MAN OF BONES

MAN OF BONES

BEN CREED

MLP

First published in Great Britain in 2024 by
Mountain Leopard Press
An imprint of HEADLINE PUBLISHING GROUP

1

Cataloguing in Publication Data is available from the British Library

ISBN 978 1 8027 9312 3 (Hardback)
ISBN 978 1 8027 9775 0 (Trade paperback)

Typeset in 11.75/17.62pt Sabon LT Std by Jouve (UK), Milton Keynes
Maps by Tim Peters Design

Printed and bound in Great Britain by Clays Ltd, Elcograf S.p.A.

Headline's policy is to use papers that are natural, renewable and recyclable
products and made from wood grown in well-managed forests and other
controlled sources. The logging and manufacturing processes are expected to
conform to the environmental regulations of the country of origin.

HEADLINE PUBLISHING GROUP
An Hachette UK Company
Carmelite House
50 Victoria Embankment
London EC4Y 0DZ

www.headline.co.uk
www.hachette.co.uk

I trust no one, not even myself.
Joseph Stalin

It is better to be hanged for loyalty than be rewarded for betrayal.
Vladimir Putin

The Party could not fail to realise that such a mass influx [throughout] 1930–33 represented an unhealthy and undesirable expansion of its membership. The Party knew that not only honest and loyal people were joining its ranks, but also chancers, careerists, seeking to exploit the Party's good name to further their own ends. The Party could not but be aware that its strength lay not only in the number of its members but above all in their quality. This raised the question of regulating the composition of the Party . . . Only after [a series of measures to suspend and verify Party memberships] was the admission of new members and candidate members into the Party resumed. As a result of all these measures, the Party was able to purge its ranks of chance, passive, careerist and directly hostile elements, and to select the staunchest and most loyal people. It cannot be said that there were no serious mistakes in the way the purge was carried out. Unfortunately, there were more mistakes than might have been anticipated. There is no doubt that we shall have no further need of resorting to mass purges. Nevertheless, the purge . . . was unavoidable and, on the whole, it produced positive results . . . for the Party is strengthened by cleansing itself of dross.

Joseph Stalin, speech to the 18th Congress of the All-Union Communist Party concerning the mass purges of delegates that had followed the 17th Congress, 10 March 1939

WESTERN USSR, 1953

CENTRAL LENINGRAD, 1953

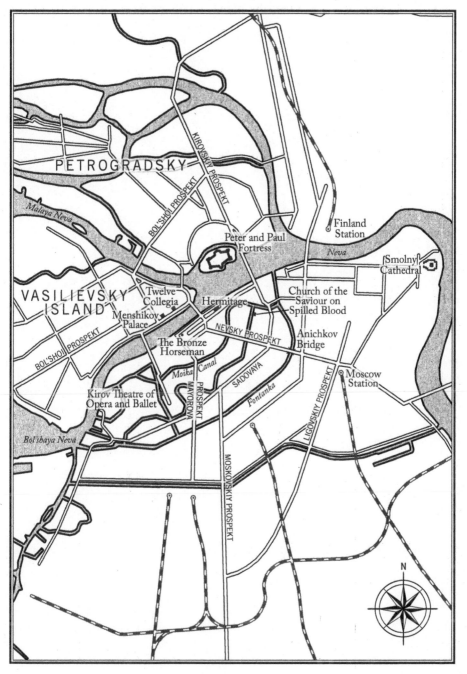

1
УТКА
Duck

1

14 February 1953

The man and woman lay on the icy ground, hands reaching out to each other, as if on a macabre date. They looked oddly contented, he thought. Almost peaceful. Love and Death frozen in a fatal embrace.

Rossel shivered. Corpses did not bother him – he had seen plenty. But the Leningrad winter gnawed into your bones, its never-ending darkness tinged with the damp that drifted in off the Baltic Sea and seeped into the streets.

The spotty young militia corporal standing next to him pointed at the two bodies he and his colleagues had dumped by the side of the road.

'Like I told you, comrade, all blood and gristle,' he said. 'A mess.'

Rossel did not reply. In his head, an orchestra growled, a chorus thundered, a hero was forced to confront his nightmares . . .

Always the same thoughts
Always that terrible dream . . .

As he stared down at the victims, the cold stung his ears, his lips, the nape of his neck.

The young officer, perhaps unnerved by the lack of reaction

from this tall, pale stranger whom he had just escorted from the opera house to the scene of the crime, filled the silence.

'Dirty old bastard and his whore, I reckon,' he said with a hint of satisfaction. He rubbed his pockmarked face. 'When a woman is all painted like that . . .'

And the dark visions of the funeral
Rise before as if they were real . . .

Rossel shook his head to dispel the music, but Tchaikovsky was not easy to dismiss. To distract himself, to gain some contact with the external world, he turned to the officer and looked him up and down. The boy's uniform was smart enough, though there was a line of grime along the top of his collar. His cheeks were scarred by his acne, his eyes tiny, a little like a pig's. More than ten years his junior, Rossel thought.

He looked over the lad's shoulder. Four or five other militia officers loitered, backs to the crumbling nineteenth-century façade of the Finland Station, staring at him. They were annoyed by Rossel's presence and let it show.

'Swarthy bastard. Big nose, too,' he heard one of them say to another as he pointed at the body of the man. 'A kike, maybe?' The other officer began laughing.

Photographs and notes had been taken, passers-by long since questioned. Dinner would be cold by now, but at least beds would be warm, with wives and girlfriends in them.

And yet they were still hanging around until this . . . well, was he from the *militsiya* or not? A dishevelled spectre who wore the boots and trousers of a standard militia uniform underneath a long civilian coat. A grubby sweater. A woollen hat. No indication of rank. How many uniform violations was that?

But the officers kept their mouths shut because he was a friend of Captain Lipukhin. Or Captain Cirrhosis, as his underlings called him behind his back, thanks to the vodka that was always on his breath. Not that they cared much about that, other than to laugh at him. The drunker the captain, the less he bothered them.

A few metres away, under a flickering street light, Lipukhin was finishing a conversation with another militia officer who was trying to lean away without making it too obvious. The captain looked around, needing a moment for the world to come into focus.

'Revol?' he said.

The other militia officers straightened. A lazy movement – resentful habit rather than obedience.

What is our life? A game!
Good and evil merely dreams . . .

'Revol . . . Rossel!'

The orchestra in Rossel's brain vanished. Only the plaintive cry of a lone violin remained – his instrument. At least, the one he used to play before a state security interrogator had put an end to that career.

'What do you think?' said the captain.

The one question every Soviet citizen did their best to avoid.

Rossel looked at the group of officers, then at the bodies. He shrugged.

'Arranged like that, they do look like lovers, Comrade Captain,' he said. 'But I can see that's not how they were found.'

Lipukhin was overcome by a short but ferocious bout of coughing.

'Love?' the captain said once he had recovered. 'You might be right. Most murders I've been involved with have had something to do with it. Either too much of it or not enough.'

Rossel twisted the end of the cardboard filter of his *papirosa* and lit the tobacco.

'This isn't a murder, though, is it?' he said.

Lipukhin raised his eyebrows and took a moment to answer.

'Yes,' the captain said. 'Well, is it? Is that what you think?'

Rossel exhaled a thin trail of smoke.

'Outside the Finland Station, at a tram stop, two people hit by a car,' he said. 'A job for the transport police, surely? Or does the State Automobile Inspectorate not operate at this late hour? Who called you out?'

'The incident was reported four hours ago, around eight o'clock. I got a call about fifteen minutes after that.'

'A call from whom?'

A pause before the captain answered.

'The blue-hats.'

Rossel gave him a sharp look.

'Ah . . . Unusual.'

Lipukhin avoided his gaze.

Rossel turned back to the unfortunate couple.

What did he think?

It depends on who is asking, comrade.

'Any witnesses?' he asked Lipukhin.

'Not so far.'

Rossel reached into his coat pocket and took out a small, sharp stone. He rolled it between his gloved thumb and forefinger and stared down at the two corpses.

'I have a joke to tell you later, Ilya. You'll like it.'

'A good one?'

Rossel leaned closer towards his friend and dropped his voice to a whisper.

'In the camps, I used to think so.'

*

Fat flakes of snow were silhouetted by the light of the street lamps – 'ice moths,' as his mother had called them. But in the middle distance was an interesting potential witness: Lenin himself, his huge hand pointing towards the frozen River Neva.

Rossel pulled hard on the *papirosa*. It felt better to fill his lungs with smoke than this dank, briny air.

His thoughts, had anyone been able to hear them, were that he would prefer not to have been greeted earlier that evening by three of Lipukhin's militia officers as he was leaving the Kirov Theatre after a performance of Tchaikovsky's opera, *The Queen of Spades*. That he would rather have walked home, lingering over the route to his dingy room in the south-west of the city, the masterpiece ringing in his skull, filling his soul and elbowing aside every other emotion he did not want to feel. That the car journey to the Finland Station in an unheated Pobeda had made him nauseous thanks to the stink of petrol and the malodorous militia officers jammed into the back seat alongside him.

That these days he was a nobody. A pen-pusher. Like most former Gulag prisoners, a husk. And – despite being recently restored to the main department of the Militia – that he'd rather keep it that way.

'Revol, your thoughts, please.' Lipukhin made a final plea.

Rossel bowed his head. Breathed in and out. Then lifted it again.

'All right,' he said.

The dead male stared into the night sky, stupefied by whatever he saw in the cosmos. Elderly, perhaps in his seventies, enveloped in a grey coat. Not one from a Soviet factory line, though – it was thicker and tougher. Tall and broad-shouldered, he looked like he'd once carried plenty of muscle. Blood had leaked out of his skull, staining the thick snow in the shape of a halo. In the harsh, unearthly blaze from the lamp above their heads, the stain was more like ink than blood. His face was dusted with stubble. The nose was large, beaky and misshapen, like a wedge of cardboard you'd shove under a wonky table leg.

As for the rest of his mangled body, the young officer had summed it up well. A mess.

Rossel sighed and fumbled for another cigarette. He turned to the female corpse.

Like her companion, she had been dragged by the militia officers out of the middle of the road, where she had fallen after being hit by whichever vehicle had struck them, and deposited on the pavement next to the Finland Station. The woman's long, brown-blonde hair covered her face and Rossel knelt to push it back. Matted and stiffening, it slid off her cheeks like a filthy curtain. She was younger than the man – late forties, he'd say. The unscathed side of her face was encrusted with make-up. Lips a crimson pout. One eye a riot of mascara.

He had seen plenty of women who sold sex. But he wasn't certain this was one of them. A woman forced to resort to prostitution didn't own a necklace like that, for starters. You'd sell it long before you'd sell yourself to a passing traveller for a clandestine assignation up against a railway station's wall.

With the forefinger of his gloved right hand, Rossel tilted the face. The other eye was no longer in its socket. Under a blazing yellow police lamp, the face was a horror, as if half of its owner was still asleep and the other half already rotting in the grave.

He looked up, assessing the surroundings again.

The approximate location at which the car had hit the two victims was on the other side of the road, about fifteen metres away. The couple, the officers reckoned, had been standing at, or next to, the tram stop down the western side of the Finland Station. None of them could say *exactly* where, though, because the corpses had been moved to get them off the tram tracks and away from the road.

Had Rossel still been a senior lieutenant in the militia – his rank until an investigation he'd conducted had ruffled feathers at the highest levels of the Party and earned him a spell in a Siberian labour camp – he would have bawled them out for that.

The victims had left twin tracks on the road with their heels, the trails bisected by the tyres of the few cars that had passed this way since the incident. If the vehicle that had collided with them had been coming from the embankment, it would either have travelled up Lenin Square or along Komsomol Street before veering right. In the latter case, it would have had to slow down to avoid skidding before . . .

He looked over at what remained of the tram shelter. One end had been virtually destroyed. The roof of it slumped to the ground.

Rossel crunched his way across the road, ignoring the tutting and muttering of the militia officers.

The tram stop split the road into two. Out of the morass of tyre tracks, one set detached itself from the rest and led straight to the shelter. A major deviation from the general flow of traffic.

He followed the tracks. The vehicle had thumped up the kerb. To have hit the man and woman with enough force to kill them

BEN CREED

outright, it must have smashed into them first before crashing into the structure. He scanned the snow for blood and found it, plenty of it. It was smeared on the wooden debris of the shattered shelter, too.

Rossel looked around.

So where – if the car had roared off, like the officers had said – were the tyre tracks leading from here back to . . .

Movement. A man, appearing out of nowhere, was walking from Lenin Square towards them. As one, the militia officers took a step forward to intercept the stranger and direct him to the opposite pavement.

As one, they froze.

A three? A seven? An ace . . .

The uniform was dark green from head to foot, save for the stiff, yellow epaulettes and the familiar blue band above the black peak of his cap.

'Touch those bodies again, you mongrel bastards,' shouted the man, 'and I will have every one of you shot.'

State security had arrived.

2

The colonel from the MGB, Ministry of State Security, searched the bodies as if he was rummaging through laundry looking for a spare shirt.

'What are you looking for, Comrade Colonel?' Rossel said.

He felt the militia officers' unease. Only fools asked questions of the blue-hats.

The colonel adjusted his cap but did not reply, as if to signal it was his prerogative to disregard anyone or anything as he saw fit. He wrenched the coat of the female victim back and forth, reaching into her bloodstained blouse. Rossel caught a glimpse of flesh, her chest and nipples stained with blood and dirt, before the colonel pulled the coat back into position and did up a button, as if to belatedly protect her modesty.

'Did anyone take her papers?' the MGB colonel asked.

His voice was cold, mechanical, world-weary. He stood and stepped under the street light. Middle-aged. Black hair over grey eyes that held yours for a second longer than you wanted. He seemed somehow insubstantial – fleeting, like a grainy figure on old film. The shadow of a shadow.

The colonel repeated the question, and the militia officers shook their heads. A line of schoolboys in front of a particularly strict teacher. Lipukhin did the same.

'How about him, the big man, Fat Rumyantsev, over there?'

The blue-hat pointed to the male corpse. Rumyantsev was a popular clown who performed on TV. 'Papers? Possessions?'

Again, they shook their heads – 'No, comrade, sorry, comrade . . .'

Rossel looked around for the car that had brought the colonel to the Finland Station but couldn't see one. Odd, he thought. MGB officers didn't walk.

'How did you hear of this incident, Comrade Colonel?' he asked.

Again, he was ignored.

'What else have you found out?' demanded the blue-hat. 'Did anyone see *anything*?'

The young officer with the pockmarked face stepped forward and flipped open his notebook. His hands were steady. His voice was not.

'A railway worker called Viktor Belov, Comrade Colonel, is the closest thing we have to a witness,' the youngster said. 'He was on his way home at the end of his shift. Lives nearby. He was round the front of the station and didn't see the incident but heard it, he said – a big bang but no screams.'

The MGB man opened his mouth, but Rossel spoke first.

'Did Comrade Belov see what he thought caused this noise?'

Pockmarks swallowed.

'Yes . . .' He tailed off, still uncertain of Rossel's status, settling for a simple 'comrade'. He cleared his throat. 'It was a large car, a Pobeda. Black. The car was going round the corner heading west. Towards the centre of town. It was almost gone by the time he got here.'

'Did he see who was inside?' Rossel asked.

'No.'

'Number plate?'

'No.'

'Were both victims already dead by the time Comrade Belov reached them?'

Rossel could see the MGB colonel's grey eyes inspecting him. Not with hostility but with curiosity, as if he were a beetle under a glass dome, about to perform another diverting trick.

The militia officer hesitated.

'Answer him,' said the colonel.

'The woman was apparently dead, Comrade Colonel, but the man was still breathing.'

Rossel was about to ask another question. But the colonel took a step towards him and poked him in the shoulder.

'I'll ask him, Comrade Whoever-you-are,' he said. 'So that your natural curiosity does not incriminate you any further.'

He turned to the officer.

'Did this still-breathing man say anything?'

A nod.

'Yes. Something strange.'

'Which was?'

The officer flicked nervously through the pages of his notebook.

'"Will it snow, Soselo? Will it rain? Is there a storm coming?" That's what the witness told me.'

Rossel knelt in the damp snow by the male victim. He began pulling back the man's coat and unbuttoning his jacket and shirt.

'You,' said the colonel. 'What *is* your name?'

'Rossel, Comrade Colonel. Revol Rossel.' He pulled the man's shirt open.

Nothing on the chest or shoulders. He inspected the man's hands.

'Rank?'

'Senior militiaman,' said Rossel.

He got back to his feet. Nothing on the hands, either. He looked up to see all the militia officers staring at him. Senior militiaman was the second-lowest rank.

The militia was under the control of the MGB, though the power and prestige of an agent of state security far outstripped the street-level officers who were tasked with maintaining good socialist order – a worthy objective but not a prestigious one.

The colonel smiled. But it did not reach his eyes.

'Your station?' he asked.

'Station 33,' said Rossel. 'Kirovsky District. This evening, however, Comrade Captain Lipukhin and his fellow officers from Station 17, in the Smolny administrative area, asked me to help them.'

He gestured at the surrounding officers, who looked as frightened as their captain.

'Despite this unusual arrangement, Comrade Colonel,' he said, 'I am absolutely certain that we all have a common goal in identifying this unfortunate couple and establishing the circumstances of—'

'And this is who I am,' said the colonel. He held up his MGB card and opened it, revealing a small photograph of himself and a name. Rossel only had time to read *Vishensky* before the colonel snapped the ID shut and stowed it in a pocket. 'I want to know why you were looking for papers on the dead man's body. You saw me search. Do you imagine I am incompetent and missed them?'

'Not papers. Tattoos,' said Rossel. 'The name Soselo is not a Russian one. If anything, it feels like a nickname, and therefore possibly a Thieves' nickname.' The Thieves were a criminal caste with their own hierarchy and code. 'If he was a Thief, it is probable that he would have spent time in a corrective labour camp and acquired tattoos which, as you know, denote criminal history, length of sentence, status and other markers of identity.'

Like the tattoo I have.

No one, and least of all a senior militiaman, would usually dare talk to a member of the MGB in this way. The colonel kept his eyes fixed on Rossel. The audience held its breath.

'Your friend is amusing, Comrade Captain,' Vishensky said at last. 'But if I were you, I'd rein him in.'

Lipukhin nodded hard enough to snap his own neck.

The MGB officer gestured at the bodies. 'A lovers' tiff, that's all this is,' he said. 'Do you understand me, Comrade Captain? They meet. An exchange is proposed, money for sex. They haggle over the price. A drunken argument ensues. Lost in it, our two lovebirds tumble into the road and, *bang*, some half-pissed factory manager driving back home to Primorsky knocks them over. Put that in your report and have it on the relevant desk first thing in the morning.'

His gaze swept over them all.

'Vigilance is crucial to the health of Soviet society. If the militia are wasting time on a pair of sordid parasites knocked over by a careless driver, then they are disregarding far more important matters. The protection of Socialist property. Political reliability among the residents of Leningrad. Maintenance of Soviet order. Have these bodies disposed of, have the tram shelter repaired. Distribute leaflets exhorting our growing class of car owners to be more vigilant on the roads. I will not hear any more of this.'

'Yes, Comrade Colonel. Of course,' said Lipukhin.

With a last glance at Rossel, Colonel Vishensky turned and began to walk away. As they watched, he veered left, across the square, striding towards Lenin's enormous statue. And, after another few paces, faded into the darkness.

* * *

A low sun flickered through the branches of the birch. The kind of burnt red sunset, she thought, only a master of broken colour like Monet could capture.

Is it preferable to die in a moment of beauty or on a day of drizzle and gloom?

Not for the first time, Zlata Sidorenko considered this.

The painter half-turned in the back of the huge limousine and watched the high metal gates clang shut behind her. The road ahead was smooth, but the trees on either side were tightly packed, suffocatingly thick.

Like the wild, hostile forests of folklore.

The ones where the Leshi hid. A shape-shifting spirit who could assume any human form. A fearsome Slavic woodland deity who led travellers astray – abducting tiny children whom he would share with chorty *– evil, black-horned devils.*

Guards bearing submachineguns and draped in ammunition lined the route. They watched the vehicle pass, scanning the number plate, the driver, the speed at which it was travelling. Looking for any signs that something might be amiss.

Inside the black Packard, the two enormous MGB agents who had knocked on her door and given her ten minutes to pack a bag – and her brushes and paints – remained still and silent. They did not have hooves, nor any sign of tails. But Zlata did not feel reassured. She had long since given up asking them the question that ran around her head.

What have I done?

She had always kept her public art within the boundaries of Socialist norms. Comrade Zhdanov, famous for his doctrine on the purity of purpose of Bolshevik art, would have been proud of her – 'The only conflict that is possible in Soviet culture is the conflict between good and best.'

Pompous prick.

Her true work, the expression of her real creative spirit and desires, she kept hidden. The blue-hats who had dragged her from her home in Leningrad had not made the slightest attempt to search for it. So they had no idea it existed, or they would have torn the place to pieces.

Nevertheless – the painter scolded herself – she had made an error somewhere.

The limousine swept on for another minute. Ahead, she could see a squat building, too large to be a house, yet too grand to be a prison or a labour camp, or somewhere worse . . . Painted green as if, like the Leshi, it had been swallowed by the forest.

Not a killing ground, then. She exhaled. A Party dacha.

More armed guards, dozens of them, some standing stiff to attention, others peering out from behind trees.

The car stopped.

'Out.'

Zlata forced her legs to obey.

'Inside.'

'My bag?'

'It will follow. Along with your other things.'

'So I'm to stay here?'

No answer. Only sullen, downturned faces.

The house was large, dwarfing any dacha she had ever seen. Just two storeys high, it stretched left and right, with a circular, glass-covered veranda at one end.

The biggest of the men who had sat next to her in the car took her elbow and urged her forward. He pushed open a heavy wooden door that creaked on its hinges and ushered her inside.

Everything was polished wood, paintings and objets d'art. *The boots of other MGB officers echoed in the grand hallway.*

Zlata looked off to the left, unsure why she was drawn to the closed door with a tiny red star on it.

'I wouldn't go in there, girl,' said the guard.

The others laughed.

I'm no girl, you big, dumb bastard.

'You are to go upstairs. Follow me.'

*

As they ascended the staircase, Zlata felt she was walking into a miasma of dust. If the ground floor had been eerie, it had at least seemed to be warm enough for human presence; up here, the air was darker and colder.

They bore right. 'Second door down,' said the guard.

But as they walked along the corridor, a different door at the end began to open. The guard stopped dead, tugging on her arm so that she did the same.

A short, stocky figure filled the frame. The sun had fallen to a level between the trees and the clouds so that light burst into the room, silhouetting this apparition.

When he spoke, there was no doubting his identity. The voice – low, quiet, with only a hint of a Georgian accent – was less commanding than the one she had heard on the radio. Yet it was still so familiar to her it might have been her father's calling to her from the next room.

'Ah,' said Iosif Vissarionovich Dzhugashvili.

The guard saluted with such vigour that Zlata thought she heard the stitching of his uniform tear.

The small man the Soviet press never stopped calling 'Great',

'Beloved', 'Bold', 'Wise', 'Inspirer' and 'Genius' stepped closer to them. His scent caught in her nostrils. Musky and cloying. *Troinoi, she thought. A mass-produced aftershave you could smell on the trolleybus.*

She hadn't expected him to smell like that.

Of what then – blood?

'Comrade Stalin,' said the guard, finding his voice again. 'This is the painter, Zlata Sidorenko.'

'Yes,' said the apparition, 'I know.'

3

He had heard other militia officers extol the virtues of the food in the dilapidated workers' canteen around the corner from Station 33. They were being generous, Rossel thought. Buckwheat porridge, black bread, mashed potato, a greasy meat stew it was best not to ask too many questions about, and tea – those were always on the menu, for Leningrad's night shifters, early risers and anyone else who needed it. It offered solitude, too, which was what Rossel craved at this hour in the morning – a place on the end of a bench where other customers would respect his wish not to be disturbed.

He ate quickly. He couldn't shake the habit. Every morsel a reminder that he was no longer starving to death in a labour colony above the Arctic Circle. A place so remote and featureless that no one had bothered to name it, other than to refer to it as 105th kilometre, in honour of its distance from the nearest human habitation.

Besides, he was a Leningrader. One of those who had survived the Blockade – the city's wartime encirclement by the Germans. About eight hundred thousand had not. Maybe more. In the years since, some had made gods of their bellies; once you had experienced starvation, it was hard to forget it.

For the most part, Rossel had shaken off the nightmares of the siege. But the struggles and privations of a corrective labour colony had changed him – two or three weeks of hunger was enough to reduce even the most civilised man or woman to an animal. He had been saving the little money he had for a glass of vodka in the *ryumochnaya* across the street after his shift. Instead, he picked up his plate and walked back to the counter. A second helping, he thought. Why not? Just one more before he headed to the station.

As he got up, an old man with bushy eyebrows carrying a bowl of stew sat down on the opposite side of the table. He dropped a copy of *Pravda* next to his meal and began eating.

Rossel glanced at the newspaper's front page. 'Glory to Leningrad, 1703–1953', read the lead article, which detailed preparations for the coming celebrations of the city's 250th anniversary. The one below it was more sombre in tone. 'Killers' Connection to International Jewry Proven!' shouted its headline. It outlined the supposed Doctors' Plot, uncovered earlier in the year, and talked of 'saboteur-doctors' and 'inhuman beasts'. Nine doctors, six of them Jews, had been accused of trying to poison their patients. A succession of similar articles since January had succeeded in creating a paranoia around doctors in general. And Jewish ones in particular.

The old man looked up from his bowl. He stubbed a fat, greasy finger down on the paper.

'Who'd have thought it, eh?' he said. 'They should hang all these Yids.'

Rossel said nothing. But when he brought back his food from the counter, he sat down at the other end of the table.

*

Rossel's new workplace bore little relation to his former militia station. The latter was an old, soot-stained merchant's house that had retained some of its pre-revolutionary atmosphere thanks to its open spaces, fireplaces, stained and battered wooden floors and chunks of ornate plaster that clung to the ceiling, crumbling but tenacious. By contrast, Station 33 was more Soviet – curling wallpaper dotted with photographs of Lenin and Stalin, a labyrinth of shabby offices, some bearing the name of the owner but many unmarked. A building without much character, though doubtless with its own secrets.

Rossel turned left at the end of the corridor and then left again. Stopping in front of a faded wooden panel with peeling red paint, he pushed open the door to his domain. A room, hardly more than a cupboard, filled with green metal filing cabinets and shelving. A kingdom of lost souls trapped between pieces of brown card. A good place for a discarded man to spend his time, among the cursory records of hundreds of other discarded people.

He set down the glass of tea he had brought with him on a small table in the corner, the only free space in the room. Around him were towers of manila files – blue, red, yellow and brown, in various stages of tattiness and disorder. The oldest ones were perched on the shelves at the far end, piled high and higgledy – the most forgotten of the forgotten.

Rossel sat. He blew across the surface of his tea, his mind turning to its task.

In theory, that was to bring these files into some sort of order so that relatives of missing Leningraders who had lived in the Kirovsky District could have their queries answered: yes, we have Ivan Ivanovich's file; no, he has not been found, come back in six months.

Before her promotion, his former sergeant, Lidia Gerashvili, had performed a similar job, though with greater diligence. It was an almost futile occupation, or at least it felt that way. These were missing-persons reports from families, factory bosses and office managers, schools and colleges, citizens' groups. Some dated back to 1937. Whatever their vintage, the state had little interest in tracking them down. In a world in which millions of people had perished, why care about one individual?

As well as being haphazardly collated, the missing-persons files were short on details.

Balakin, Pyotr Petrovich. Left home to go to work at the public library on 8 March 1948, last seen by citizen Elena Ivanovna Genrikh on the afternoon of the same day. Balakin's wife reported him missing the morning after his disappearance. Body not found.

Lopatin, Dmitry Yegorovich. Left Leningrad by train on 14 August 1946, towards Vyborg. Friends claimed he was going mushroom picking and swimming near the castle. Missing, body not found.

Vyborg was close to the Finnish border. Perhaps Comrade Lopatin had attempted an unauthorised departure from the Soviet Union. Maybe he had got lost in the dense Karelian forests, or encountered a wild animal, or gone out too far in the water. Either way, after six years, Rossel concluded, Dmitry Yegorovich was unlikely to be returning to his loved ones.

Fateyev, Vladimir Borisovich. Went ice fishing near Roshchino with three friends, 3 December 1950. The three friends caught the train back to Leningrad in a state of inebriation, believing that Vladimir Borisovich had also joined the train. It turned out that he had not. Missing, body not found.

Wiping dust off the front sheet of some of them, Rossel opened more files. He took time to read each report with care, though most were only a few sentences, and even fewer had any useful information in them. Only hints of tragic accidents, drunken misadventures, undetected vengeance.

Yet he was content with this drudgery. For one thing, he had no choice.

Your survival depends on keeping very quiet, Revol. On keeping your head down. Unless you want a bullet in the back of it.

That had been the advice. He was happy to obey. Survival was all that mattered.

Well, almost.

'Galya.' He said his sister's name out loud. And then, as if half-expecting a reply, glanced around the room.

There was one missing person he was determined to find.

Rossel removed his gloves, something he did when alone, and rubbed his fingers. Not that they could feel the cold much. Two were missing on the left hand, the result of a vigorous interrogation from the secret police. Just after he had left the Leningrad Conservatoire to embark on what everyone assumed would be a brilliant career. The right hand had all its fingers, but the bones and tendons had been broken in the same encounter. All that had put paid to his life as a violinist before it had begun.

He tapped at his chest, at the tattoo of the seabird hidden under his shirt – a memento from his spell in the camps in north-western Siberia. His lungs still gave the occasional rattle from the experience. A seabird was meant to be his lucky charm. So far, he thought, it hadn't been much use.

No more trouble, he thought. Last night had been foolish. He'd let that blue-hat get to him. But he wasn't going back to the camps, to the cells, to the agonies that both ensured.

Rossel was pulling his gloves back on his hands when the door swung open. It was Lieutenant Shishkin – a corpulent, sweating nightmare to those under his command.

Shishkin glared at Rossel through two sly eyes embedded above a thick moustache. He took in the dingy records room for a moment before speaking.

'Alone again, Senior Militiaman Rossel?' he said.

'It seems that way,' replied Rossel.

'Not any more. You have a visitor.'

*

Captain Lipukhin smelled a little better but was still not looking well. He had washed, combed his hair, and had tried to shave. A bloodied piece of gauze was stuck to his chin.

Shishkin stopped at the door, glanced sceptically between Rossel and the captain – as if undecided as to which was the more likely to bring shame upon his department – then closed it.

Lipukhin nodded after him.

'Who shoved the stick up his arse?' But the tone of the captain's voice didn't match the bravura of his remark. He sounded confused. Lost.

Rossel shrugged. 'Just another lieutenant who wants to make captain. His men tell him what he wants to hear and compete to polish up the buckles on his uniform. But I've met worse.'

Hemmed in by two unwieldy, overflowing cabinets, Lipukhin looked around the untidy room.

'So, this is you now?'

Rossel nodded. 'This is me.'

Lipukhin blinked hard. Rossel saw his fingers twitching.

'I could use a detective at Station 17. I have already talked to Shishkin about a possible transfer.'

Rossel shook his head. 'An old friend advised me to find a little corner of nowhere, to keep my head down and my mouth shut,' he said. 'Doesn't this look like nowhere to you?'

Another look of pain crossed the captain's face. He pinched the bridge of his nose.

'A headache,' he said, catching Rossel's eye.

'You look . . . tired, Ilya.'

Lipukhin let his arm fall to his side. Moisture was beginning to leach into the collar and the armpits of his jacket.

'My sister,' he said. 'You remember Raisa?'

'I don't think we ever met,' replied Rossel. 'But you lived in the same apartment, am I right? Along with her little daughter.'

Lipukhin nodded. 'Raisa had a tongue like a rusty saw. Vicious. But she was a good mother.'

'Had?'

'Something to do with the blood,' Lipukhin said. 'A few months back. Cancer. She went so fast we barely had time to say goodbye.'

'I'm sorry to hear that.'

Rossel had a hazy memory of meeting Raisa's daughter once. An earnest child with a broken doll that Lipukhin had put back together in return for her silence about an illicit bottle of vodka.

'And little Dasha?'

'I am responsible for her now,' said Lipukhin. 'I am not good at it. The child does not respect me.'

'How old is she now? Eight?'

'Nine.' Lipukhin pressed his knuckles into his temples and tossed his head from side to side as if to shake the last droplets of alcohol out of his brain. 'There is an autopsy of the Finland Station victims tomorrow, Revol,' he said.

What did Lipukhin want from him? Ilya wasn't even an investigations officer – Station 17 was for pavement walkers who did the dirty work of clearing up after domestics, drunken stabbings, unruly behaviour under the general heading of 'hooliganism', petty or malicious.

'An autopsy? Colonel Vishensky won't like that. Why not just order the city's garages to report all vehicles coming in with human-shaped dents in the bodywork?'

Lipukhin looked up. 'They think I can't do it. They think I'm an idiot. Worse, they think I don't care. But they don't know I have *you*, Revol. I need you on the case.'

His tone had changed. Now, he was Rossel's superior officer, aware that his order would not be welcomed but not caring.

'Respect, redemption, whatever you are after, they won't come from solving this Finland Station case, Ilya – if there is even anything to solve,' Rossel said. 'It will come when you finally screw the cap back on the bottle.'

Over Lipukhin's face flitted surprise, pain, outrage and shame. Finally, the flame in his eyes and pinch of his mouth settled on anger.

He walked across to the desk and picked up one of the files of the missing.

'My redemption. Really?' He dropped the file into a bin. 'You're the one who's missing, Revol. Lost, just like your fucking sister.'

Rossel stood. 'Take that back!'

'*Comrade Captain*,' Lipukhin said. 'Take that back, Comrade Captain.'

Rossel stared at him. 'Very well, Comrade Captain. I have been given this job to stay out of the way. I need to do that. A year ago, I was in the Gulag. On the verge of having molten metal poured into my eyes by the Thieves. Beria himself . . .' He forced himself to lower his voice. 'I'm told Beria himself wants me gone.'

Lipukhin shook his head. 'It's well known you have a guardian – what's that bastard's name again? Major Nikitin. That's why you gave that MGB colonel – what was his name? Vishensky – so much lip. Because you're protected.'

'It's Nikitin who told me to lie low,' Rossel said, trying to keep his voice level.

'I understand,' said Lipukhin, breathing hard. 'You're well connected now, eh? Coveting your own place in the Party hierarchy, perhaps? So, you won't help out an old friend.'

Rossel jabbed a finger at Lipukhin's chest. 'You haven't been to the camps, Ilya, I have. I'm not going back. I am a filing clerk, not an investigator. You can forget about me. You want to sit down and have me describe what they do to a man? Maybe then I'll finally get through to that permanently pickled brain of yours, eh?'

'You know what?' said Lipukhin, drawing his coat around him. 'You can do one.' He yanked open the door. 'Autopsy, tomorrow morning, Station 17 after that, or I'll file a disciplinary complaint to the MGB, the Party, the Komsomol, the fucking Composers' Union and anyone else I can think of.'

He stalked out, almost running into Lieutenant Shishkin, who looked intrigued and startled at the same time.

'Lovers' tiff?' he said to Rossel.

Rossel sighed and tried to push the door shut. But Shishkin stopped it with his foot. The lieutenant thrust a scrap of paper at him.

'The world's been turned upside down, it seems,' he said sarcastically. 'I'm running errands for you now, Comrade Senior

Militiaman. A message from a *friend* from Moscow. He wants to meet you.'

*

As Rossel left Station 33 that evening, he passed two junior officers discussing plans for the weekend.

'It was minus twelve out there,' said the first man. 'Not bad for February, might even head to the dacha, a friend has a *banya*, could even take the wife . . .'

The other man grinned. 'My advice is to ditch that sour-faced bitch and take your girlfriend instead.'

'Can't, Sveta wants a baby.'

'They all want that,' said the older man, 'and when you give them one . . . take it from me, that's when the days of heaven are over, comrade. It's nothing but nappies full of shit and nagging after that . . .'

Their voices trailed away as Rossel stepped outside.

Station 33 was on a nondescript street off Prospekt Stachek, a long road in Leningrad's southwest that was blasted by the sea winds that whipped off the Gulf of Finland. Rossel's room was fifteen minutes' walk away, but, although this was a convenient arrangement, he would have preferred an apartment in a suburb or satellite town further away. Somewhere even more anonymous.

Not far from the station was a small park, and within that was a bench with a view. The view was not alluring: an industrial vista with cranes that bent in the wind and rusted in the salt-sodden damp, while at least one in three of the vessels that came this way ended up moored to a forgotten monolith of metal and concrete, listing and abandoned.

He sympathised.

Beyond this unprepossessing nearline, however, you could see the red, yellow and green lights of the ships that drifted in and out of Leningrad's docks and waterways. Ships bearing good Soviet cargo to the rest of the world. Perhaps the odd one bringing the fruits of the working classes in the West into Leningrad. Ships that carried a few adventurous souls. Ships that might have borne Galya to a new shore. She could have taken many routes towards her disappearance, why not this one? Would he be more likely to pick up her trail if he did the same?

The image of the broken body of the woman who had been killed outside the Finland Station floated into his mind.

Once upon a time, two mangled bodies broken by the violence of a car crash might have piqued people's interest. No longer. Leningraders were experts in filtering their nightmares. Of pretending not to see or listen. Of pretending not to hear the Black Ravens pulling up outside. The MGB footsteps on the stairs, the nocturnal hammering on citizens' doors. Of German shells thumping into grimy, desolate homes. Of snowplough engines buzzing as their scoops shovelled heaps of corpses into mass burial pits. Decades of the sounds of death. Covering your ears became a habit. It was not that Leningraders were indifferent. Just that they had little choice. Death was run-of-the-mill. Why get hysterical about it?

So what was Galya's worth? What was one more dead Soviet citizen among many? Who cared about another lost soul swallowed up by . . .

But that was the point. What *had* his sister been swallowed by?

4

The six-floor building in which Rossel lived had been built just before the war.

Already, it felt old, assailed by the damp, salty air and Leningrad's unrelenting winters, which had scoured its walls and windows. The saturated floorboards creaked, the wallpaper bubbled. And his floor, the fourth, had its resident ghoul, who went by the name of Valentina Semyonovna.

She was waiting for him this time, as if affronted that he had managed to get to his bed the night before without her noticing.

'You're home,' she said, looking him up and down as if he was on parade.

Valentina Semyonovna, who was perhaps in her fifties, wore an indeterminate number of layers under an all-encompassing shawl decorated in a traditional rustic style. Under a less bitter face, a less twisted expression, the shawl would have indicated a warm and welcoming abode, perhaps even hinted at matriarchal homeliness. But Rossel had little doubt that she would inform on him to the MGB if he gave her half a chance. One loose word, one sarcastic remark, one lapse in Marxist-Leninist devotion . . .

'Good evening, Comrade Valentina Semyonovna.'

He took off his hat and coat and hung them next to the front door of the apartment. She lived off to the left and down another left. His room was to the right, close to the bathroom, a position she resented. A tiny kitchen divided them. Beyond his room lived an elderly couple whose room smelled of decay.

'*Vsyo v poryadke?*' he asked. 'Is everything in order?'

She thought about it, testing her assessment of the world as it currently was against her instinctive understanding of *poryadok*. Order. Good order. Soviet order.

Rossel removed his boots.

'I will now brew some tea. Will you join me?'

Without hesitating, Valentina Semyonovna turned her back and padded towards her dark, silent lair.

'I am not in favour of unnecessary familiarity,' she said.

'Then good night, fair Valentina Semyonovna, I hope you enjoy a splendid evening.'

She did not look back.

*

Rossel entered his room and closed the door. The elderly neighbours had their radio on, and the strains of classic Soviet songs did battle with the wind that rattled his windowpanes.

The building had taken some bad blast and shrapnel damage during the war but no direct hits. It was not rickety enough to be demolished, and it clung to its gas and electric supply. Perhaps in compensation, the *kvartplata*, the monthly demand for maintenance costs, was negligible. In a city where there was constant pressure for housing, the district authorities were happy that the resilient citizens of Leningrad were prepared to put up with such a home.

Through his window, Rossel looked out upon a former flour warehouse. Little remained of its exterior; in front of it, snow and ice had covered a huge mound of rubble, and the local children spent their afternoons sliding down it on metal trays or re-enacting scenes from Stalingrad in violent games of hide-and-seek. Further down the street was a fresh building site; cranes towered above it, part of Leningrad's faltering attempts to rebuild after the Blockade.

Rossel had a cupboard for clothes, in which he also stashed a few basic provisions. The springs in his bedframe had long surrendered any useful function. His prized possession was a battered Sokol radio-gramophone with a worn green leather case. The gramophone produced a surprisingly good sound, even if its ageing stylus was in the habit of getting stuck. But it produced music, and that was all he needed.

Yes, his room was small, barely furnished and poorly heated. But to share the entire floor with only Valentina Semyonovna and one other family was, after the crowded claustrophobia of his labour camp barracks, luxury on a palatial scale.

He removed his militia jacket, hanging it up on a hook on the wall. From the inside pocket, he retrieved the message that Lieutenant Shishkin had handed him that afternoon.

On it was a time and a place. Tomorrow afternoon. And a simple message:

I trust you have a good reason for making contact.

Rossel went over to the table that stood opposite his bed and opened a drawer. He pulled out a photograph of a young woman. She looked back at him with the same eyes as his, the same high cheekbones, the same natural insolence. He carried her over to his bed and sat down, pressing the photo to his chest.

5

As a half-Jewish doctor who by reputation dabbled in the black-market caviar trade, Maksi Bondar's longevity was impressive.

Perhaps, Rossel thought, the pathologist had learned from the dead. A hint of something behind their eyes. A glimpse of eternal life presented to the damned at the very end, eluding them even as they grasped and flailed for it.

As the headline he had read in the canteen suggested, the editors of *Pravda* and *Izvestia* seemed to be injecting anti-Semitism into their veins each morning before they sat down to type. To judge by the venom of their diatribes, the ruinous anti-Bolshevik activities of Jews, doctors, capitalist speculators – and especially Jewish doctors and Jewish capitalist speculators – were everywhere.

And yet here was Maksi, seemingly unperturbed, large as life – an ever-cheerful reaper.

Rossel had always found Bondar to be oblivious to the political weather. Maybe the rumours about caviar stashed in his mortuary refrigerators were true. Perhaps that was what gave the pathologist a dependable, all-weather *krysha*, or protection, provided he kept up a decent supply to the right people. People who could advise him on keeping a low profile when it mattered. To leave town on certain nights or to attend medical conferences in distant places at certain times – for an unexpected beluga bonus.

34

Bondar grinned as he prepared to examine the two mangled victims who had been felled outside the Finland Station. Standing slightly apart from each other, the air between them still frosty from their last exchange, Rossel and Lipukhin stood further away from the mortuary trolley. The captain was keeping his distance from the corpses in case the pathologist set to work with his scalpel and he saw someone's innards without warning.

Bondar worked in the basement of The Crosses, Leningrad's most notorious prison. The joke among the inmates was to call the occupants of the morgue 'the lucky ones'. The autopsy had been assigned there because of its proximity to the Finland Station.

'The male is one hundred and eighty-five centimetres tall and weighs ninety-five kilograms,' said Bondar. 'He has some scarring on his left side, close to the abdomen, though this is faded, and it is not possible to discern the cause. I will do the usual checks into his basic health, but I understand the cause of death is not in doubt. There are no tattoos or other major distinguishing marks.'

On a second steel table a couple of metres away lay the female. In the fierce light of the examining room, her face appeared contorted. In fear, perhaps. Or fury that life had been taken from her.

'The woman is one hundred and sixty-seven centimetres in height. She weighs fifty-nine and a half kilograms. She has a large red birthmark on her upper leg, just above the knee. Otherwise, no distinguishing marks.'

At the scene of her death, the woman had noticeably thick hair. She was bald now, shaved for inspection.

'I can, at the most fundamental level, confirm that these two unfortunate citizens had an encounter with a car or a truck,' said the pathologist. 'Traces of black paint on their coats, most likely of the type used in car factories – analysis will confirm. And

that's before we get to the massive bruising and internal haemor-
rhaging, and the damage to bones and internal organs.'

He turned to Lipukhin.

'Have you managed to establish who our two friends are?'
Bondar spoke of his charges in the present tense.

Lipukhin shook his head. 'Neither was carrying their papers.
Nor anything else useful, like a factory pass or their work
record,' he said.

For a law-abiding Soviet citizen, this was rare. But not
unheard of. Some people preferred to 'forget' to carry their identity documents. It made the militia's cursory efforts at social
scrutiny a little harder.

'A pity. As I mentioned on our way down here, comrades, if
these two citizens were struck by a fast-moving vehicle, the force
would have thrown them some distance from the point of impact.
A simple thing to verify. Was this the case?'

'According to the local militia officers who were first on the
scene, yes,' said Lipukhin. 'Unfortunately, they dragged the
bodies out of the road and onto the pavement without marking
the exact position in which they had found our happy couple.'

Bondar tutted. 'Blood loss at the scene?'

'No one took a note on that,' said the captain.

'Were any fragments from the vehicle recovered from the
area?' asked the pathologist. 'Glass, a chunk of metal. Cars are
not complex objects – we're not looking for rare elements that
might decay before our eyes.'

Rossel glanced at Lipukhin. But the captain was looking at
the floor.

'The captain was called out late, Maksi,' Rossel said. 'The
local militia and transport inspectorate did not follow procedure
as they should.'

Bondar's face was not one that kept his inner thoughts secret.

'Late,' the pathologist said. 'Yes, of course.' From nowhere, he produced a scalpel. 'Comrades, do you care to stay?' he asked with a sly smile.

Lipukhin was already heading for the exit.

'I think we are busy, Maksi,' Rossel said.

'I will get on with it then,' replied Bondar. 'A busy day for me today, too. There was a big fire last night in an apartment block in Moskovsky. I'm shortly expecting a large delivery of very well-done steak.'

*

Come with me, Galya. I want you to come with me.

In the town of Kostroma, eight hundred kilometres to the east of Leningrad, on the evening of 25 November 1935, Rossel's sister had walked into a snowstorm and vanished. It had been a few days after their joint eighteenth birthday.

But well before that, she had started avoiding him.

I never see you these days, Galya. Where do you go?

You have your place at the conservatoire, Revol. Once the paperwork is done, you'll be in Leningrad with your violin to keep you company.

What will I do?

What do I have here now?

Come with me, Galya. I want you to come with me.

I don't have permission. You know that.

Three months ago, Rossel had written to the Kostroma Militia Directorate requesting any files they held on Galina Rossel, with particular interest in any records dating from November 1935 onwards. The reply had not yet come. He had followed up with a request to his superiors to visit Kostroma and go through whatever militia archives were available. He had been awaiting a response for weeks.

It was more likely, of course, that he would find any trace of her in the filing cabinets of the Ministry for State Security, perhaps in Kostroma, perhaps in Moscow or Leningrad. If anyone knew what had happened to Galya, it would be the MGB. No other organisation was as obsessive in its documentation of Soviet citizens. No other organisation knew as much about their fates.

But for a low-ranking *militsioner* to poke his nose into such affairs was unwise. Especially if he was the son of two Old Bolsheviks who had been dispatched to a labour camp before facing a firing squad. Especially if he had his own history of dissent.

That was why he needed help.

6

In a city of spectacular parks, palaces and churches, the Mikhailovsky Garden held its own. The well-kept path along one border of the manicured gardens ran parallel to the Moika, a section of Leningrad's elegant lattice of canals that in summer lapped at the grassy shore but in the depths of winter was frozen, dusted white. Usually, the garden was a popular place for people to stroll, but the temperature had fallen overnight to minus twenty-five. The few Leningraders passing Rossel had their hats rammed down to meet the tops of their coats, scarves tightly drawn.

A stocky, brooding figure who looked to be examining the tips of his own boots stood by the water's edge, as still as the canal's ice. If he heard the crunch of Rossel's boots, he did not look up.

Finally, Major Nikitin turned. 'Well, look who it is. Tchaiko-vsky's bastard son. You look like shit,' he said. His voice was muffled inside the upturned collar of his coat.

Rossel stopped a few paces away. He looked Nikitin up and down, from the sea of scars on one side of his face to the pol-ished caps of his boots.

'I like your coat,' he said. 'Very expensive. Who did you borrow it from? Ivan the Terrible?'

Nikitin dusted a few flakes of snow from his pocket. It was

black sable, exquisite – the kind only someone at or near the peak of the Party hierarchy could afford. His broad, brutal face – disfigured around one missing eye by wartime scarring – broke into an uneasy grin.

The major pointed at his feet. Underneath, a pair of well-creased trousers and gleaming half-leather, half-felt *valenki* peeked out. 'New boots, too,' he said.

'At this rate, you'll have yourself a Party dacha out near Lake Ladoga.'

'What makes you think I don't?'

Rossel shrugged. 'Good point,' he said. 'Which Politburo hack are you working for this week? You must be running out of arses to kiss.'

He enjoyed the glare that Nikitin gave him, satisfied that the remark had hit home.

Oleg Nikitin, formerly of the Ministry for State Security, the MGB, and for a short period of its bitter rival, the military's Main Intelligence Directorate, GRU, had more recently become an aide to Nikita Khrushchev, a member of Stalin's inner circle, a position that was at once powerful and precarious. Along the way, Nikitin had acquired innumerable enemies, including Lavrentiy Beria, who was, after Stalin, the most feared man in the Soviet Union. But he had survived by ducking under the wing of other influential figures – doing deals, revealing secrets, offering his services. As many had found, the journey from the Kremlin to the Vorkuta labour camps could result from just one misstep. But for now, for today at least, Nikitin was somebody. And he knew it.

The major's voice softened. 'I can certainly get *you* a better job, Rossel, I'm sure of it. A better apartment, at least. As I said to you a few months ago, all you have to do is—'

'They're my parents. I won't denounce them as enemies of the people for a second time, just so you can get me a Party job re-arranging Khrushchev's sock drawer or cracking heads for the blue-hats.'

'Your parents are already dead. Even if you denounced them a thousand times, they would never ever know it.'

'But I would.'

Rossel swallowed, coughed a little – acid in his mouth from a breakfast eaten in haste. Or maybe, he thought, the contempt he felt for this man, his former torturer. The man who years ago had destroyed his hands, severing two of the fingers, in an effort to get him to confess to treason. Yes, the two of them had twice been forced into a strange alliance in recent years. Such were the times. But it didn't mean he had to like it.

Nikitin drew his collar up around his neck. 'So, why ask me here? I told you not to contact me without good reason.'

'Galya.'

Nikitin snorted. 'Again?'

'Yes, again,' said Rossel, trying to keep his voice level. 'My sister is the reason I agreed to help you last time. I still can't find a trace of her in militia records. I've contacted as many depart-ments as I could get hold of two hundred kilometres east and west of Kostroma, where she disappeared. Rang them myself. It's taken months. Nothing.'

'Militia records. Pieces of shit. They've probably still got one open on the Tsar. No one's told them he's dead yet.'

Rossel nodded. 'The MGB's files, on the other hand, are comprehensive. And you can—'

Nikitin spat on the snowy ground. 'No, I won't help you with that. Comrade Beria is not a man to forgive and forget, and I don't believe he has forgotten you. Or me, for that matter. I have worked to keep you safe. Got you this new job, out of the way.

Helped you when you won't even help yourself . . .' He pointed at Rossel's left hand. 'I've paid my penance,' he said. 'Don't mess it all up now by getting yourself noticed again. Forget about Galya.'

Rossel took out a *papirosa* and lit it. 'You might as well ask me to forget about myself,' he said, pulling hard on the cigarette. He tapped the back of his left hand with his right. 'And you still owe me. Not just for this. For how I helped you out with the Vronsky and Pletnev investigations.'

Nikitin scanned the park. No one close. Only a woman rocking a pram sitting on a distant bench.

'Stalin is tired,' he said, his voice no more than a murmur. 'Getting old. His paranoia is no longer just a necessity for survival but a disease. The shadows he hides among have begun to consume him. Everyone – and I mean everyone, not just the Jews or the doctors – is under suspicion. Some think even Beria is about to go under the water.' His voice softened again. 'Why not wait? That's all I'm saying. In a year or so, everything might be different. You have that girl, Natalya, am I right? A real beauty. A queen. Why not spend more time with . . .'

Rossel looked away. Like most of the woman he met, Natalya had not been able to put up with his obsession with missing-persons files for very long.

They walked side by side for a while. A grimy fog was descending, blotting out the cupolas of the nearby Cathedral of the Spilled Blood. They were alone in the snow-covered park now, two indeterminate figures, blotches of black ink on white paper.

After a minute or so, Rossel spoke. 'There is something else,' he said. 'An investigation.'

Nikitin stopped. 'I got you a job as a records keeper, not an investigator,' he remarked.

'I'm afraid that a senior comrade officer in the militia has insisted on my involvement.' He held up a hand to repel Nikitin's objections. 'It's all right – I can wrap this up simply enough. But there is an oddity. An MGB man, a colonel. He has taken an interest in the case.'

'Another case? Another bloody murder?'

Rossel hesitated. 'Not sure. A car accident near the Finland Station. The name is Vishensky. Other than his surname and rank, I don't know anything about him. But a run-of-the-mill car accident hardly seems relevant to state security.'

'Everything is to do with state security,' said Nikitin, 'if they decide it is.'

'Nothing on the surface, I mean.'

Nikitin rolled his eyes. 'Can't you stay out of trouble?'

'I want nothing to do with this case,' Rossel said. 'This is . . . just something to clarify.'

Nikitin stared at him. Finally, he clapped a hand on Rossel's shoulder. 'I'll see what I can find out.'

Rossel did not return the smile. 'About Vishensky?' he said.

'Yes.'

'And Galya?'

Nikitin stretched out a hand and squeezed Rossel's left glove.

'Penance,' he said. 'All right, more of that, if it makes you happy. What are old friends for, after all, if not to help each other?'

7

Senior Lieutenant Lidia Gerashvili pushed through the doors of Station 17 at 7.30 a.m. exactly. She manoeuvred her small frame through the morning bustle with caution, trying to avoid colliding with larger colleagues who moved and talked over and around her.

At one end of the main hall were the stairs that led to a large room for the more senior officers. Only a couple of years ago, it had been Rossel's office.

Station 17 was a former merchant's house on Vosstaniya Street, dubbed the 'Black House' by its occupants because of its soot-covered walls. It had no modern heating, only a number of fireplaces. Many of those were currently dark because the station could not find or afford enough coal or wood to burn.

The station had been raided by MGB troops two years earlier after an informant – they never knew who – had tipped off the secret police that a militia sergeant had fought for the monarchist side in the Civil War more than three decades before. Not that Rossel mourned the betrayed man, Sergeant Pavel Grachev, whose favourite method for dealing with any arrested woman was to offer her freedom in exchange for sex. The MGB had taken everyone in the station for robust interrogation. Not everyone had survived the experience. Gerashvili had been arrested. But then freed.

She began to climb the stairs. Her hair, Rossel noticed, once blonde, was now black and cut shorter. Her brief encounter with MGB interrogators had changed the way she moved. As if each step brought a faint echo of those torments. Before that, he remembered, her eyes had always been filled with a refreshing candour. A direct, searching honesty, almost reckless, which her time among the blue-hats had, at least for a while, extinguished.

Gerashvili had taken no more than four steps when – sensing the presence of the man sitting alone in the far corner of the room – she turned, met his eye and descended. The chatter in the station sank to a low hum as she threaded her way between desks and cupboards towards him.

By getting in at six that morning, Rossel had had a chance to choose the darkest, coldest corner of the police station. Not that he had needed to worry about having too many awkward conversations. From those who had no idea who he was, which was almost everybody, he got a few puzzled glances.

One or two recognised him but avoided contact. Word must have got around, he thought: Lipukhin had summoned him, he was there on the senior officer's orders. A former comrade-in-arms of their ill-starred captain. One who had been sent to the camps. And yet returned.

Rossel stood and readied himself to salute a senior officer. Gerashvili waved it away.

'Revol,' she said. 'Captain Lipukhin said he was hoping to persuade you to join us.'

Rossel inclined his head forward and then felt foolish for the formality. 'Comrade Captain Lipukhin would not accept no for an answer,' he replied.

Gerashvili studied his face, but he had been ready for that.

'I am very happy to see you again,' he said. 'Thank you for . . .' He stopped himself.

A year ago, Gerashvili had uncovered and passed on some vital information for Rossel in a case he had not officially been part of. The less said about that, with people about them, the better.

'Understanding,' Gerashvili nodded. Then looked him over. 'What has the captain got you working on?'

Rossel opened a thin file to show her half a dozen photographs of the two victims of the collision. 'A couple of ghosts,' he said. 'A woman in her forties and a man considerably older.'

She tapped a finger on the picture of the male. 'Georgian, I'd bet,' she said.

'I'd already had him down as being from the Caucasus,' Rossel replied. 'But that could mean he's from several places. You sure?'

'A raven is the aunt of a jay. That's what they say out there for someone who might be a distant relative. He is almost identical to every man in my extended family in Tbilisi, where I grew up.' Gerashvili shuffled through the photographs. 'She is not, though. She's as Russian as they come. A northerner.' She dropped the images. 'Have any missing-persons reports in other stations turned anything up?'

'I have not filed one yet, Comrade Senior Sergea— I mean Comrade Senior Lieutenant.'

He said this last part a little louder on purpose. It was not an issue that they were acquainted, but it was best if the militia comrades around them did not know how close they were as friends.

'I need appropriate authorisation to make such a request,' he added.

Gerashvili's eyes met his. A little mischief in them.

'The dead woman has something about her,' she said. 'An unusual presence. A nobility of bearing. She will be missed. I would not be surprised to find a male friend, or at least a concerned colleague, wondering where she is, why she has not reported for work . . . Request granted, Senior Militiaman Rossel.'

Gerashvili saluted. Rossel mirrored her.

'Thank you, Lieutenant.'

*

Less than two hours later, a response came in.

'I am most grateful, comrade,' Rossel said down the telephone.

A wheezing sergeant from a militia station on Vasilyevsky Island gabbled on for another twenty seconds. Gerashvili had been right. A report had been made by a concerned colleague, an academic at a research institute affiliated to the Hermitage Museum.

Anna Dmitriyevna Orlova, forty-eight, had not been in her office for three days. Usually, she would give her *administratsiya* ample warning of any absences – family business, annual leave, medical appointments. She had done so without fail for sixteen years. An unauthorised, spontaneous absence was out of character. The description of Orlova provided by the sergeant closely matched that of the corpse in the basement of The Crosses.

'Who was this colleague?' asked Rossel, pen pausing over his notepad.

'Let me see,' said the voice down the line. 'Here we are. Lapshin. Lev Abramovich Lapshin. Professor of Mediaeval Slavic Studies at the Philological Faculty of the university. Know it? It's based inside the old Menshikov Palace. And he heads a research institute that is affiliated to the Hermitage – or something along those lines, anyway. He came in looking very worried.'

The Menshikov was just over the water from the Hermitage. He could walk it in less than half an hour.

'Did he say if she had relatives?' asked Rossel. 'A husband?'

'No husband, no children,' said the sergeant. 'If she's got any family, they're not in Leningrad. What happened to her?'

'Car accident,' said Rossel.

'Dead?'

'Very.'

'This Lapshin will be upset, poor bastard,' said the sergeant. 'I will send someone to tell him.'

8

Professor Lapshin looked like an Orthodox priest, albeit one who had swapped his vestments for a brown suit and a pale-yellow tie.

'I am almost angry at her,' he said, blinking at Rossel, his lower jaw swivelling to the left and right, a motion that waggled his grey, wiry beard. 'Anna was a very private individual, very respectable. Dedicated. Vigilant. To be ... to be ... That she should meet her end in such a fashion ...'

'What do you mean?'

'The other militia officer told me something of the circumstances in which she was found,' said Lapshin, bobbing and shaking his head. He had the slightest lisp, which gave his sibilants an unfortunate dampness. 'At a rendezvous with a ... a ... a ... *southerner*. A lecherous Georgian. Perhaps ...' He looked up in hope. 'Perhaps she was simply too trusting?'

Rossel felt that the professor's feelings for Anna Orlova were not merely protective, his concerns not only for her reputation.

'Aren't we all, Comrade Professor,' he said. 'Did she ever mention a friend who fitted the description of this Georgian?'

'No, never.'

'Was she married?'

'Once, yes. But not any more. There was a tragic accident.'

Lapshin seemed to notice that his own voice had risen.

He took a long breath.

'She would work, day and night, staying here to examine her manuscripts until long after the rest of us had gone home.'

'What can you tell me about her work?'

Lapshin's beard did another dance. Rossel could see him trying to pull himself together. Repositioning his glasses over an angular nose, the academic rose from his seat, stumbled on his way past his desk and set off along one of the long, elegant corridors of the Menshikov Palace. Rossel followed him.

Long since deserted by its aristocratic occupants, the palace now served as an outpost of the Hermitage. It was used for minor exhibitions and academic research. They walked under gilded crystal chandeliers and past ornate candelabra until Lapshin stopped and opened the door of another, smaller office.

This one was dominated not by books but by large folders and files.

'Manuscripts,' Lapshin said. 'Some of them extremely rare. Look.'

He laid one out on the green-topped table.

'So,' said Rossel, looking around, 'this was Anna Orlova's office?'

'For many years,' said Lapshin. He opened the folder.

At a first, upside-down, glance, Rossel thought he knew what it was: a manuscript in Old Church Slavonic. A biblical text, a sermon, or a letter from a supposed saint to his flock. It was a copy, he realised, a facsimile of a more delicate, yellowing material. The letters were intricate, scratched out in an angular hand. Although some of the characters had faded over time, the individual words should be decipherable.

But they were not.

As he turned his head to take a better look, Rossel realised he could read none of it. It was a collection of crosses, loops, minute geometric shapes with almost childlike decorations and extensions.

ⰗⰟⰀⰎ ⰎⰡⰀⰞⰟ ⰔⰟⰟⰀⰜⰓ ⰥⰍⰅ· Ⱎ ⰀⰠⰠⰆ
ⰏⰅⰞⰜⰌ ⰅⰀⰏⰆ ⰒⰟⰞⰅⰞⰅ ⰓⰀⰟⰜⰆ
ⰆⰥⰌ· ⰆⰏⰀⰒⰆ ⰠⰆⰞⰏⰆ ⰞⱀⰆ· ⰆⰏⰟ
ⰟⰄⰆ ⰆⰀⰥⰆ ⰓⰆ· ⰒⰒⰆ ⰞⰆ ⰆⰜⰆⰗⰀ
ⰞⰜⰟⰗⰆ ⰠⰆⰎⰆ· ⰆⰥⰆⰎⰆⰜⰓ ⰀⰆ ⰥⰒⰆ
ⰌⰅ ⰗⰆ ⰀⰆⰀⰅⰀⰆ ⰠⰆⰅⰠⰆⰅ ⰜⰆ ⰥⰅ ⰎⰡⰀ
ⰔⰟⰟⰀⰜⰓ·

'Defeated?' said Lapshin. He leaned in so that he was shoulder to shoulder with Rossel. 'This,' he added, tracing the lines of the manuscript, 'is Glagolitic. The oldest alphabet of the Slav peoples. This text is from one of the Gospels. Anna was the real expert, but my guess would be that it was written in the tenth or eleventh century.'

'How can you tell?'

'The verb conjugations, the tenses. The orthography. Some of the vocabulary, which later fell out of use. There are clues. But it's not my field. Anna was so familiar with her work, she could recite some of these manuscripts from memory. And were it not for the modern paper instead of the parchment, you would be hard-pressed to tell the difference. She could spend hour after hour studying, reading, finding new things . . .'

Lapshin's finger hovered over the manuscript and moved from one letter to the next. He muttered under his breath as his finger travelled over the strange letters, sounds that were familiar, though the overall meaning was impenetrable.

Rossel stared at the manuscript's ornate lettering.

How beautiful . . .

Writing, yes, certainly. But the writing of wizards, or of a lost civilisation.

'So Glagolitic was replaced by Cyrillic?'

Lapshin smiled. 'I see I have piqued your interest,' he said. 'Broadly speaking, yes. But Anna's research was more extensive.'

He shuffled over to her records and weaved from left to right as he searched for something.

'Ah, there it is.' He pulled out a box. 'Only facsimiles, I'm afraid, but look at this.'

The script was more akin to Cyrillic. But the letters lined up before Rossel's eyes as if on the verge of making sense – only to deviate from the familiar alphabet and defy comprehension at the last moment.

'What is it?'

'Old Permic,' said Lapshin, delight in his voice. 'A script devised by St Stephen of Perm, who converted the pagans of the north – what is now the Komi Republic – and devised this script for their language. Which, as you know, is related to Finnish.'

Rossel had not known. But many territories throughout the Soviet Union had their own languages. Perm was a few hundred miles further east, but his grasp of the region's geography was shaky. North of Sverdlovsk?

'Is it still in use, this Old Permic?'

Lapshin shook his head. 'Sadly, no. It died out in the seventeenth century. Replaced by Cyrillic, of course. That was a time when Moscow was asserting greater authority over the country, not least in matters of religion. And Moscow could churn out more bibles and prayer books than a far-flung outpost of empire. Thus it overwhelmed alternative sources. Only a few people, such as Anna, kept the memory and knowledge of Old Permic alive. It is a fascinating academic subject but an orthographic dead end.'

Rossel cast a glance over his shoulder before asking his next question. 'Did Anna Orlova's work attract any . . . official attention?'

Lapshin stuffed the pages into their file and shoved them back on the shelf. He did not answer straight away. This was potentially hazardous terrain.

'On occasions,' he said at last.

'Because of the religious aspect?'

The professor studied Rossel's face for a few seconds. 'No,' he said, his voice low. 'Because of her opinions on the origins and movement of the peoples who now inhabit our glorious Soviet Union. Papers she wrote for her doctorate. She painted a picture of ethnic complexity, of the ebb and flow of different peoples of different origins. And when the official position on the origins of Russians switched to a theory of immutability and permanence, she was forced to retract.'

'But she must have defended her doctorate a long . . .' Rossel stopped himself. The observation was a stupid one. Words spoken or written a long time ago could be made to seem very recent in malevolent hands.

'Excuse me, comrade,' said Lapshin. He looked at Rossel

dolefully. 'This man. The one she was with. Do you know who he was? His background? His education?'

That soft lisp again on the last syllables of the question. The professor looked forlorn. As if he would have preferred Anna Orlova to have fallen into the Neva River rather than meet her end in the middle of a sordid entanglement with a common Soviet citizen.

Rossel shook his head. 'At present, comrade, he is as much a cipher to us as one of your Glagolitic texts.'

9

Rossel stuffed his notebook into his jacket pocket and sat down at his desk.

He was about to start work when he heard Gerashvili's voice cutting through the habitual murmur of Station 17. He turned to see her talking, voice raised in fury, to a tall young man whose face had turned bright red. The youth looked familiar.

'Why are you standing there like you've got a mouth full of water? Explain yourself, Volodya,' she demanded.

The militia officer, the same rank as Rossel but more than a decade his junior, stared down at her, mute and blinking. Rossel recognised him as one of the group who had kept watch over the two corpses outside the Finland Station.

'Well?'

'I . . .'

Almost every other officer had stopped to watch.

Gerashvili noticed the sudden quiet and glanced around. Most of them began inspecting their feet or addressing invisible paperwork.

She turned back to the red-faced junior. Only now did Rossel notice that she was holding a large photograph.

'Out of my sight,' she shouted.

Volodya walked away, the leisurely speed of his departure an obvious act of defiance. Rossel caught sight of his expression, his bitterness clear – *dressed down by a woman, and a Georgian to boot.*

Gerashvili walked towards Rossel.

He stood and saluted. 'Comrade Senior Lieu—'

'A few moments ago,' she cut in, 'a woman came in to report her uncle missing. Senior Militiaman Volodya over there thinks – *thinks*, mind you, though he didn't write it down – that the name she mentioned was Tamas.'

She stopped in mid-flow to draw breath.

'So he wanders over to your desk, knowing that you have photographs of those two poor people and that you are on the lookout for missing-persons reports, and takes this.' She held up the image in her hand; it was a death portrait of the male victim. 'Waves it in her face. At which point, she screams and runs out of the station. And we lose her, without learning her name, and potentially lose vital information, perhaps never to get it back.' She tossed the photograph onto Rossel's desk. 'Idiot,' she said through clenched teeth.

Rossel watched as she turned and disappeared up the stairs. He looked around for Senior Militiaman Volodya and saw him standing by a fireplace, staring into the black hearth. He walked over to him.

'You all right, comrade?' he asked.

Volodya shrugged. 'Iron Balls – that's what we call that bitch. She's full of herself since they made her senior lieutenant. Fuck your mother, you think she'll report me?'

'No,' said Rossel. 'She's good at what she does. Asks the same of others. But she's not vindictive. I've worked with her before.'

Volodya looked unconvinced.

'This woman you spoke to about her missing uncle,' Rossel said. 'What did she look like?'

'Small. Pretty,' said Volodya.

'How pretty?'

He smiled. 'Big eyes like Klara Luchko. You know, the one in *Three Encounters*. Except she was *chyornaya*, a proper blackarse – Georgian, Armenian, I don't know. Dyed red hair, a bucketload of slap.' Volodya patted his groin with proprietorial pride. 'Makes my *khui* glow just thinking about her.'

'And she definitely said her uncle was missing?'

Volodya nodded.

'Then what?'

'I told the blackarse we had a candidate in the fridge at The Crosses.'

'And you showed her the photograph?'

'I'm not an idiot,' said Volodya, 'despite what Iron Balls says. First, I checked the file on the corpse and quizzed her, and she got it all right – rough age, height, shape, looks and so on. Right down to the scar on his belly, the lot. That's our man, I said. And, to be honest, she didn't seem that upset.' He picked at his nose. 'But as soon as I said he'd been hit by a car that hadn't stopped, she turned white as a sheet. Then I held up the photo and she started sobbing and pissed off.'

Odd, Rossel thought, that it was the manner of death, not the death itself, that had scared her.

'So you didn't get his name?' asked Rossel, trying and failing not to sound too irritated.

Volodya's face flushed. He straightened. 'Enough of the interrogation, comrade,' he said. 'You're just another militiaman like me. I did get a name, even if just a first name – Tamas.' He thrust his neck out. 'T . . . A . . . M . . . A—'

'Half a name, thanks so much. That will reduce the length of my search from around two decades to one,' said Rossel.

Volodya took a step forward. Rossel stood his ground.

A sergeant got up from his desk and strode towards them.

'That's enough from you, new boy,' he said, stabbing a hand at Rossel.

Rossel returned the sergeant's glare. 'I know my place, respected Comrade Sergeant,' he said. 'But when a witness comes in off the street, you make sure your junior officers at least have enough brains to get their name down.'

The sergeant stared at Rossel. 'Listen, you condescending bastard. You might be an old friend of the captain, but I'll drop you in the Moika if you talk to me like—' He started to raise his fists.

'I did get a name,' whined Volodya.

Almost nose to nose, Rossel and the sergeant turned to look at him.

'Not his,' Volodya added. 'Hers.'

The sergeant stepped back and sighed. 'What was it then, fuck your mother?' he shouted.

Volodya fumbled inside a pocket and retrieved his notebook. 'Dzagnidze,' he said. 'Elene Dzagnidze.'

10

Elene Dzagnidze lived in a small, shabby street in the Kalininsky District, almost at the city's northeastern limits. Opposite her building was a skating rink and a small shop with an enormous red sign saying *Shoes*. Two of the letters had fallen off.

Dzagnidze inhabited a room at the far end of a large communal apartment on the third floor. Rossel could see she looked after it. The floor was covered by a large green and red rug decorated with winter scenes, the chairs were draped in damask coverings, of rough cotton but in tasteful patterns, and the room was softly lit by a plain but elegant standing lamp with a fading pink shade.

It was almost two rooms, in fact. The bed was part-hidden behind a wall that someone had started but given up on less than halfway through, perhaps surrendering in the face of the impossibility of making this house even more minuscule. She had a couple of shelves, one filled with dog-eared paperbacks, the other for photographs, trinkets, pieces of jewellery. Jars and tins of food – pickled vegetables and preserved fish, mainly – were stacked in, on and around a cupboard.

She had opened the door to the apartment herself, and her attempt to look surprised at being visited by the militia had been short-lived and unconvincing. Volodya had been right about her. She was beautiful, with smooth, dark skin, black eyes and broad, symmetrical features. Yes, she did have a touch of the film star Klara Luchko about her.

For a moment, Rossel was left on his own, Dzagnidze having gone to the kitchen to make them some tea. The way this communal apartment had been divided meant that some rooms had radiators, while others, like hers, went without, and so her lodgings were chilly. Rossel's room in his old *kommunalka* had been the same, while his neighbour's place was as hot as a *banya* throughout the entire winter. Once the building's management committee turned on the radiators in mid- to late October, they stayed on until the spring.

On a table was a tin box, stuffed with photographs, its lid half closed. Rossel picked it up and riffled through the images. Holiday snaps, for the most part. One caught his attention. A lakeside scene. A girl of nine, obviously the young Elene, with a middle-aged man, fat belly spilling over his swimming trunks. A younger version of the corpse lying on Bondar's trolley back at the morgue. Rossel pocketed it, then replaced the lid and sat in a low-slung armchair, gloved hands on his knees. Even through his thick coat, he could feel several springs digging into his back. He guessed Dzagnidze was using the time to get her story straight, playing out all the possible conversations ahead of her.

The interesting question was why she felt the need to do so.

*

After ten minutes, Dzagnidze returned, carrying a tray set with two cups that she placed on a small table at one end of the room. She offered him sugar. In the labour camps, sugar was like gold. If you came across any, you'd devour it, even if you had to lick it off the floor. Like so many other Gulag habits, the worship of it had stayed with Rossel. Right now, it was hard to get in the shops and Leningraders were enduring an enforced period of abstinence.

For Dzagnidze to offer him some was a generous gesture.

Another trip to the kitchen elicited some biscuits, hard and dry but edible. If there had been jam, she would probably have produced that, too – when they had guests, Russians set the table for tea with iron rules. But jam was also in short supply that month.

Giving him an uneasy, fleeting smile, Dzagnidze retreated to her own chair, keeping some distance between them.

'Your uncle,' he said, breaking the silence. 'Can I take his full name, please?'

'Abazi,' she replied. 'Tamas Abazi.'

'What can you tell me about him?'

She picked up her cup and took a sip. 'Not very much. I didn't see Uncle Tamas often,' she offered. 'He lives near Tbilisi, and I left Georgia several years ago. Not long after the war.'

'He is on which side of your family?'

'My mother's.'

'A big family?'

She nodded. 'Georgians count a lot of relatives as "family". I have two aunts and one uncle on that side, and three uncles and two aunts on my father's side.'

'And what is your own profession?' Rossel asked.

'I am employed at the Lomonosov Porcelain Factory. A designer there.'

'For how long?'

'Since the war,' she said.

'And during the war?'

'I worked on a production line at a military aircraft factory outside Tbilisi,' she said. 'We made Yaks there.'

Rossel nodded. 'Beautiful aircraft. An invaluable contribution to the Soviet war effort, comrade.'

She smiled at the compliment.

Rossel straightened his back. 'Why was your uncle in Leningrad?'

Dzagnidze thought for a moment. Then took another sip. 'I don't really know,' she said. 'He turned up, out of the blue. A few days ago.'

'He didn't give a reason?'

'He said he had come to see some old friends. I was puzzled – he'd never mentioned them to me. I didn't know he knew anyone in Leningrad.'

'Who were these "friends"?' Rossel pressed her.

'I asked,' she replied, 'but he just laughed and wouldn't say. Can I ask you something, comrade?'

'Of course.'

She leaned in a little. 'You appear to be an ordinary *militsioner,*' she said. 'I thought, perhaps, they might send someone more senior.'

Dzagnidze blew on her tea and looked at him over the rim of her cup. She must suspect he was from the MGB. Or from the Party.

Play the part, then.

'My superior officers are very busy,' he answered. 'You must have seen the papers, all this talk of Jewish doctors and their plots. Our great Socialist state is under constant attack from capitalist exploiters and fifth columnists. So I have been given some small tasks to fulfil in relation to the incident you refer to. Tell me, Comrade Dzagnidze, what did your uncle do in Tbilisi?'

'Oh, he was long retired,' she said. There was a nervous edge to her voice, cowed by the mention of fifth columnists. 'Before that, he was a labourer, doing this and that. A warehouseman, also, loading and unloading goods. Welding. Carpentry. That sort of thing. He was good with tools.'

'How many times did your uncle visit you here in Leningrad?'

'Just the once,' she said. 'He turned up at my door a few days ago – relatives had given him my address. There are no secrets among folk in small towns in the mountains.'

'In the mountains? I thought you said he lived in Tbilisi. That is a city, not a small town.'

Under make-up, applied to accentuate her already sharp cheekbones, Dzagnidze reddened. It took three more sips of tea to compose herself.

'Gori,' she said. 'He came from Gori. People move between the two. Family all over the place, in the sense of extended family.'

It was Rossel's turn to lean forward. The tone of his voice changed, became more conspiratorial. 'These friends he had in Leningrad, comrade. Was one of them called Soselo?'

Dzagnidze's right hand began tapping on the edge of the table, making her cup shake in its saucer.

'I don't— who . . .'

'Soselo,' Rossel said again. 'Who is he?'

Dzagnidze set her cup on the table. 'I don't know him,' she said. 'Perhaps, you can enlighten me?'

She did not smile, but something in her demeanour changed – as if he had revealed his weak point. As if she had turned the tables.

Rossel did not move. 'Who is Soselo?' he repeated.

Dzagnidze took out a handkerchief, dabbed at her mouth and replaced it. She said nothing, only gave him a measured, confident stare. A display meant to convey she had found him out. That she was sure he was only an ordinary *militsioner*, after all.

'Comrade,' she said. 'I urge you to see to it that bureaucracy does not hold up the repatriation of my uncle's body. Now I would like you to leave.'

She stood and crossed to the door. Seeing there was nothing to be gained by persisting, at least for the time being, Rossel followed. Before she opened it, she turned to face him. Her jawbone flexed under her skin. She stepped closer, reached up to touch his collar. A confusing mix of hostility and intimacy.

'I also urge you to forget all about him,' she said.

Rossel looked down at her, unnerved by her cold flirtatiousness. He glanced at the hand and then reached up and removed it.

'Forget that he was hit by a car whose driver clearly intended to kill him, you mean, Comrade Dzagnidze?'

Without another word, she opened the door, ushered him through it into the corridor, and closed it behind him.

11

Arm outstretched in the evening gloom, Lenin struck his famous pose, exhorting the city to greater feats of Bolshevik zeal, entreating the proletariat to further throw off the shackles of imperialism and overturn the bourgeois lackeys who propped up the corrupt capitalist system – to take their glorious revolution not just to Russia but to the world.

For a moment, Rossel was Lenin's only companion, two men standing outside the Finland Station lost amid the snow. If Rossel shut his eyes, ghostly crowds raised cheers for the Bolsheviks and hurled abuse at the Tsar. But the din of the rabble was soon drowned out by the morning trams and lorries rumbling along the embankment and up and down the square. Rossel turned away from the statue and walked towards the railway station.

Anna Orlova and Uncle Tamas, whoever the old *muzhik* was, had probably emerged from the station, turned immediately right and right again, and come to a halt at the tram stop in the middle the road.

If they had arrived by train, they might have spent the day, or a few days, somewhere in the Leningrad Oblast. A discreet fleapit in a sleepy satellite town, perhaps, or a spa, or the apartment of someone they both knew. Or maybe it was a day trip to find time for some quiet canoodling. Alcohol had been consumed.

Consensual – they had returned together, waited for a tram. He pictured them both, laughing, clinging to each other . . .

And then their expressions of alarm, disbelief, terror as the car had headed straight for them. If they'd had time to register it at all.

To hit the two victims and then smash into the shelter so hard that the roof came off, Rossel reasoned, the car must have been travelling fast and either skidded so that the brakes were useless – signifying an accident – or not have braked at all, indicating a deliberate act.

The roof of the tram shelter was thin sheet metal, flimsy and light. It was propped up against the remains of the wooden structure that it had covered – tilting stumps and a couple of small, splintered planks that had once been a bench.

But if the driver had merely made a terrible mistake, he would have stopped. He would have got out and run to the bodies. Found them bleeding, unconscious, perhaps not quite dead. Even if he'd panicked, he'd have jumped back in and roared off – leaving a clear set of single tyre tracks, a few vital metres of them, from the ruined tram shelter back to the road.

There had been nothing like that visible the other night. Which meant the car must have reversed, and with care. Then re-joined the road and driven off.

This is murder. No doubt about it.

Glancing around, Rossel tried to spot any unwanted observers. None made themselves obvious and making yourself obvious was often the idea. Men in trench coats lurking in cars. Intimidation was the point.

That was odd, too.

No car for Colonel Vishensky?

The blue-hat had arrived on foot and departed the same way, marching off into the night. Back towards the embankment.

But instead of keeping strictly to the road, Vishensky had veered onto the park and towards Lenin's statue, following a course that took him towards Arsenalnaya Embankment and out of sight.

Rossel retraced Vishensky's footsteps as best he remembered them, deviating at what he thought was the correct point. After a few more paces, he paused before the giant statue again.

He stopped to read the inscription:

Da zdravstvuyet nasha revolutsiya. All hail our Revolution.

Rossel peered up at the wet flakes swirling around Lenin's bald pate.

While his huge left arm was stretched out in front of him, his right was curled and held close to his breast. A large lump of snow was covering the top of it, giving the oddly surreal impression that Vladimir Ilyich was eating an ice cream.

Rossel turned and began to walk away.

What's that?

Something was resting against the statue's plinth. Rossel pushed away the snow around it. He stood and inspected the object.

It was a wooden carving, approximately fifteen centimetres long, five centimetres across its base and shaped like a crooked truncheon. A face, of a sort: eyes, a nose and mouth. But it did not look human, nor as if the carver had even attempted to depict a human face. It was long and lugubrious. Rossel turned it over in his hands. From one angle, it looked to be wearing an expression of infinite patience. From another, it seemed ferocious – no, more than that. Enraged.

A joke?

It was hard to understand what might be funny about leaving such an object here. Hard to see any purpose at all, in fact.

The snow that covered it had fallen since the night they had found the bodies.

Did Vishensky see it?

The thought of the blue-hat made Rossel glance nervously around him again.

He turned a full circle, but unless a driver in one of the few passing cars was paying attention to him, no one had seen him retrieve the piece of wood. He slipped it into his coat pocket, not quite sure why he was doing so, baffled by what it might signify.

But at the same time, certain it meant something. As he walked towards the station, he looked back at the statue, half-convinced the little carving had somehow slipped from Lenin's grasp.

2
ПТИЦА
Bird

12

He woke early to a changed world.

Blinking, Rossel tried to shield his eyes against the onrushing snow with his gloves. Blizzards like this one engulfed the canals, palaces and pavements. Out on the street, he felt like the only human left alive, stumbling through Leningrad's maze of water and stone, every other soul obliterated in this whiteness. The tram stop he was searching for had also disappeared – surely he must have reached it by now? Or had he passed it? Was he even still on the pavement? No, there it was, abandoned in a white desert.

It offered little protection, but he clung to it, waiting for a tram.

At last, one arrived, heralded by dim headlamps and tiny orange sidelights. Its doors clanked open and Rossel tumbled inside with relief.

A *babushka*, wedged into a seat, tutted in alarm at his appearance and asked if he was all right.

'Fine, but thanks for your concern.'

He sat and tried to get his breath back.

As the tram rumbled north, Rossel stared out of the window into the nothingness and thought again of his sister, who had disappeared into an all-consuming snowstorm such as this one.

It had been almost two decades ago, and in another place. Maybe, in the years since, she had indeed sought him out in Leningrad? Perhaps she had been a face in the crowd, a whisper on a stairwell, a passenger behind the misted window of a tram, trundling past on a city street. But if this was so, why had she never tried to contact him? He pushed the idea away.

A fantasy.

They inched along the Obvodny Canal until Rossel had to change trams to one that ran a little faster up Ligovsky Prospekt. Stop by stop, the carriage took on more passengers until dozens were rammed in. Those with seats were trying to fend off upright comrades who were being pushed into their laps.

A young man smeared a hole through the condensation on the windows and, away to the left, Rossel caught a glimpse of the four bronze horses that reared up over the Anichkov Bridge, the snow swirling and eddying around them. The horses were fighting four human figures who were trying to tame them – Man versus Nature. Classical in design, commissioned by a Tsar, they depicted an epic battle that appealed to the Soviet mindset. Why else create new cities in Arctic wastelands where the winters were fifty degrees or more below? Why else try to build railways in Siberia over terrain that was ice for half the year and stinking swamp for the other half? Bending nature to the will of Socialism was the goal of the Soviet leadership.

Memories of his sister Galya came back to Rossel again. The bridge had been one of the last places in Leningrad where they had spent time together. Teenagers full of Marxist-Leninist slogans and Komsomol platitudes, before the Bolshevik Leviathan consumed their family. Before their parents had been arrested and had vanished into the galaxy of Soviet corrective labour camps. And they had been sent to an orphanage in the small town of Kostroma.

Barely a year later, Galya had disappeared. The last sight he'd had of her was from a window. She had stepped out from beneath a light and disappeared, lost in the dancing flurries.

Tamas Abazi had done something similar.

The old man had gone out one night and not come back. But at least the Georgian's niece knew where he was, even if it was on a cold metal bench in a morgue.

Not that she seemed to care.

The tram braked hard, eliciting gasps and curses from its passengers. As they settled again, Rossel closed his eyes.

He saw Galya's face staring at him from the open door of a room just before she had disappeared. He had looked up from practising his violin – his audition for the Leningrad Conservatoire was in a few days' time. Something in her eyes and a redness in her cheeks made him feel she was about to tell him something. His playing was drawing it out of her.

A secret.

A confession.

At school, they'd both been taught by a sad-eyed science teacher who loved examining things under a microscope. Pollen, onion skins, yeast cells, mould.

'Tiny worlds filled with secrets.' Galya would often repeat the teacher's phrase, Rossel remembered. The man was right. Up close, mould on black bread looked like tiny balloons tethered by a piece of string. An onion skin like the cobbled floor of a great castle.

And a snowflake . . .

No two are alike – did you know that, Revol?

His stop was approaching. All around, passengers were making ill-tempered inquiries as to who was getting out.

So you may think we're the same because we're twins. But we're not, Revol. I will never be just like you, nor you like me . . .

Rossel muscled his way as close as he could to the middle of the carriage. The doors burst open and a rabble of citizens bundled tight in coats and scarves spilled into the busy street.

Somehow, he had ended up on Nekrasova; he had overshot and would have to take a detour. But he didn't mind.

Unlike the living, the dead weren't in a hurry.

13

Even slit down the middle, the corpse looked better than Captain Lipukhin.

The captain – dark rings around his eyes, mottled blotches on his nose and cheeks – looked as though if he were to lie on the metal table next to the fat, naked Georgian, Tamas Abazi would be the more likely of the two to get up first.

Rossel and Lipukhin stood in the centre of the mortuary next to Dr Bondar. The woman lay covered by a sheet on another table in the corner.

'Verdict?' said Rossel.

The pathologist scratched his chin. 'In theory, accidents like this are motiveless,' Bondar began. 'The driver leaves home having planned nothing, merely intending to live a perfectly normal day. By the time they get home that evening and shut the door behind them, he or she is a killer. Such a perpetrator, like the victim, never sees it coming. Fate simply introduces each to the other. However, that may not be the case here.'

'I could do without the rhetorical flourishes and bullshit philosophy, comrade,' said Lipukhin. 'Just tell us what happened.'

Bondar nodded his head in exaggerated apology. 'There are three important aspects,' he clarified. 'First, the physical. The internal organs reveal the severity of the impact. The kidneys and liver are ruptured – possibly this man turned his back to the vehicle at the last minute in a futile effort to absorb some of the impact. The spine is fractured in several places. Well, not so much fractured as crushed on one side – the, ah, right side – so he must have twisted to that side as the vehicle hit. Both of his legs are broken, as is the case with the woman. I would say they were standing perfectly still at the moment of impact.'

'Frozen to the spot, then,' said Rossel. 'Unable to get out of the way, unable to do anything except brace for the killing blow.'

'Or they simply didn't see the danger,' added Lipukhin.

'Wouldn't you hear the engine of a vehicle coming towards you at speed?' said Bondar.

'Perhaps they were distracted?' replied Rossel.

'By what?' countered Lipukhin, turning to him.

'A good question,' said Bondar, pleased to take this cue. 'And I think I have the answer. Both victims had considerable levels of alcohol in the blood – not enough to be incapacitated, but enough to indicate they had been having a good time. More revealing was the man's mouth, once we had cleared away the blood. His lips were still red.'

'Lipstick?' said Rossel.

'Correct.'

The pathologist picked up the right hand of the male corpse, and then sauntered over to do the same to the woman.

'No ring on either of them,' he said with a grin. 'A couple of free spirits here.' Bondar let the woman's arm drop. It hit the table with a thud. 'But now Fate has decreed they're married for eternity.'

If Bondar was right, that was one theory that appeared to have been confirmed, thought Rossel. The liaison had been a romantic one. Until it had been interrupted.

'And the third aspect, Maksi?' he said.

'The third aspect is the most intriguing,' replied Bondar. 'You may or may not like it.' He moistened his lips.

'Go on,' said Lipukhin, his voice so quiet, it was barely audible.

Bondar pointed to two folded piles of clothes. One male, one female. 'Those tell a different story,' he remarked. 'For example, the woman's coat. White, which made this task easier.' He held it up. 'As well as some specks of blood, it is covered with black marks. Grease and oil.'

'They were hit by a car or van,' said Rossel. 'Surely, you'd expect that, Maksi?'

Bondar put the coat back down. 'Generally, when the person has been hit while standing, as indicated by both victims having spiral fractures of the lower leg, the impact throws them clear.'

Rossel tapped his right index finger against one of the missing stubs of his left. 'Thrown clear. So, the car does not pass over the body.'

'Correct. But despite the snowy conditions, the clothes of these two unfortunate souls have dirt and grease on both the front and back *and* right and left sides.'

Lipukhin slumped into a chair. 'Shit,' he muttered.

'So, the car hit them once, and then rolled over them again to make sure,' said Rossel.

'Exactly,' said Bondar. 'There was a secondary impact when the car followed through, crushing the victims against either the tram shelter or the road, or both. Put bluntly, some of our unfortunate couple's insides were ruptured, some were crushed, and by two different types of force. Collision, and then weight.'

Rossel felt for his cigarettes. 'Murder, then,' he said.

Lipukhin stood and pointed at Rossel. 'I knew it. A murder and they've handed it to the poor fools in the Workers and

Peasants Militia, to a department headed by a . . .' He stopped just short of self-condemnation. 'So, we are meant to sweep it all up and forget about it,' he continued, muttering through clenched teeth, and pacing up and down between the two ashen corpses.

'I am not an investigator, of course,' Bondar interrupted, 'but I can tell you that such a collision will have caused significant damage to the vehicle concerned. Smashed headlights, dents in the bodywork, traces of blood and fragments of clothing. The blood may have been washed off, but a thorough examination of the vehicle should find fibres from the victims' clothing. The traffic police should be able to find the car.'

Rossel did not voice the alternative, which was that its owner might not be a citizen but an organisation, with the means to conceal the vehicle until it had been repaired, or to have it dismantled and sold for scrap because it was one of many at their disposal.

Lipukhin was still agitated, wagging his finger at the unheeding bodies. 'That's why that blue-hat turned up out of nowhere, why he told us to do the paperwork and leave it. Well, to hell with them . . .' He stopped. 'I won't be taken for a fool again . . .'

But the other men were no longer listening. Dr Bondar gripped Rossel by the arm. With his free hand, he pointed to the door. Through the small double window, they could see a number of men in a distinctive uniform arriving.

At their head was Colonel Vishensky.

*

The morgue was always cold, but the temperature managed to drop another couple of degrees as Vishensky and two other MGB officers, wearing their blue-topped caps with red bands, strode in. Two more of Vishensky's men stood guard outside the room.

The colonel looked at each of them with those pale and unblinking eyes, before his gaze alighted on the dead bodies. With heavy, deliberate steps, he walked over to Abazi's bloated corpse. He removed his cap and placed it next to the body.

'Even now, so many years after the Blockade,' said the colonel, 'whenever I see a well-fed man in Leningrad, I think, "There goes a traitor in our midst." Back then, you could only fill a fat belly like that with stolen rations.'

'Black bread, sausage and a lot of red wine,' said Dr Bondar. He swallowed hard and added: 'That's what was inside this unfortunate comrade. His name is Tamas Abazi.'

Vishensky turned towards him. The pathologist took a step back.

'A feast, then?' said Vishensky. 'A celebration of sorts? A happy death day for Comrade Abazi? What else have you discovered, Comrade Bondar?'

Dr Bondar tried to smile but only managed to open his mouth and close it again without speaking.

Rossel stepped forward. 'We have established that he has family in Leningrad, Comrade Colonel,' he said. 'Or, rather, had. A niece. She came looking for him. As for the woman, so far only her work colleagues have come forward. No relatives in the city to grieve.'

That's right – I have been looking into this, comrade, despite your advice, despite even my own inclinations.

'Grieve, Comrade Senior Militiaman Rossel?' Vishensky raised his eyebrows. 'Did not Lenin tell us our collective power is established on the sublimation of the individual will? Now, if Socialism died, I would grieve for that. But not these two.'

Vishensky walked over to Orlova and drew back the sheet that covered her, exposing the jagged welter of stitching up and down her corpse.

'I'm disappointed in you, Captain Lipukhin,' he said.

'Disappointed?'

Vishensky dropped the sheet. 'To waste the resources of Comrade Bondar, such a highly respected scientist, by further examining two bodies that I thought we had already concluded were victims of nothing more than an unfortunate car accident.'

He picked up a scalpel from Dr Bondar's tray of instruments and held it up to the light. Then he placed the flat blade against the woman's forehead, turning it from side to side until it marked the pale brown skin.

'Don't . . .' said Bondar. His voice trailed away.

Vishensky looked up. 'Don't?'

'I am always professional, Comrade Colonel. I only make the marks that must be made. The ones that help turn the pages of their stories.'

Vishensky took the tip of the blade and traced a mark in the dead woman's forehead.

'Let me close your book on these two, then, Comrade Bondar,' he replied. 'As I have said, a simple car accident. That, I assure you, is all that has happened here.' He began to trace another line. The guards flanking him couldn't take their eyes off the twisting scalpel. 'In the Bolshoi Dom, the inmates envy the dead, comrades. I have seen them look up as the bodies are carried away. *They're safe now* – that's what they are thinking. Gone to where no one can hurt them.' Vishensky smiled softly. 'But, perhaps, they're wrong about that? And wherever it is they go, someone like me is waiting?'

Vishensky took the scalpel off the body and further tested its point with his little finger. 'No crime has been committed here. As I said, a car accident. Abazi and Anna are . . .' He stopped himself.

'Are you referring to Comrade Orlova, Colonel?' said Rossel.

Vishensky's cheeks darkened. He shouted out an order to his men. The two standing guard at the door came in and all four MGB officers began wheeling the two trolleys out of the morgue.

'Colonel, I must protest,' said Dr Bondar.

'Must you, Doctor?' asked Vishensky. 'I would be careful about that.' He pointed at the fresh cuts he had made in Anna Orlova's forehead. 'I can already see this examination has been botched, the evidence tampered with, and thus rendered worthless. Be careful what you say, or I will have to report your negligence. And as recent arrests of treacherous metropolitan elements, these Zionist doctors, make clear, now is not a good time to come to the attention of the authorities.'

He picked up his blue cap and placed it on his head. The metal trolleys thudded against the doors of the morgue as the corpses were taken away.

'Bravo, Comrade Vishensky,' said Rossel. 'It takes exceptional revolutionary zeal to arrest the dead.'

The colonel closed his eyes and inhaled. 'I have read your file, Comrade Senior Militiaman Rossel,' he said. His eyes opened a fraction. 'You seem to be the kind of fellow who sees thin ice as an invitation to tap dance.'

Vishensky walked towards the door. At the last moment, he turned.

'Be careful, comrades,' he said. 'Ice can break.'

14

In silence, Rossel and Lipukhin drove back to Station 17.

As they pushed through the station doors, Rossel spoke. 'Well?'

'Well, what?' snapped Lipukhin.

'This investigation's over, isn't it? Vishensky has drawn a line. We can't cross it.'

Lipukhin held his gaze for a moment, turned his back and headed for the stairs that led to his office.

Rossel shrugged.

He walked over to his desk, intending to tidy up a few files and take his leave. On the top of one of the folders lay a scrappy note. He read it, tucked it into a pocket and hurried back out into the street.

*

Less than a minute after entering the grand Komsomolskaya Square entrance of Leningrad's Moscow Station, Rossel spotted Nikitin at the other end of the main hall. The major was standing next to one of the large Italianate arched windows, pretending to examine train timetables.

'About time,' said Nikitin. 'I've virtually memorised the departure time of every weekday train leaving this station. I was about to move on to weekends.'

'I get to talk to you twice in a week,' said Rossel. 'I'm honoured.'

'More than you know, comrade,' said Nikitin, stamping his feet. 'Fuck your mother, is there no heating in this station?'

Rossel didn't answer.

Nikitin sniffed. 'No small talk, today, I see. All right, I'll get on with it. I must return to Moscow, anyway. My train leaves in half an hour. But I have made some inquiries on your behalf. And something else turned up on its own. You'll want to hear both.'

A couple of other people, men in suits and long coats, began to study the timetables. Nikitin took Rossel by the elbow and led him towards the platforms.

The station was not busy, but a former MGB officer was not about to take any chances. Being on the platform gave him an excellent vantage point to spot anyone who might be interested in their conversation.

'Number one. I was wrong to dissuade you from your investigation,' said Nikitin, once he was certain they could not be overheard. 'Pursue it.'

'But last time we spoke you said not to?'

'Last time we spoke, I had not mentioned it to my friends in Moscow. Now I have.'

'That may prove difficult,' said Rossel. 'The MGB colonel who first warned us off this case has confiscated the bodies of the two victims.'

Nikitin frowned, the mass of scars on one side of his face wrinkling. He adjusted his scarf. 'Colonel Vishensky, yes?'

'Correct.'

Nikitin pointed at a large poster on the wall of the furthest platform. The slogan read: *Smert' shpionam*. 'Death to spies.'

'Not just a slogan,' he said. 'A direct order to state security from Stalin himself. Your Colonel Vishensky is in MGB counter-intelligence. It is his role, along with others, to eliminate enemy agents. Root out traitors. By reputation, he is relentless. Pitiless.'

Rossel scrutinised Nikitin. The note in the major's voice was hard to interpret. It could have been caution, or admiration for the colonel. It might have been fear. But Nikitin was scanning the platform and gave no clues away. He turned towards Rossel.

'Ever since the Revolution, émigré White Russians have clustered in Paris and Istanbul, Belgrade, Berlin, Switzerland, London. Plotting to restore the monarchy, even though the brains of the Romanovs were long since splattered on a wall. Nearly all of them are hopeless dreamers, and those who had the capacity to be more than that are dead, largely because of Vishensky. In the thirties, he posed as a ringleader in one of the most prominent anti-Soviet groups, which enabled him to lure its other leaders into Russia to lead fake coup attempts and assassination plots. And have them arrested, interrogated and shot.'

Rossel glanced at the poster and back at Nikitin. 'So, why is a senior counter-intelligence officer rummaging through the pockets of two road accident victims at the scene of a supposed accident?' he said.

'Good question.'

'And also, presumably, the reason your friends in Moscow want me to keep looking into this affair . . .'

Nikitin patted Rossel on the shoulder, as if he was a dim-witted pupil who had finally got a mathematics problem right.

'After the war, he continued in counter-intelligence. The Second Directorate of the MGB. Promoted to colonel. Doesn't drink or smoke. No loose talk, no pillow talk. Leaves no traces of himself in anything he does – quite literally, in fact.'

'I'm not following.' Rossel was growing impatient.

'No fingerprints.'

'I still don't understand.'

'There's an odd remark on his file, on the health assessment. Otherwise, fit and healthy. But he has . . .' The major reached into a pocket and pulled out a scrap of paper on which was written a single word. 'Words of more than two syllables give me a headache. I had to get a doctor to tell me what this meant. Adermatoglyphia. No ridges on the skin of the fingers, or toes, or even the palms of his hands. He could sneak into your room at night, pick up everything you owned and not a single print.'

A train began to pull into the platform, obscuring the poster on the opposite wall.

'Even a ghost leaves a chill behind,' said Nikitin. 'Vishensky leaves nothing.'

The train, an old steam class L converted from freight to passenger use, belched out a plume of smoke as it pulled to a stop. Its passengers began to disembark. A woman in a red headscarf, carrying a baby in one arm, was having problems getting her suitcases down with the other. Rossel stepped forward and picked one up. Nikitin picked up the other. She nodded her thanks, as they carried them to her waiting mother at the other end of the platform.

'Always happy to help,' said the major.

Rossel stayed silent, resenting anything that suggested co-operation between the two of them.

A loudspeaker burst into life. The Moscow train was announced.

Nikitin straightened the buttons of his coat and picked up his small case.

'What was the other thing?' said Rossel.

'The other thing?'

'The thing that turned up on its own.'

Nikitin fastened his top button. 'Oh yes, that,' he said. 'Well, now. Cast your mind back a few years before the war.'

Rossel said nothing.

'As you may recall, a troubled time,' Nikitin went on.

This was an understatement. In the years before the Great Patriotic War, Leningrad endured a long, dark period of para-noia, terror and violence. Missing faces, empty desks at work, silence on the other side of the walls of your room where once you had heard laughter or arguments or sex or toasts to happi-ness or to the health of members of the Politburo.

Those mass arrests and disappearances had not come out of nowhere, for they had had their omens. Portents of slaughter. Among the omens was the fate of two Old Bolsheviks, believers from the start in Lenin and his Revolution. Two people who had paid for their devotion with one-way trips to the labour camps, shortly after their denunciation and arrest. Rossel's parents.

'Not everyone, however, was deterred by this great purge of anti-Soviet metropolitan elements from indulging in anti-Bolshevik activities,' said Nikitin. 'One small group, indeed, remained as zealous as the most committed Party member. Christians.'

The crackle of the loudspeaker again. A last call for the Moscow train.

'Christians? So what?'

'Back then, all the churches were shut, or ransacked for any-thing useful to the Party or the people,' said Nikitin. 'Then used as dumps, or grain depots.'

'I know what happened.'

'Of course you do. But in perusing some of the paperwork

from the time, I found an interesting document from November 1937. A low-ranking officer in the People's Kommissariat of Internal Affairs, the illustrious forebears of today's MGB, filed a report after a raid on a modest and supposedly disused church on the northern edge of Leningrad. Thanks to an informant, a small religious gathering had been identified and disrupted. Some of the gathering escaped, but two people were arrested. Too slow, too terrified, or too trusting in the Lord's protection.'

Nikitin paused. Rossel held his gaze. The major's teeth retreated under a set of bluing lips.

'Under interrogation, they gave up some names. One caught my eye,' Nikitin said.

Rossel felt like he was falling through space. 'Galya?' he whispered.

Nikitin nodded. 'Precisely so. Rossel. Galina Rossel. Almost exactly two years after she disappeared, your sister was back in Leningrad, getting high on the opium of the people.'

15

In daylight, Lenin looked different, Rossel thought, and not just because a passing seagull had left its verdict on the progress of Socialism on his bald, bronze pate.

He seemed less imperious, his power diminished. But there he was, standing outside the Finland Station, one arm stretched straight in front of him like a knife slicing through the icy air to emphasise a point – another polemic about the dictatorship of the proletariat or the overthrow of bourgeois supremacy. Or perhaps by now, after exhausting his list of counter-revolutionary threats, the Bolshevik messiah had fallen back on more mundane topics, such as phosphorite mining in Kazakhstan. Rossel had always suspected the young Lenin was not the kind of revolutionary comrade you wanted to sit next to on a long train journey.

He walked on and left the statue behind.

Crossing the road, he looked around him. As buses and trams crawled through the heavy snow, lines of people trudged in and out of the station in a meandering parade of thick winter coats, fur hats, boots and scarves. Only a smattering of red and yellow posters exhorting Leningraders to lend their efforts to rooting out traitors or glorifying the Soviet armed forces livened up the monochrome morning – "Fight for a good harvest! Listen, country, the dream of the people is calling! All power to the Soviets!"

Rossel pushed his way into the station building.

The militia officers who had arrived at the scene of the accident – or murder, as he now knew it was – had reported that a railway worker had been first to get to the victims. A worker who had seen a black Pobeda disappearing round the corner after he'd heard the bang of a collision. And who had heard the male victim's final words.

Will it snow, Soselo? Will it rain? Is there a storm coming?

As agreed with the chief engineer of the Finland Station in a brief conversation down an almost inaudible telephone line, one of his employees was waiting next to the ticket office. He was a square-shouldered, middle-aged man with a broken front tooth, wearing overalls and thick coat. The man did not look pleased at the prospect of the forthcoming interview.

'Comrade Belov?' Rossel asked.

A curt nod.

'Is there somewhere private we might go to talk?'

Viktor Belov forced a smile, exposing the jagged front tooth. 'Now there's a question everyone wants to know the answer to,' he said.

*

Belov picked at his broken tooth with the dirty nail of his little finger. His accent was rough, that of a peasant. A Belarusian, maybe.

The railwayman led them to a small hut between two of the platforms, about a hundred metres down the line. To judge by the levers, pulleys and handles that sat next to the oil-streaked windows, at some point it had been used as part of the signals system. Now it was filled with junk – coils of rusting barbed wire, boxes of nails, planks of wood, a pile of rotting sleepers.

Nevertheless, it seemed Belov spent plenty of time here. The samovar was on.

Belov poured himself some tea into a tin mug. Then took out a hip flask.

'Something to keep out the cold,' he said.

He offered the flask to Rossel, who shook his head.

'I would like to clarify the exact time of the accident you saw,' said Rossel. 'Around ten past seven in the evening is what you said. Am I right?'

Belov shook his head. 'Heard, not saw. I didn't see it happen.'

'What did you hear then?'

'A *bang.*' He thumped the wooden wall of the signals box so hard the windows rattled.

'No other sounds?' asked Rossel.

'No.'

'Then what?'

'I'm just coming out of the station,' said Belov, 'about to go home to Rzhevka. Know it? A real beauty spot. So, I should turn left, but then the *bang,* so I look right. I can see a car that looks like it has got stuck on the tram tracks. It's gunning the engine but only moving slowly. I think, some total *durak* is behind the wheel. I turn away – I'm late finishing work on the signals and it's cold and the wife is waiting and it's not my bleeding car – but then the engine really screeches, so I turn again. The car bumps off the tram lines and starts moving forward again. And that's when I see them.'

'Them?'

'The bodies.'

Belov looked at Rossel as he worried at his tooth again. 'Hers, anyway. Like I told the rest to your militia comrades. The man is still alive but only just. I ask him, what the fuck happened, comrade, he mumbles some shit about the weather, and then he's gone. So, we're done now, gun dog?'

'And the car?' asked Rossel. 'Did you get a good look?'

Belov sucked at his fingers and took a big swig of his tea. 'My wife is clever, not like me,' he said. 'I can't even read. Not books, anyway.' The railwayman picked up a metal shovel and tapped it on a sleeper. 'These I can, though. I've laid so many of them, I only have to put my ear to the tracks and listen to what they say. It's in the way the whole thing vibrates and rattles. With a little practice, you can tell what's coming – an old pre-war steam Kolomna or one of these new diesels they're building in Luhansk.'

Belov sniffed and took a pull from the hip flask. He grimaced as the rank spirit went down.

'That's who I am, gun dog. An honest Soviet worker with the hands of a peasant, an ear for the rails and . . .' He tapped his right nostril. 'A nose for trouble.'

'The car you saw,' said Rossel. 'Did it run over the man and the woman after you heard the noise?'

Belov dropped the shovel on top of the pile of sleepers. It made a harsh clanging sound. 'The wife says, "Don't ask questions, Viktor. Don't answer any, either. That's how we'll get through." That's what my wife says and—'

'She's the clever one, I know.'

'"If people ask, just say no to everything", she tells me. So that's what I do.'

'People?'

'Administrators, bosses, blue-hats, militia . . .'

'Ah.' Rossel understood. But despite his bombastic nature, Belov had a certain charm. He decided to play along. 'Even if the answer's yes, you say no?'

'No,' said Belov, with a grin. It wasn't just the front tooth that needed the attention of a good dentist. There was a queue of molars, too.

'Did the car run over those two people after the initial noise?' asked Rossel again.

Belov prodded at his tooth. 'No,' he said, winking.

'Did you get a clear look at the people in the car?'

'It was snowing and very dark. There were two of them, that's all I can say for certain.'

'And the car?'

'By the time I got there, it was going round the corner, but I'd say I did *not* see a GAZ Pobeda, or an eleven-eighty—'

'Colour of this car you did *not* see?'

'Dark blue, or it could have been black.' Belov's little finger drilled into the back of his mouth. His cheeks coloured. 'I won't get into trouble, will I, gun dog?' He gave Rossel a plaintive look. 'My wife won't like it if I do.'

'If anyone asks, I only asked you one question – about the time of the accident,' said Rossel. 'If you do that for me, I won't have to mention to anyone about the vodka you're taking with your tea in a clear breach of regulations. And much frowned upon by management. Especially as you say you still occasionally work the signals.'

'One question. Got it. You sure I won't get into trouble?'

Rossel thought for a second. 'No,' he said.

Uncertain of Rossel's meaning, Belov scratched his brow. 'A no that might mean yes, right?'

Rossel shrugged.

The railwayman sighed. 'Bloody teeth,' he said. 'Men like me don't need them anyway. What the fuck have I ever had to smile about?'

*

Back at Station 17, Rossel walked up the stairs to the room where the more senior officers spent their days. Two years ago, he would have barged straight in. Now, his low rank prohibited that. He knocked.

A man with the insignia of a junior officer yanked the door open. 'What?' he said.

'Begging your pardon, Comrade Junior Lieutenant,' said Rossel with a cursory salute. 'Is Captain Lipukhin available?'

The officer shook his head. 'Captain Cirrhosis administered himself a fortifying restorative and went home an hour ago. He's probably already snoring in his bed.'

Rossel looked past the man's shoulder. Everything was familiar. Almost as he had last seen it. His old desk in the same place. The usual feeble fire flickering in the grate. The tarnished metalwork around it, especially the carving of a seagull Rossel used to rub for a little luck – the same bird he'd had tattooed on his chest while in the labour camp, as a kind of guardian angel.

He reached into his pocket and found the little stone there. The reality of the Gulag had robbed him of all his foolish superstitions. Except this one, he thought, smiling to himself, as he rolled it. One of many that had lodged in his boot during the long, forced marches there.

Not for luck, though.

As a daily reminder to see the world as it really is.

'Anything else, Comrade Senior Militiaman?' said the officer. 'If not, I'm busy.'

'No, nothing else, thank you, comrade . . .' Rossel began.

The door slammed in his face.

16

On the wall of the captain's apartment was a poster of a young, virile, heroic Ilya Lipukhin in the ubiquitous socialist realist style. Lipukhin in profile – blond quiff, blue eyes, a chin that looked as though it was about to storm Berlin all by itself. A slogan declared: *Keep the motherland safe from capitalist elements! Join the militia!*

Next to a scratched wooden chest and a standing lamp with a faded brown tasselled shade lay the real version, slouched on a dark yellow sofa. Rossel looked at his friend through a haze of cigarette smoke. The air in the apartment was almost unbreathable. There was now little left of the police department's former golden boy.

Lipukhin's hair was greying and receding, the eyes bloodshot, the chin unshaven and jowly. A single long grey hair, twisting like a corkscrew, had sprouted in the middle of his right eyebrow. As well as being dressed only in a stained white shirt and blue striped dressing gown, the captain was clutching a half-empty bottle of Armenian brandy. Holding it tight to his chest like a mother cradling her firstborn.

Rossel glanced at his watch. It was only half past two.

'When she was very young, my niece Dasha used to stand on that chest and kiss that image, as if it were an ikon. When she did that, my heart would sing,' Lipukhin said. He pointed at the poster. 'My whole family used to say it was me, the likeness is so strong.'

The brown liquid sloshed in the bottle as he upended it.

'Now Dasha kisses a different heroic picture. One in her schoolbook.'

'A picture of whom?'

'Pavlik Morozov, of course.' Lipukhin said 'of course' with a sneering whine. 'You know, the little shit who informed on his dear papa.'

Rossel did know. Morozov had become a Soviet martyr for denouncing his father for forging documents for bandits and parasitical landowning peasants. His grandparents decided the best punishment would be to murder the boy – an act that led to their immediate execution. Little Pavlik's actions were glorified in song, poetry and theatre. And schoolbooks, in which children were exhorted to follow Morozov's example and keep a close eye on family members for un-Soviet activity.

'Little shit,' said Lipukhin again.

Once, even at home and drinking, Rossel's friend would have tempered his speech. These days, he seemed incapable of doing that – like a man standing on the edge of a precipice who decides that now, at last, he can tell the world what he thinks of it.

'Dasha's in the Pioneers. Worships the boy. These days, she's giving me odd looks.'

'Odd?'

'Like I was Trotsky, and she was the ice pick.'

Dasha had been young the last time Rossel saw her – a serious but sweet girl.

Lipukhin put the bottle to his lips and tipped his head back. 'My sister had been very anxious about things before she became ill. I don't think that helped.'

'Anxious?'

'Raisa was accused of making derogatory remarks about Stalin. Which she had. She often let her mouth run off.' The captain put the bottle on the floor and sprawled on the sofa. His body was sad and sagging. 'But only within these four walls.'

It took Rossel a moment to understand him. 'Dasha? You think she denounced her own mother?' He shook his head. 'I don't believe that. Surely not?'

Lipukhin patted his pockets for more cigarettes.

'I do,' he said, his voice rising. He clambered to his feet and began to shout. 'You can't get lower than that, eh? The little bitch. These children are having their minds poisoned.'

Rossel raised a finger to his lips. Then pointed at the wall. 'Ilya . . .' he said.

He turned on the radio, lit another cigarette and poured himself a glass of brandy.

Lipukhin belched.

'I need to take a piss,' he said.

Rossel turned the volume on the radio up. His exchanges with Lipukhin were exhausting him and he needed a diversion. With a burst of pleasure, he heard the strains of a familiar song – a Schubert *lied*.

Lipukhin walked back into the room and began waving his arms like a conductor.

'What is she warbling about, Revol?'

'It's by Schubert. *Death and the Maiden*. A girl is dying, but she is begging Death to leave her alone. *Away, wild man of bones, I am still young – leave me, dear one, and do not touch me.*'

'And does Death listen?'

Rossel paused and let the mezzo-soprano sing out.

'No,' he said. 'He soothes her, tells her to come with him, tells her there is nothing to fear.'

Lipukhin lowered himself onto the sofa and groped for his bottle. Without the captain seeing, Rossel moved it out of reach with his foot.

'I like it,' said Lipukhin. 'It is sad, but I like it. Man of bones. Who is the singer?'

Rossel didn't know, but she was superb. At the conservatoire, he had once been in love with a girl who had a voice like this one.

Frustrated by the absence of brandy, Lipukhin tried to get up again. His hand knocked over a stray glass that smashed on the floor. Ignoring the mess, the captain staggered towards the poster on the wall and, straightening his back, saluted.

'Keep the motherland safe from capitalist elements! Join the militia!' he sneered. His shoulders slumped. 'That's who I used to be, Revol,' he mumbled. 'A picture of Soviet health, vigilance and sobriety, all in one. If we solve this case, these bodies at the Finland Station, find the killer . . . Maybe I can be that person again?'

He hurled another glass at the poster. It shattered. A man in the apartment upstairs started banging on the ceiling. His cursing was muffled but audible.

'No record for this Anna Orlova, no clues as to why she ended up in a fatal clinch with an old Georgian goat,' slurred the captain. 'We simply do the MGB's bidding. She will just be another corpse lying on a slab waiting for a drunken militia captain to come and rubber-stamp an accident.'

He stared at Rossel, trying to focus.

'She's like my Raisa, this woman, she's like your Galya, don't you see?'

He slammed his fist on the table. The man in the apartment above banged on the ceiling again.

Lipukhin raised his head. 'Piss off, Golubev, you piece of shit,' he roared, 'or I'll come up there and arrest you.'

He slumped into the chair again.

'Can't you see that, Revol?' he said, breathing hard. 'Nobody will even remember the misbegotten bitch unless we – you and I – find out what really happened to her.'

Rossel was about to answer. He wanted to ask why they should bother – why, in a country in which unnumbered people disappeared, should anyone care about Anna Orlova or her lover, or anybody else.

But if that was true, why should anyone care about his missing sister?

It was hard to argue for any interest in her fate if he himself could not summon up the desire to look into the reasons why a quiet academic and a visitor from the Caucasus had been rammed and crushed and silenced for good.

Lipukhin scanned the room, his neck struggling to control his heavy head. It was as though he was looking for some piece of incontrovertible evidence that would make his case for him. But he seemed stumped. Finally, he placed his little finger over his top lip to form a Stalinesque moustache.

'A "man of bones", you say, according to your beloved Schubert,' he said, forcing out the composer's name with a cascade of spittle. He sought out Rossel's left hand, with its two stubs where fingers had once been, and placed his own hand over it. 'A man of bones sent you to Siberia, Revol,' he whispered. 'A man of bones made your parents disappear. Maybe Galya, too . . .'

Rossel tried to pull his hand away, but Lipukhin tightened his grip.

'A man of bones took these fingers from you. This case can be your chance – our chance – to do something about *all* of that.'

Rossel stared at his hand. Then at Lipukhin. He sat forward. 'I . . .'

An almost imperceptible squeak on the parquet in the hall outside made them both jump.

The door to the room swung open. Nine-year-old Dasha, her blonde hair in bunches, wearing a plain blue dress and a small, red, five-pointed star badge with the portrait of the young Lenin on it, stepped into the room. She stared at them.

Rossel got to his feet.

'Dasha, how good to see you again,' he said. He pointed at her badge. 'And now a Little Octobrist. Soon to be a Young Pioneer?'

Dasha nodded curtly.

Rossel recited the Pioneer mantra. '"Pioneer, to fight for the cause of the Communist Party of the Soviet Union – be prepared!"'

Dasha walked across to the table and picked up the brandy bottle. Lipukhin, still swaying, reached out and tried to tousle her hair. But she stepped away from him and dropped the bottle into a bin before giving Rossel the correct response.

'Always prepared,' she said.

The little girl knelt and began to pick up the pieces of broken glass from the floor.

17

Valentina Semyonovna had not even spoken to him tonight as they passed each other in the apartment's hall. He had been a little too sarcastic with her the last time they met, Rossel thought. He needed to be more careful.

He was listening to Rachmaninov, the third piano concerto. Sitting in his armchair, he stretched his arms behind him and yawned.

The needle on his old Sokol radio-gramophone stuck again. He repositioned it. Then sat again.

Rossel picked up the wooden figure he had found at the feet of Lenin and turned it over in his hands. The crude face glared back at him. He looked up at the walls, where he had, only that evening, after returning from Lipukhin's apartment, pinned up photographs and autopsy notes, a militia map of the area around the Finland Station, with the possible routes to and from the crime scene taken by the vehicle that had killed the two victims, a list of names to contact for questioning... The criminal investigations department of the militia would not be impressed by it, he thought.

Normally, he turned for comfort to a pile of files on the other side of the drawers, material he had stolen from the archive at Station 33, and began his nightly work. Looking for something, anything, some tiny piece of information that would lead to the whereabouts of his sister. But tonight was different. At last, he knew something. Galya had been seen in Leningrad in '37.

She's alive, I'm certain of it . . .

As he reached for another *papirosa*, the wooden figure caught his attention again. Its eyes were without expression, like the eyes of the dead Anna Orlova.

Rossel grimaced at the memory of the MGB colonel's work with the scalpel; at the thought of Lipukhin's drunken entreaties and the dangers they represented; at the indifference, even hostility, of his militia colleagues in Station 17.

None of that mattered. His sister was still with him.

He stood, picked up his gun and placed it in its holster.

I'll look around the dead woman's lodgings just for the sake of appearances. That's all.

Even as he said the words to himself, he knew they were a lie.

18

Anna Orlova's *kommunalka* was on a small street off the Moika embankment, not far from Palace Square. Rossel and Lipukhin had walked there through the morning traffic from the station; driving would have been quicker, but the captain needed the icy air to clear his head.

As they climbed the staircase and reached the apartment, they saw a piece of torn notepaper stuck behind a grubby sliver of glass. It detailed the occupants' surnames with a different number of times to press the buzzer – one for Petrov, two for Timofeyev, three for Babin, and so on – next to each name. A common strategy adopted by residents who shared only one bell. You needed five buzzes to summon Orlova, but there was no chance of a response.

'Well, we need to choose someone,' said Lipukhin. 'Three is a good number – God loves His trinities.'

He rang for Babin, whoever he was, and they waited.

Lipukhin examined the mud on his boots. 'Thank you for coming, Revol,' he muttered.

Rossel gave him a curt nod. He was about to ask after Dasha, but the door opened before he could say anything.

There stood before them an old man wearing a gaudy red dressing gown, felt boots and a woollen hat. He admitted that he was Comrade Babin.

Babin led them down the entrance hall and into the *kommunalka* – crowded lodgings, half a dozen families bumping shoulders and not liking each other for it. No one had volunteered to give the place a lick of paint or nail down the curling linoleum floor.

Six or seven rooms led off the hall, one per family. There was only one bathroom, outside which two young women – a moon-faced blonde and a stocky redhead – were arguing about a hair they had found on a bar of soap.

'The soap is mine, it's TeZhe, I bought it, and look . . . it's a ginger one,' said the blonde.

The redhead sang the popular ditty about the beauty brand back at her in a shrill, mocking voice. '"TeZhe on your eyes, TeZhe on your lips, TeZhe on your cheeks. Where am I supposed to kiss?"'

The blonde stuck her hands on her hips. 'You know what you can kiss, Lyuda? You can kiss my . . .'

But then, seeing Babin trailed by two militia officers, her voice fell away.

'Comrades.' Rossel nodded to them as he walked past.

The women drew their dressing gowns up around their necks and took a step back. Their eyes followed Rossel and Lipukhin down the corridor.

'Militia, you say,' said Babin to the world at large as they approached the door to the kitchen – the heart of every *kommunalka*. 'If bad news comes, I always say it could be worse. And, well' – the old man winked – 'seeing as how you two comrades are *militsiya,* we both know it could be.'

The old man's voice was loud and filled with exaggerated bonhomie – a clumsy attempt to warn his neighbours that the authorities were now among them, and to mind their language.

The kitchen was shrouded in steam from innumerable metal pans bubbling away on the three big stoves. Wet washing hung on lines across the ceiling and two small children were playing with three mangy cats in one corner of the room.

Lipukhin sniffed and smiled. '*Shchi*,' said the captain to two middle-aged women standing at the stoves. 'I hope you have put potatoes in it. It's not a proper *shchi* unless you add potatoes, my mother used to say.'

The women stopped stirring and eyed them.

'I disagree,' one of them said at last. Her friend elbowed her in the side and the woman added: 'Forgive me for contradicting your mother, comrade, but, for me, a little extra cabbage always does the trick.'

'Militia,' Babin said. 'Only militia. They want to ask a few questions about poor Anna Orlova.'

One of the women held up a ladle. 'Want a bowl?' she asked Lipukhin.

The captain nodded.

Rossel patted his stomach. 'I'll have one, too,' he said.

*

Rossel and Lipukhin sat on one side of a large kitchen table covered with a green tablecloth. Babin and the two young women who had been arguing in the corridor sat on the other. The middle-aged women who had been stirring the stew had shooed the children and the cats into the corridor before sitting next to them. The other occupants of the *kommunalka* were either at work or queuing for groceries. A rumour had gone around the block that *Vostochnye Sladosti* – a store that specialised in foreign delicacies and was therefore usually empty – was about to release some bananas.

Two steaming bowls had been placed before them. Despite the divergent views on the correct ingredients for cabbage soup, two fat potatoes bobbed on the surface of Rossel's helping. It was part hospitality, part bribe – a little kindness in exchange for the goodwill of the city's law-enforcement authorities. After his privations in the camps, it was a well-placed one.

As it turned out, the women needed little encouragement to start talking.

'Do you know what happened to Anna?' said the blonde owner of the TeZhe soap who revealed herself to be a doctoral student in Egyptology from Leningrad University named Natasha.

'That is what we are trying to discover,' said Rossel.

Lipukhin looked up from his bowl. 'Delicious,' he said to the woman who had served him.

She reached up with one hand and straightened her pink hairnet. 'I put in two potatoes, Captain. Just for you. Because you said you liked them.'

'What can you tell us about dear Comrade Orlova?' Rossel asked Natasha. 'We know that she was an academic, of course.'

Natasha took out a handkerchief and dabbed at her eyes.

'She worked in the mediaeval manuscripts department at the Hermitage. Not the main part of the museum but in an annexe, in the Menshikov Palace on Vasilyevsky Island. She was an expert in Cyrillic and pre-Cyrillic scripts like Glagolitic.'

'She showed me once,' said one of the older women. 'But I didn't understand any of it. All those strange symbols—'

Natasha interrupted her. 'Anna wasn't stuck-up like some academics can be. She knew lots of things, but she'd give you time; listen to what *you* had to say. She was kind. She helped me get my room here. At New Year, she gave me a box of dried figs, and we all shared some jellied meat that she'd kept out on the balcony.'

Rossel took a picture from his pocket. 'Then I'm sorry to have to show you this.'

He laid the crime scene photograph of Orlova on the table. Babin and the four women leaned forward to get a better look. Death, Rossel thought, was a film star who always managed to get top billing.

'Note how she is dressed, comrades,' said Lipukhin. 'Were those her normal clothes?'

'No,' replied Lyuda, the redhead, shaking her head. 'She must have had a date, the sly one. Dressed like that, I mean, and with all that slap on.' She turned to Natasha. 'I bet it was Anna who borrowed your precious soap.'

Natasha ignored her. 'I have never seen her dressed like that before,' she said to Rossel. 'And she kept herself to herself. The only man Anna was interested in was St Kirill and his precious alphabet.'

Lipukhin finished his stew and dropped the metal spoon into the bowl. 'She was religious, then?' he asked.

Natasha shook her head. 'Glagolitic was the first script for Slavic languages. It was the creation of St Kirill, a monk from Thessaloniki, in the ninth century.'

Lyuda smirked. 'You think you're so clever.'

'It's true. I heard her talking about it to someone in her room,' said Natasha, staring Lyuda down.

'She had visitors?' asked Lipukhin. 'From work?'

'No, on the phone.'

Rossel leaned forward. 'She had her own personal phone?'

Most *kommunalkas* had one phone that all residents shared. Having a phone to yourself was unusual. A privilege.

'Oh yes,' said one of the older women, setting off vigorous nodding around the kitchen. 'She was very well regarded at her institute. That's how she got it.'

Natasha sat back. 'Anna was so lovely,' she said. 'I think the university got the phone put in to help with her research. She was always calling round students, giving them advice. Comrade Orlova was *not* the type of woman who would borrow your soap without asking.'

Lyuda stood and pointed at Orlova's photograph. 'So why is she dressed like a whore about to knock on the Devil's door?' she sneered.

The others looked embarrassed.

'Please sit, comrade,' Rossel said, pointing at her seat.

The girl obeyed – the militia were not the blue-hats, but they still represented the state.

Rossel looked around the room and smiled some encouragement. 'We'd like to see Comrade Orlova's room, if that's possible?'

Natasha stood up.

'I'll show you,' she said.

19

Anna Orlova's bedroom was large for a single occupant in a *kommunalka*.

Natasha sat on the edge of a small metal bed that was covered in a purple quilt embroidered with yellow flowers. Two dresses were laid out on it – one red, one light blue.

A small desk and stool stood in a corner. Opposite them was a worn green armchair, used for reading by the look of the pile of books on the floor beside it. Orlova's prized phone – a black Bakelite VEF – sat next to them. On a chest of drawers was a mirror, some family pictures, a simple musical box with a slender brass lever and a plastic tub containing tubes of cream, face powder and lipstick. The walls were covered with bookshelves, mostly filled with hefty academic tomes.

Lipukhin was examining the books, taking out any volume that caught his eye and leafing through its pages.

Rossel stood next to the desk. It was covered in rough sketches of some sort of symbol. On top of the pile was a large circle, drawn in ink, standing on the tip of a precise, sharp-cornered triangle, the tip just penetrating the circumference, like a ball that had impaled itself on a pyramid. As Orlova had not finished the drawing, Rossel assumed it was the last thing she had been working on. He picked it up.

'Do you know what this is?' he said to Natasha, who was looking over his shoulder.

'A Glagolitic letter. Like I told you, it was her speciality.'

Rossel held up the sketch so she could see it better. 'What letter is it?'

She shook her head. 'I don't know. I'm an Egyptologist. Show me a hieroglyphic and I can tell you whether it's New Kingdom, Late Period, Persian or Ptolemaic. But with these, I only know a few of them. But Glagolitic is not the only strange alphabet she was an expert in. Early Georgian scripts, Old Permic . . . she loved the more obscure ones, the letters and scripts that nobody used any more, the ones that history had left behind. "If I don't remember them, who will?" That's what she used to say to me.'

Lipukhin took a book from the shelf and sat in the armchair. He began to turn the pages. The older women, who had clustered around the doorway, lost interest and began to drift away. Rossel walked to the musical box and pressed the little gold lever. A mournful tune began.

'It's from a ballet, *The Pharaoh's Daughter*,' said Natasha. 'I gave it to Anna as a thank you for helping me get my room.'

'I know it,' said Rossel. 'Pugni. Everyone takes opium inside a pyramid where the coffin of the pharaoh's young daughter is lying. Then strange things begin to happen – who'd have thought it? *The Pharaoh's Daughter* was a ballet that Anna liked?'

Natasha smiled. 'Yes, I took her to see it once and she loved it. Afterwards, she told me a sad story about a little boy who had died very young. One, she said, she often dreamed about. She said Pugni would have been the perfect composer to score her nightmares.'

Lipukhin placed the book he had been reading back on the

floor. He pointed to the two dresses lying on the bed. 'Dreams don't interest me,' he said. 'Basic police work does. She laid out three dresses and chose one. Put some effort into her assignation. Tries them all on. Rejects the red and the blue. Chooses the one we found her in.'

Rossel nodded, then pointed to the cosmetics. 'They look new, too. Some of the bottles aren't even opened.' He turned to Natasha. 'You're sure she wasn't one for make-up?'

She shook her head. 'Even if she had a date, which I doubt, she just wasn't the type to . . . well, you know, put the goods on display,' she said.

Rossel noticed something. Propped up against the musical box was a miniature portrait in a round frame, with green velvet on the back. It was a cartoonish scribble of a duck, probably drawn by the same hand that had etched the symbols, Orlova's. But he could not be sure. It seemed an inconsequential thing. Odd then, he thought, that she had framed it.

He opened the chest of drawers, pulled out a battered, leather portfolio and opened it – more sketches of Cyrillic symbols. He sat down at the desk and began to leaf through it. Lipukhin began rummaging through the wardrobe, but there wasn't much to sift through.

'None of this makes sense to me,' said Natasha, picking up the blue dress. 'The clothes, the make-up, finding her with a man like that.' She turned towards Rossel. 'I don't believe it was an accident. Do you?'

Rossel held her gaze. 'The MGB do,' he said.

As if only just discovering it was contaminated by a virus, Natasha dropped the dress.

'Can I go now?' she asked. 'I'm . . . I'm working on my thesis.'

Rossel nodded. 'Of course.'

She moved towards the door. But stopped near the chest of drawers.

'May I, Comrade Captain?' she asked of Lipukhin, pointing at the musical box. 'That little tune reminds me of her.'

Lipukhin shrugged. 'If you wish.'

She reached out and started up the box.

'He used to sing,' she said to them both. 'That I do know.'

'Who did?' said Rossel.

'The boy Anna dreamed about. She told me he used to sing to her.' She sighed and pressed the box to her chest. 'I don't suppose he will any more.'

*

With a grunt of irritation, Lipukhin sat down in the armchair. The two men had searched the room for another twenty minutes but found nothing.

'I think we should go now, Revol,' he said. 'What's left to know? She was an expert in Cyrillic symbols, or Glagolitic, or Permic, Gothic, mythic, classic, whatever. Her room is full of sketches and books about them, which is as you'd expect. She obviously had a date with the fat Georgian. She bought some clothes and lipstick in advance of it. Maybe she did really like him – made more of an effort than she usually did? Maybe she just needed a good fuck. Sometimes we all do.'

Rossel shook his head. He took out a *papirosa* and lit it. 'Something's not right, Ilya. Natasha thinks so. I do, too.'

A distant look crossed Lipukhin's face. He drummed his fingers on the arm of the chair but made no effort to get out of it. 'Ever been out near Olonets?' he said.

'No. Where is it?'

'On the other side of Lake Ladoga. Out on the road to Petrozavodsk.'

'And?'

Lipukhin leaned back in the chair and closed his eyes. 'When I was young, my father used to take me every year to see the geese in the spring. There are thousands of them, an amazing sight. As a child, the first ones you see land in the water, well, you look at them and swear they're the exact same geese you saw last year – look there's Ivan, Papa, and isn't that good old Olga? And my father would talk about how reliable those birds were, how you could almost set your watch by them.'

Rossel paused in the act of rummaging through a drawer. 'So?'

'"Rely on the birds, Ilya." That's what my father used to say. Perhaps you're right to believe this Natasha, that's all. The girl seems like a dependable type who knew Orlova well.'

'You've never spoken to me about your father before. Was he proud when you joined the militia?'

'Very,' said Lipukhin. The captain got to his feet. 'All right, five more minutes then.'

Rossel gazed down at Orlova's desk and the sheaves of paper on it. Looking for inspiration, he riffled through them. None came.

What are we missing?

He sat down at the desk.

The papers were intriguing, comprising more sketches of enlarged letters of unknown alphabets, but hardly incriminating.

Eye-catching, he thought. And distracting . . .

The desk had an ornate carved drawer, which he had already searched. There was nothing of significance in it, only more of her sketches. He opened it again and leafed through them.

After another minute of staring at it, something caught his eye. The bottom of the drawer was lined with a bit of green-and-white wallpaper. It was curling up in the back left corner. He pulled the drawer out as far as it would go.

'Something?' said Lipukhin.

Rossel emptied the drawer and pulled back the wallpaper. Underneath was a new piece of plywood. He slammed down the palm of his right hand. The plywood sprang up – only a little but enough to get a fingernail under. Rossel lifted it further and then pulled it away.

Underneath was a flat, black leather case.

He held it up to Lipukhin. 'Yes,' he said. 'Something.'

Rossel unzipped the case and lifted out the contents. It was a sheaf of a dozen or so papers covered in small, densely drawn symbols. On one paper was drawn a table. A classification perhaps, of Cyrillic letters, including some he did not know, and perhaps therefore from ancient texts. The surrounding explanations and definitions were hard to decipher.

The two militia officers could recognise a few words and phrases. 'Creator'; 'peace bringer'; 'seventh day of the tenth month'; 'beginning of the Apostles' era' . . . interspersed with words they half-recognised but could not quite define. In the Soviet universe, such texts did not often come into the public domain – citizens were dimly aware of them, and their place in Russian history, but close study was not encouraged.

The papers grew stranger. On one was a series of circles within circles, like a code wheel devised by mediaeval monks, which grouped certain letters or letter-couples into families, though the common factor was impossible to discern. A third paper consisted of a series of concentric circles inside which were two rectangles forming a cross; where the shapes intersected, more letters were grouped in classifications that defied under-standing, at least to laymen like themselves. It was esoteric, almost occult.

Lipukhin exhaled. 'Well. It isn't *Das Kapital* – I think we can conclude that without fear of contradiction.'

Rossel stared at the papers. Orlova had spent her life study-ing ancient scripts. Why were these worth concealing? What made them so different?

'They look very old,' Lipukhin added, fingering the papers. 'As if they should be behind a glass case in the museum. Stolen, do you think? She was taking things from work for the black market? Maybe that's why she was meeting a strange man in the middle of the night – to sell them to him.'

Rossel tried to think. Did that make sense? Orlova did not seem the type to be dealing in contraband. But many people were good at not seeming to be something.

'Or was it just that these were valuable,' he replied, 'and she kept them well away from the prying eyes of Natasha and Lyuda and anyone else who might want to . . .' His voice trailed away. Orlova's black Bakelite phone was ringing.

Rossel and Lipukhin looked at each other. The captain raced to the armchair. He let the telephone ring twice more. Then picked it up.

Lipukhin listened for several seconds but did not speak.

Finally, the captain looked up.

'Well?' said Rossel.

Lipukhin appeared baffled. 'Music,' he said.

'Music?'

'Just a few bars. But, yes, they played some kind of tune down the phone. From a record player. I could hear the crackle. Then the call ended.'

Rossel waited for more explanation, in vain. 'Come on, Ilya,' he said. 'What music? Did you recognise it?'

Lipukhin shrugged. 'Well, it wasn't Lidia Ruslanova, I can tell you that. I've always liked "Charming Eyes" – the perfect accompaniment to the bottom of any glass.'

'Classical, then?'

'Maybe, yes, but—'

Rossel sighed. 'Come on, Ilya, tell me exactly how it sounded. Sing it.'

Lipukhin stood and patted down his coat as if ready to take the stage at the Bolshoi. But the noise that came from his mouth would have scoured clean a burnt pan.

Rossel waved his arms about. An enraged conductor silencing an unruly orchestra.

'Fuck your mother, you sound like one of those Olonets geese you were going on about,' he said.

Lipukhin picked up a couple of pens off the desk. He tapped out a rhythm. 'Does that narrow it down?' he said.

Rossel listened. 'You started with Beethoven's Fifth, moved on to Brahms's Hungarian Dances and ended with Stravinsky and *The Rite of Spring*,' he replied. 'So, no.'

Lipukhin shrugged again. 'It could be a code, a message of some sort to Orlova.'

'Yes, it could.' Rossel tapped his own fingers on the desk in frustration. 'But from whom? And about what? And why to Anna Orlova when she's dead?'

Lipukhin tried humming the tune again but caught Rossel's eye and stopped.

'No words, only music?' Rossel said.

'A few mumbled words at the very end. Only a sentence – but it gets stranger.'

'How?'

'Because I *think* the man who mumbled was speaking a few words of Ukrainian,' said Lipukhin. 'Mostly Russian, but he used the word *khlopets*. That's "boy" in Ukrainian, right?'

Rossel shrugged. 'Maybe.'

The two languages were closely related but far from mutually intelligible.

'Something about "memory", or "remember",' added Lipukhin. 'It might have been "Remember the boy Petro," in Ukrainian. Something like that. Then in Russian, "Remember the boy who should not exist." And then he put the phone down, whoever he was.'

'Petro? And "Remember the boy who should not exist." You're sure?' asked Rossel.

'As sure as I can be.'

Rossel realised he knew next to nothing about the Ukrainian language. Or Ukraine, for that matter. The place had been torn apart during the war, he was aware of that, but not much more. Didn't most of them speak Russian? Or was it that many had been deported, leaving the Russians behind?

'You can't make any sense of it?' asked Lipukhin.

Rossel shook his head. 'But at least there's one thing we know for certain,' he said. He picked up the black case that had been hidden in the drawer and slipped the miniature of the little duck into his pocket.

'We do?'

'Whoever made that phone call doesn't know she's dead yet.'

* * *

Nine days and still no sign of Stalin.

And now the ninth night.

Lying, mostly awake, in a small bedroom with a lumpy mattress on the second floor.

Listening . . .

Each sound a gunshot.

Drunken laughter. Loud toasts – To luck! To love! To happiness!

Singing, shouting. More laughing. More toasting. To Comrade Khrushchev! To Comrade Molotov! To – always followed by prolonged applause – Comrade Stalin!

Then, two nights ago, she had awoken with a start. A figure was standing in the doorway, staring at her half-clothed body.

'Who are you?'

Then she had realised. After Stalin, the next most recognisable figure in the Soviet Union.

Lavrentiy Beria had smiled at her.

'Good evening, Comrade Sidorenko,' he'd said. Before she could answer, he'd slipped inside and shut the door behind him.

She had struggled, but he was stronger than he looked, and his terrible reputation gave him supernatural powers over her. Until her legs bent as she tried to curl into a ball and her left knee had caught him hard near the groin. She had felt his gasping breath on her neck as he'd slithered off the bed.

So far, he had not come back. But she was expecting him to return at any moment.

The nights were endless. But the days were worse.

All she could do was stare at the closed wooden office

door – the one with the red star on it – and wait for the polished brass knob to twist and turn.

She was sitting at a large table. Next to it was an easel on which were set out an array of her paints, a clean palette, a box of brushes, some cloths, turpentine and other items of her art.

Zlata Sidorenko preferred staring at the door. Because it stopped her thinking about her secret.

A rattling sound. She sat up straight.

Stupid girl – it's only the wind again.

An icy chill that blew across the snow-covered lemon and apple trees in the garden would sometimes judder the door in its frame.

Nothing to worry about.

Zlata jumped to her feet. It had not been the wind, after all.

The apparition, its mouth twisted in encouragement, gestured with his pipe for her to sit again. The door clicked shut behind him. Then Stalin sat down opposite her.

'My apologies, Comrade Sidorenko,' he said. 'I have been busy with these accursed metropolitan elements, Zionist doctors, reactionary plotters . . .'

A puff on the pipe.

'Doctors are the cancer now,' he added. 'How can that happen?'

Two Sphinx-like eyes – black-brown pupils, a muddy, yellowing tinge in the whites – settled on her. The dying suns of a distant planet, she thought. One on which it was always night. In them, she felt she could make out the smoking chimneys and crumbling rooftops of Gori. His birthplace. A dusty, mountain city of brigands and bandits.

'Do you know why you are here?' he asked her.

Don't think about your secrets. Think about something else. Give him only your purist proletarian thoughts.

She shook her head. But then pointed with hope at the canvas.

'*To paint something, Comrade Stalin?*'

Another draw on the pipe.

'*Not something. Me.*'

Zlata pushed her hands further under the table. They were not trembling with fear but with relief.

A commission. That's all this is.

'*I have greatly admired your work ever since I saw another portrait of yours,*' *Stalin added, contemplating the stem of his pipe.* '*It was of Marshal Tukhachevsky. It used to hang in the Hermitage. It caught my eye.*'

She did not answer.

'*I read about you and your methods first in* Pravda. *Then I asked someone to draw up a report. Tell me more.*'

She tried to speak. But her mouth was dry.

A magnanimous wave of the pipe.

'*You must say what you wish.*'

In front of almost anybody else, that is what she had always done. That was why Mikhail Nikolayevich Tukhachevsky, also known as 'the Red Napoleon', had liked her. No one had expected her to survive the Thirties – through the long years of the Terror. She was known for airing her views.

Zlata cleared her throat.

Very well, then . . .

'*I pride myself on the truth, Comrade Stalin,*' *she began.* '*At least, I mean . . . on my search for it, and my ability to find it. An inner truth. What I try to capture is an instruction, one the* sitter does not even know they are giving me. "Tell me who you are without speaking." I ask people that. Sometimes, to aid me, I also ask them to show me something – an object, usually – that helps to reveal who they really are.'

Stalin blew out some smoke.

'What did Tukhachevsky bring?' he asked.

'A little wooden statue. A carving. Something he had made himself while he was prisoner of the Germans in the First World War.'

'A statue of what?'

Careful . . .

'He didn't say.'

Stalin stared. His pupils dilating.

'The eyes,' he said, 'it's all in the eyes. That's what made Repin such a great painter.'

He turned his pipe over and tapped out the embers into a metal ashtray.

'An interesting person, Tukhachevsky . . .'

His eyes on her again, searching for secrets.

'Moghalat'eebi khshirad arian,' he said.

She didn't understand the Georgian.

Stalin translated: 'Traitors often are.'

Her heart was beating so loudly, she was certain he could hear it too.

'I'll think of something,' Stalin said.

'Something?'

'To bring you. Something that will tell you who I am without speaking. But . . .' He pointed to the canvas on the easel. 'Let us begin without it.'

He reached up and touched his cheek, running a finger across the smattering of smallpox craters there.

'They never include these, on the official ones. You must do. My son, Vasily, one day he was feeling a little sorry for himself. Some minor official had disrespected him. He came to me and said, "But I am Stalin too." No, you're not, I told him. You're not Stalin and I'm not Stalin. The Stalin in the newspapers, official portraits, on the posters, banners, stamps, banknotes, boxes of chocolate, postcards, lapel pins ... that Stalin has been painted a thousand times. He's not me. He is Soviet power. I want you to paint someone else, Comrade Sidorenko.'

She understood. 'Iosif Vissarionovich Dzhugashvili?'

The moustache twitched above a reluctant grin, the black-brown pupils, set deep in their sockets, unmoving and unreadable.

'What was he like when he sat for you – Tukhachevsky?' he asked.

Beautiful, wondrous ...

'Much gentler than I thought ... for a military man, I mean,' she said.

'Blokhin thought so, too.'

Don't let him know you know.

'Blokhin? Is he an artist?'

The apparition allowed itself a small smile.

'Of sorts ...'

20

A knifing wind had stripped the grand boulevard of Nevsky Prospekt almost clean of people. Rossel pulled his coat tight around his body.

Gogol's line came back to him, a line most Leningraders knew. *There is nothing better than Nevsky Prospekt... This, the beauty of our capital – what does it not glitter with?*

Right now, he thought, Nevsky wasn't glittering at all. In keeping with the weather, its shops looked glum and lifeless, light barely escaping through the windows, their goods rejected by the city's citizens. The writer's depiction of a devil-may-care St Petersburg, full of young bucks and beautiful women, a place of endless indulgence, inhabited solely by flâneurs...

A foolish summer fantasy, that was all.

It wasn't just the city's name that had changed. That carefree character had gone, too – eviscerated by a bloody revolution, war and starvation, and the brutal nocturnal activities of its secret police.

Rossel crossed the street. Then stopped. In front of him, in defiance of the elements, stood a wrinkled *babushka* behind a large trolley. The woman wore two big coats, her face almost entirely covered by a thick, red headscarf.

A single word was scrawled on a piece of cardboard taped to it: *chebureki.*

Rossel's stomach groaned. Since returning from the labour camp, it seemed convinced each meal would be his last.

'What's in them?' he asked.

'Meat.'

Without waiting for a direct request, she opened the lid of the trolley and pulled out one of the steaming pasties.

He fumbled for some kopeks and handed them over. As he bit down into the crust, hot juices oozed out and scalded the corners of his mouth.

Turning his back to the wind, Rossel stared up at the neoclassical façade of the State Public Library. A place he hoped would tell him more about the mysterious Anna Orlova.

The last time he'd stood here was during the siege, when the much-loved building had remained open. A literary sanctuary for Leningraders.

Back then, like everywhere else in the city, they'd had no working heating, so Rossel had sat shivering in a reading room, turning the pages of Gogol's short stories, like 'Nevsky Prospekt'. And 'The Nose', a surreal tale about a man whose nose had gone missing and was apprehended at a coach station by the police while attempting to flee the city. Half-starved and half-hallucinating as Rossel had been, in a Leningrad surrounded by German Army Group North and with bodies lying where they fell on the streets, he'd become obsessed by the disconcerting notion that all the decomposing and discarded noses, arms, legs, hands, heads and fingers of the city's dead had hatched a plan to make a run for it.

Rossel pushed the last of the pasty into his mouth. 'Would you not be warmer inside, *babushka*?' he asked the old woman.

She shook her head. 'I don't like to read, *synok*.'

'What do you like, then?'

She opened the lid of the trolley, gave the pies a poke with an ancient spatula, and slammed it shut again.

'I like cooking *chebureki*.'

*

Leather, paper, ink . . . the library's scent was intoxicating.

Rossel loosened his scarf, took off his gloves and ran the tip of a finger along the great staircase's balustrade. He held up his hand to examine it. Black dust. As if the leather-bound volumes on the shelves occasionally shed their skins.

He looked around and was greeted like an old friend by regiments of brown wooden shelves, guarded in places by large bronze statues and imposing busts of literary icons – Pushkin, Tolstoy, Dostoyevsky.

A tall, thin, middle-aged man with grey hair sat at the front desk.

'I'm looking for works published on the Glagolitic alphabet,' said Rossel.

'Scholarly, then?' said the man.

Rossel nodded. 'Unless you have anything more exciting on the subject.'

The man pointed down a long corridor lined with little brown shelves full of card indexes. 'First right,' he said. 'Then take the second left after the statue of Voltaire and follow the signs. I imagine most of the books in that room will be happy to see you.'

'Why's that?'

The man gave a wry smile. 'It is an underused part of the library,' he said. 'As a rule, nobody reads them.'

Rossel followed the directions until he reached an almost deserted section of the building. He shrugged off his coat and draped it over a wooden desk with black leather top and a green, mushroom-shaped reading lamp in one corner. Every desk had the same style of lamp on it, lined up like a small parade of inscrutable toads.

He began to take out and fan through the little wooden drawers containing index cards. On the third attempt, he found her – *Orlova, Anna D.*

Her name was cited on at least six academic papers. But she was the main author of only one: *God's Love, St Kirill and the Slavic Nations: How the new symbols of the Glagolitic alphabet gave voice to the souls of the Slavs.*

Rossel took the index card to a librarian and retrieved the paper. But the text was abstract and filled with obscure academic citations. After half an hour, he sat back and sighed. He could understand hardly any of it.

Then he noticed something. The paper had another name attached to it. Not a co-author, but a contributor – one Professor Lapshin.

*

'Professor?'

Lapshin stopped in his tracks. The professor glanced around the embankment of the frozen Neva as if assessing, with all due academic rigour, his chances of escaping across the ice.

'You're here about Anna again?'

Rossel nodded.

Lapshin looked relieved. The light grey eyes in his round, sallow face darted from side to side. Rossel offered him his pack of *papirosy* and the professor took one with swift, pecking fingers.

The militiaman nodded towards the Menshikov Palace. 'You like working there?'

Lapshin pointed across the river, in the direction of the golden dome of St Isaac's Cathedral, on the opposite bank. It was glinting in the winter sun. Before it reared the blurred silhouette of *The Bronze Horseman*, the famous statue of Peter the Great – at this distance, a model in miniature.

'I like being close to Peter,' Lapshin said. That soft lisp again. He puffed at his cigarette without pause. 'Anna did too. "Great Peter is our city's heart," as she used to put it. Have you found out who was driving the car that hit her?'

'Not yet.'

Lapshin's back straightened a little. He nibbled away at his cigarette, looking Rossel up and down, as if he were a curious symbol the semiologist did not quite recognise.

'Then why are you here?'

Rossel took out Orlova's sketch of the circle with the triangle drawn underneath and handed it to him.

'What can you tell me about this?'

Lapshin glanced down. 'It's from Glagolitic,' he said. 'The oldest Slavic alphabet.'

'What does it stand for?'

'Ah, well, that is not so easy to answer,' said Lapshin. 'In the simplest sense, the sound it represents is an "s". But it is also symbolic of the eternal Trinity. The circle for eternity, the triangle for the indivisible nature of Father, Son and Holy Spirit. And it even had a name: *slovo*, which is to say, word, or speech.'

'A letter that meant "word",' said Rossel. 'Can you tell me more?'

The professor looked at the paper again. 'In the sense of the Word of God, comrade. *In the beginning was the Word, and the Word was with God, and the Word was . . .*' He stopped himself and looked at Rossel with a little apprehension. Soviet Russia's Holy Trinity was Stalin, Marx and Lenin; it did not do to deviate from this dogma.

Rossel gave what he hoped was a reassuring nod.

'For St Kirill and his brother Methodius,' Lapshin continued, 'creators of this new alphabet, the task was to bring the Gospels to the Slavic people on their own terms, to more accurately reflect the speech of the Slavic people in ways that the Greek alphabet – they were Greeks, you see – could not. They were not just inventing letters. They were evangelising, bringing the Word itself into being, imbuing each sound with sacred meaning, both visual and aural. Without St Kirill, comrade, you and I and all the rest of the world's millions of Slavs would have no voice.'

Lapshin sighed.

'That was a point that dear Anna made repeatedly and passionately to everyone she met.'

'Did this letter have any particular significance for her?'

'I don't know.'

'It appears that she drew it. Not just wrote it out, but enlarged it to this size. It was on her desk. Perhaps it was the last thing she ever committed to paper before . . .'

He saw Lapshin's face crumple and began to wonder again if the professor had harboured more than just comradely feelings towards Anna Orlova.

Lapshin composed himself and studied the paper again. Then he gestured across the white sheen of the frozen river towards the statue.

'She used to say to me, "Think of Peter's vision – three hundred years ago, there was nothing here but marshland and mosquitos. But the emperor built a city on it. He took what was in his heart and made it so." Though I should add that she was not blind to the human cost, nor indifferent to the suffering.'

Lapshin flicked the butt of his cigarette into the snow.

'But it made her think about the creation of something out of nothing. About permanence and impermanence. That's why she loved these ancient scripts so much. She felt protective of them, striving to save them from oblivion. Peter willed a civilisation into existence. Anna believed she could save another from disappearing into history's impenetrable mists.'

'How did her husband die?' asked Rossel. 'You said an accident. What sort?'

Lapshin drew the collar of his coat up against his neck and recentred his ushanka.

'Let's walk along the embankment a little,' he said. 'When I talk of the past, I often find I need to stretch my legs.'

*

The two men had stopped next to some stone steps cut into the embankment that led to a tethered rowing boat that was marooned on the ice.

'Do you believe in luck, Comrade Militiaman?' asked Lapshin.

Rossel felt his left hand begin to move towards the inked bird on his chest but stopped it. Instead, he pushed it into his pocket and found the small stone at the bottom.

'I used to,' he said.

Lapshin nodded. 'Anna always did. But she was not really blessed with good fortune. She did not speak about it much, but I think she witnessed some terrible things back in Ukraine when she was young, before the war. She wanted a child with her husband, but it never happened. Then he died very young.'

'How, exactly?'

Lapshin sighed again. 'Drowned at sea.'

'A sailor?'

'A philosopher.'

Rossel dropped his own cigarette butt into the snow and ground his boot on it. He was growing tired of the academic's evasiveness.

'I haven't got time for lessons on metaphysics, comrade. I'm investigating the accident in which your friend and colleague was killed.' Rossel took a pad and pencil from his pocket and thrust it at the professor. 'Please write down all the names of friends, people in her circle, people with whom she associated,' he said.

Once again, Lapshin looked crushed.

The professor spent a few moments writing some names on the pad, and then returned it.

'Thank you, comrade,' said Rossel. 'And the husband?'

'These are not easy things to talk of.'

Rossel understood the man's dilemma. Academic tenure was a fragile thing. Not so easily awarded. But quickly rescinded on the whim of some Party bureaucrat.

'It will go no further, comrade,' he said. 'You have my word.'

Lapshin swallowed and looked again towards the statue of Peter. He wiped at his nose, which was beginning to stream in the frigid air.

'They were called "philosophers' steamboats",' he said. 'Not long after the Revolution, hundreds of academics whose views and writings were deemed problematic – philosophers, but also artists, scientists, journalists – were rounded up and exiled. Rounded up, pushed onto steamboats and shipped off to Germany.'

'And Orlova's husband was one of them?'

Lapshin nodded. 'Nikolai Orlov. A Ukrainian philosopher, a man of great ideas, but also a mediaevalist and Christian. Something of a nationalist. He was from Kiev, where he joined the Theological Institute. An unwise move in the early 1920s. I have not read his work since it is . . . not readily available in Leningrad. But, evidently, it was not what the Soviet Union's new intellectuals were looking for.'

'So he was exiled,' said Rossel. 'Did she never see him again?'

Lapshin took his handkerchief from a pocket and blew into it. 'No, she never saw him again. The ship he was on was not as seaworthy as it should have been. A storm blew up in the Baltic Sea and it tried to take shelter in the Gulf of Riga but was sunk.' He replaced his handkerchief. 'After that, Anna pursued her own career far away in Ukraine. She did not come to us at our research institute until later.'

'You mentioned before that she had seen some terrible things out there in Ukraine,' said Rossel. 'Such as?'

Lapshin looked him in the eye.

'During the Siege when my belly was hollow, I blamed the Germans for that,' he said.

'We all did.'

The professor stared at Rossel. 'But we Leningraders weren't the first to experience such things.'

'No?'

Lapshin brushed a few flakes of snow from his coat collar. 'I do not know. I was not there. Ukraine is another country. And I doubt that you even want to know,' he said.

Rossel straightened the sleeves of his coat.

'In spite of my own best interests, I find I do,' he replied.

Lapshin shook his head. 'I have said too much already. If you want to talk to me again, I suggest you first contact the administration of the Hermitage and go through official channels.'

Lapshin began to walk back in the direction of the Menshikov Palace. 'All those dead philosophers bobbing up and down like croutons on a bouillabaisse,' he mumbled, as if in a trance. 'All those unasked questions . . .'

Rossel called out to him. 'One more, question, then, Comrade Professor.'

Lapshin stopped walking. He turned around with reluctance.

Rossel took from his pocket a photograph of the wooden figure he had found next to Lenin's statue. He held it up. 'Does this mean anything to you?' he said

Lapshin took it from him and examined it.

'An easy one to finish, then,' he replied, relaxing just a little. 'That's Perun . . . Perun, the old Slavic god of war.'

21

Of the six names Lapshin had written down, Rossel was able to cross off four in short order.

Two were academics from Leningrad University: a sad-eyed female professor of history and a male lecturer with a bulbous nose and a grandiose russet moustache. The latter, an expert in Stoic philosophy, had greeted Rossel with a quote from Seneca – 'We suffer more in imagination than reality.' But he had delivered this pearl in a voice that told the detective he didn't really believe it.

The third person Rossel crossed off the list was a minor Lenfilm actress who lived near the Leningrad Zoopark. She smelled giddily exotic, as though she bathed nightly inside a bottle of Red Moscow, and claimed to have dated the director Grigori Alexandrov – 'People who don't know anything say he and Eisenstein were, shall we say, *tête-à-fifou*, but it's all nonsense.'

She and Orlova had become friends when the actress had lost a shoe on a crowded tram and Orlova, travelling more sensibly in boots for the commute, with her work shoes in her bag, had come to the rescue. They had met for the occasional dinner, party or screening. 'We didn't demand things of each other, dear comrade. We were just friends.'

The fourth was a thin, jolly woman in her late forties, a former neighbour of Orlova's who spoke of how kind she had been to her when her mother had died. 'Always popping by with flowers or a little gift, until I was quite myself again.'

Rossel rubbed his temples. After several hours of questions and knocking on doors all around the city and with the day fast disappearing, he did not feel much further forward.

On seeing the sketch of the Glagolitic letter Lapshin had identified as *slovo*, the two academics *thought* they remembered Orlova doing similar drawings of the same symbol, and the neighbour recalled seeing it doodled on a pad on her desk, 'although it might have been something else, among those strange squiggles and shapes.' All recoiled when shown the crime scene photograph. All said they'd never seen her dressed or made up like that before.

Name number five on Lapshin's list was different.

Rossel stood in front of a large Art Deco apartment block on the banks of the Fontanka River. It had been simple to locate Viktoria Kovalyova.

In a similar vein to the descriptions handed out to her fellow poet Anna Akhmatova, *Pravda* had once designated Kovalyova a 'slut' and, more ornately, a 'cosmopolitan jezebel'. *Sovyetskaya Literatura* had been more restrained, settling for accusations that she 'undermined the workers' class consciousness and went against Soviet ideals'. More mundane criticism, but equally dangerous. People said that it was only her friendship with the writer Gorky that had saved her from the camps.

Before the Great Patriotic War, Kovalyova had been one of the Soviet Union's most celebrated literary figures. After it, she had written a poem called '*Pevchaya Ptichka*', or 'Songbird', and fallen foul of Andrei Zhdanov, ultimate arbiter of what was and was not acceptable in the sphere of Soviet culture. The *Zhdanovshchina* was now the ideological rule by which all artistic output was measured. Or, as Comrade Zhdanov himself had put it,

'The only conflict that is possible in Soviet culture is the conflict between good and best.'

In practice, you wrote poems, plays and novels the Party liked, or you didn't write at all.

'Songbird' – a subtle, abstract poem in which the bird of the title sat silently on a perch, her cage surrounded by a preening, purring band of black cats – had been widely seen as a direct and foolhardy challenge to *Zhdanovshchina*. The literary critic of *Pravda* had wasted no time in sinking his own claws into it, deriding the work as 'the last, desperate mewlings of the recidivist, bourgeois sensibility'. Before he had died, Zhdanov had personally seen to it that Kovalyova was culturally isolated, which generally led to physical and economic isolation, too. As had happened to many others similarly cast out, it was rumoured that, for a time, she had not even been allowed to claim her full ration of writing paper.

As Rossel crossed the street, he remembered a stanza from another now banned poem by Kovalyova.

Death stands outside the circle,
And sings a silent song,
A song of bones.

He entered the Art Deco apartment block, climbed the stairs to the second floor and rang the bell.

*

Vika Kovalyova was a thin, stately, dark-haired woman who trailed sadness behind her as if it were the hem of a great cloak. The poet was in her late forties and walked with a slight limp.

She led Rossel down a long, cold corridor and into her room – a decent size, but sparsely furnished and draughty. Next to a coat stand, he noticed a small brown suitcase.

She's already packed.

He was a little saddened by the sight. But not shocked.

That a Soviet citizen could experience a sudden and catastrophic downturn in fortunes at any point was something Rossel knew too well, so the fact that Kovalyova had a bag ready to take with her should state security officers knock on her door at four in the morning should not have bothered him. It was a standard precaution taken by many who went to bed each night with reason to expect such a visit. Like Young Pioneers, they were 'always prepared'. But as he knew from personal experience, someone like Kovalyova was unlikely to survive a labour camp.

Two tabby cats had followed her along the corridor, one on each side, as if standing sentinel to her solitude. As they entered her room, the two broke ranks and joined another five of differing colours, shapes and sizes who were purring, tumbling and snoozing around a large wooden table. Half of them eyed Rossel warily, the others ignored him.

Books lined the walls, not on shelves but in teetering piles. In one corner, beneath a red ceiling lamp, was a desk fashioned from four piles of books, on which had been laid an old door, sawn in half. On this surface was a silver bowl in which the embers of some papers were still smoking.

She followed his gaze.

'A poem I didn't like,' she said.

'A healthy capacity for self-criticism is to be valued, comrade.'

Kovalyova stared at him with wide, sceptical brown eyes as though he were an errant comma in an otherwise exquisite stanza.

'A militia officer, you say. Come to enquire about poor Anna.'

He nodded. 'How did you know about her accident?' he asked.

'Friends told me. Can I see your identity card again?'

He handed it over. She glanced at it and gave it back. Leaning down and scooping up a black cat that was rubbing around her ankles, she nodded at the bowl and its smouldering contents.

'A poor first effort,' she said. 'I wish I could drive the words out of my mind. But once they have been there, I can never really forget them, comrade. Not even the bad ones. That is my curse. I often wake in the night, ears flayed by the creaking hinge of a dissonant couplet.'

'But an exceptional memory is a gift, surely.'

She pulled a face. 'As a child, I was confined to my bed for months with polio,' she said. 'I passed the time reading and memorising poetry. This routine gave me exceptional powers of recollection. Before my fall from grace, I could recite in public, word for word, any of my poems that those attending might request, and quite a few of the output of several others. On the other hand, my mind is now, what was it, "polluted with a bourgeois sentimentalism". And my famed memory keeps this unfortunate quality locked away, "like a *kulak* counting his hoard", according to *Sovyetskaya Literatura*. They rushed to condemn me once Comrade Zhdanov made his pronouncements on what was or was not allowed to be considered Soviet art. So even my special talent has been turned against me. Forgetting would be easier.'

Rossel picked up the silver bowl and examined the embers. He recalled some lines from another poet who'd had his own brush with the cultural authorities: 'As in summer a swarm of midges, Flies into a flame, Did snowflakes fly from the courtyard, Towards the windowpane . . .'

He stopped reciting and turned to Kovalyova, half-inviting her to pick up as he left off.

'A policeman who quotes Pasternak,' she said, pushing her hair out of her face. 'A somewhat unnerving phenomenon. Like a priapic priest or a poet with a gun.'

'You are an admirer of Pasternak?'

'Much of the man's work I find somewhat overwrought. But I admire some. These days, of course, I think it wise to wait for the Party to tell me which of his lines are worthy of praise. Marx, it turns out, was every bit as expert on cadence, rhythm, symbol and rhyme as he was on historical materialism.'

Rossel put the bowl back on the makeshift table. Next to it was a notepad and a pen. The pad had a few lines scribbled on it.

'Good enough to cheat the flames?' he said, pointing to the words there.

Kovalyova gave the faintest of smiles. 'Not really,' she replied. 'But redemption, of sorts. A libretto, a work for children. Natalya has asked me to write it. She thinks if the piece is accepted for performance, that my own work may be published again. In time.'

'Natalya?'

'Natalya Surkova. The director of the Moscow Children's Theatre. Prokofiev himself has been writing the score. But he has been very ill. The great man suffers terribly from headaches and nausea these days. So, the project has been delayed.'

'I hope he gets better,' said Rossel. '*Sarcasms* is a piece I love. Only Prokofiev can tell jokes with his dissonant harmonies and unusual time signatures. Jokes that people actually laugh at, that is.'

Vika stroked the cat in her arms. 'First Pasternak, now Prokofiev . . . Perhaps you write poetry, too, Comrade Militiaman? I can see in your eyes you have at the very least lived enough to produce a stanza or two.'

Rossel liked her. He sensed a kindred spirit, someone who had also suffered from the Party's capriciousness, who saw stoicism laced with mockery as the best way to stave off despair. But he had work to do.

He took Orlova's sketch of the *slovo* symbol from his pocket and held it up in front of her.

'A symbol even Marx can't explain,' he said. 'Do you recognise it?'

She leaned down and let go of the cat. It slipped away and joined its comrades by the table.

'I—'

The doorbell buzzed.

'Who could that be?' she said.

But her voice sounded mechanical, almost as if she had been waiting for the interruption. The bell, fixed above her door, sounded again, vibrating like an enraged insect against the wooden wall.

'May I?' She gestured towards the hallway.

Rossel nodded.

'I'm not expecting anyone,' she assured him, opening the door.

'Not even the ghost of Comrade Zhdanov?'

Kovalyova pointed to the suitcase on her way out. 'I've long expected a visitation from that particular spectre,' she said.

As soon as Kovalyova left the room, Rossel picked up the silver bowl and examined its contents in more detail. But the paper was completely charred.

He was curious to see who was visiting her, and instinct told him this was a more pressing issue. He opened the door to her living room and peered into the gloom; it was a straight line to the front door. Kovalyova's austere figure obscured his view of whoever had come calling, but Rossel glimpsed the outline of a broad-shouldered man in a black hat, perhaps a homburg.

No ghost, then.

The poet sensed his eyes on her and looked around. The man turned and began walking away, and Kovalyova slammed the door shut. Apart from his hat and a nondescript coat, Rossel had not been able to make out anything else that was distinctive about the visitor.

Rossel stepped back inside the poet's room, knelt on the rough floor and scooped up one of the tabby cats, which emitted a murmur of protest but was otherwise happy to be held.

As he stood up again, he noticed a collection of black-and-white family photographs that Kovalyova had framed and displayed on the wall opposite the desk. The first was a laughing group sitting around the garden of a dacha in an unidentifiable location; the second showed a smiling Kovalyova and a short, grey-haired woman, perhaps her mother; and the third comprised a more sombre collective standing outside what looked like the broken remains of a modest Orthodox chapel. Next to this picture was an object that Rossel found more interesting than the family album. A small illustration of a bird, a raven, perhaps – a miniature, in a green velvet frame, in precisely the same style as the one he had seen of Anna Orlova at the academic's *kommunalka*.

Preceded by light footsteps, Kovalyova reappeared.

'A polite enquiry from the Kirov,' she said. 'They are anxious that I finish my libretto. I am sorry they had to interrupt your questions.'

Rossel held up the cat and then put it down on the floor. He offered the poet a friendly smile.

'I interrogated this little lady while I was waiting,' he said.

'Did she give you the answers you were looking for?'

Rossel shook his head. 'No. Like her owner, she is somewhat evasive.'

The poet's face fell. She crossed her arms. 'I have never seen the symbol you showed me before,' she said, her voice quiet. 'If that's what you mean, comrade?'

'Never?'

'Never.'

He folded the paper and tucked it away. 'Don't you want to know, Comrade Kovalyova?' he said.

'Know what?'

'Who it was who was driving the car that killed your friend, Anna Orlova? I have been here for twenty minutes, and you have not asked me a single question about any of the details of the accident.'

'Anna, she . . . In recent years, we had drifted apart some-what . . .' The effort to gather her wits was visible. 'And I told you, a friend has already described the basic facts,' she said. 'A car accident. In the snow, it lost control and hit her. She was with a man, whose identity is not known. Or at least not known to me, though I am sure your rigorous investigation will soon shed light on it. As I say, we had not been close for some time. My *position* has made that difficult for many of my friends.' She stopped. Her voice, and the bitterness within it, had started to rise.

'Just one more question.' Rossel pointed to the miniature on the wall. 'A raven, a lark, a blackbird? What is it?'

Kovalyova looked at it as if seeing it for the first time. 'Just a bird, that's all.'

'By whom?'

The poet's eyes flickered between the drawing and her interrogator. The pause before she answered him was a fraction too long.

'Anna drew it for me,' she said. 'She gave me it as a gift when my poem "Songbird" came out. Do you like it?'

Rossel buttoned his coat and picked up his hat from the table. He could have pressed her harder – how she and Orlova had met, what their relationship had been, what they knew of each other's work, who else was in their circle, when had they last met. But he had decided on another course of action.

He shook his head. 'It looks a little melancholy, Comrade Kovalyova. As you do.' He pointed at the embers in the ashtray. 'I'm beginning to suspect you're worried someone may be able to read those poems you keep buried inside your head.'

22

Enveloped in a black fur coat and scarf, Kovalyova stepped into the street and closed the door to her building behind her. A large icicle fell from the gutter above and shattered at her feet. Instead of jumping to one side, she gazed at it for a moment, unflustered. Then she set off down the Fontanka Embankment towards the Anichkov Bridge.

After she had gone fifty metres, Rossel emerged from the darkness of the doorway of a building opposite the poet's house and began to follow her. When she reached the bridge and its four huge guardian horses, she turned right and began walking up Nevsky Prospekt. Despite the snow and ice on the pavement, and the crowds – people were coming home from work – the poet walked at a brisk pace.

The snowploughs had scoured the city first thing in the morning, but by now, at nearly 5 p.m., there was again a thick blanket on the roads and every bus and car driver was having to crawl along, keeping their distance from each other as they slid and slipped from one lane to another.

After ten or fifteen minutes, the poet turned right towards Palace Square and the Hermitage Museum. Her head was bent into the sharp wind that blew off the river. But she walked with purpose. She was in a hurry.

*

As he reached the huge granite pillar in the centre of Palace Square, Rossel stopped walking and stood behind a workman's awning that was flapping like a flag in the icy wind.

From here, he could track her movements without risk of her detecting him. Next to the awning were two grimy trucks filled with scaffolding poles.

A night officer at the militia station had heard that the statue of the angel on top of the Alexander Column was soon to be replaced by one of Stalin, as part of the coming celebrations of the 250th anniversary of the founding of the city.

Looks like it's true, then.

Kovalyova stopped outside the main portico to the museum, next to a short queue of people waiting to go in. Some of the city's culture addicts, hoping for a quick fix of El Greco or Degas before the museum closed.

After she'd stood in line for less than five minutes, she glanced to her left. A man in a black homburg hat was moving in her direction. From where he was standing, Rossel could just make him out. He was in his sixties, a thin face, pinched cheeks, wearing small round spectacles and with a grey goatee.

Rossel waited until they were at the front of the queue and preoccupied with buying a ticket before marching to the back of it, concealing himself behind a large group of teachers and teenage students.

After a few minutes' wait, a flat-faced, lethargic woman on the door looked at his ID without reacting.

Rossel entered the museum, scanning the crowd for them.

There . . .

Kovalyova and the man in the hat were wandering down a long corridor lined with Roman busts, Renaissance marbles and paintings – Rembrandts, Titians, Renoirs.

He fell in behind them.

The two spoke little but paused from time to time to admire a particular painting or a statue. After ten minutes, they came to a long, crowded room that contained a new exhibition of paintings of military scenes by Pyotr Krivonogov, the celebrated war artist and painter of visceral battle scenes from the Great Patriotic War.

Huge canvases filled with bloody carnage hung on three of the walls. They had stirring names like *The Bloody Battle at Korsun*, *At the Kursk Salient* and *The Defenders of the Brest Fortress*.

Rossel stopped in front of one – *For the Motherland!*, a depiction of the heroism of the 2nd Shock Army at Volkhov.

In a doomed attempt to break the Siege of Leningrad, the 2nd Shock Army had become surrounded by German forces. Retreat, even if it had been possible, was not permitted, and as a result, there had been few survivors. The huge painting showed a defiant winter scene – Red Army soldiers repelling the German advance against a background of giant shell holes and broken tree stumps. A fearless lieutenant stood on top of one of the trenches about to hurl what Rossel recognised as an RGD-33 stick grenade.

He examined other details with the eye of a man who had been there.

In his depiction of the mounds of corpses half-buried in mud and whipped by the snow, Krivonogov had got it right, Rossel thought. And there had indeed been idiots like the lieutenant, officers driven insane by the shriek of falling bombs and sheer patriotic fervour, officers who would get their men killed. Unless, of course, one of them put a bullet in his back. Which was not the kind of incident the Party would have encouraged the artist to commit to canvas.

At the end, on the furthest wall, were some older, more sombre permanent paintings of military figures, past and present – members of the Red Army and Soviet High Command who had fought the Whites in the 1920s, or the Germans in the 1940s. Legendary names like Ivan Konev, Semyon Timoshenko and Georgy Zhukov.

Kovalyova and the man had taken a seat on a wooden bench and were staring up at this group of legendary Soviet heroes. They sat in silence for several minutes, neither of them moving, except when the man took off his hat.

Rossel scanned the room, half-expecting someone else to join the poet and her companion, and hoping for the two to some-how incriminate themselves – exchange information, prepare for action. To do something, drastic or otherwise. Something that revealed their connection to Orlova and her work, or to the Georgian, Tamas Abazi.

Anything but this quiet contemplation of military glory.

Two more minutes went by. Then the man stood. Holding his hat in his hands, he said goodbye to the poet and walked away.

Rossel decided to follow him rather than keep an eye on Kovalyova. But as he tried to leave the room, a troop of excited schoolchildren was pushing past two of the museum's storemen, who were wheeling a large frame down the corridor on a trolley. By the time they had passed, and Rossel could get out of the door, the man in the homburg had disappeared.

Rossel stepped back into the hall of heroes.

The poet was still there.

A few moments later, she stood and advanced towards a gap

between two of the paintings. She reached down and touched a small plaque, something he had not noticed was there – a tarnished rectangle of brass at knee level. The poet paused, her fingers still in contact with the metal, as a worshipper might touch an ikon to receive a divine blessing. Then she stepped back and exited the room into the one next door.

Rossel waited until he could no longer see her, then walked towards the brass plaque. It was dirty, covered with black and brown spots, like an old man's hands. Its screws were corroded, the heads almost melded into the rest of the metal, perhaps the reason it had not been removed. It looked like someone had determinedly scraped away at the lettering, rendering most of it illegible. But he could still make out a few letters.

IKOLA

His first thought was a name – Nikolai. But did that mean the Tsar, whose palace this had once been? Hardly – the Hermitage administrators would have removed the entire wall rather than let a trace of the Romanov dynasty remain visible.

But it was a trace of someone. The trace of a man's imprint on history. The question was, who?

3
ДЕДУШКА
Grandfather

23

Pushkin had a line about tea and women. Something about them speaking in a cunning fashion as they beckoned the objects of their desire towards the samovar.

But then Pushkin had a line about everything.

The tea Senior Lieutenant Gerashvili had poured him was strong and sweet. Rossel sat back in his chair and let it warm him through. It was early, only 7.30 in the morning, and he was still feeling the effects of trudging all over Leningrad in pursuit of Anna Orlova's associates.

He was tired, frustrated. This investigation was complex, confusing. He didn't feel like he was making any progress. Right now, all he had were strange symbols, portraits, missing paintings, half-remembered names . . .

He put his glass on the table. 'Thank you,' he said.

Gerashvili nodded and stifled a yawn. She had spent a busy evening looking after her sister's children. At another of the station's desks sat Lipukhin. Or, rather, the soles of his boots rested on the desk. The rest of him was slumped at an awkward angle.

Rossel got up and put another log on the small fire in the senior officers' room – once *his* room. There wasn't much wood left next to the grate, but he didn't care; he felt that his readmittance to this inner sanctum was worthy of an extra flame. Besides, no one was objecting.

He sat next to the captain, who had opened his eyes and lit a cigarette.

Rossel took a drink of tea, then sniffed the air and reclined his head. The captain could do with a wash.

Laid out on the table in front of them was the miniature illustration of the duck in the green frame, taken from Orlova's room, and some photographs taken later at the same place by a young militiaman who was yet to master his camera.

Lipukhin scratched at the two-day-old stubble on his cheek. He picked up the little painting.

'And she had one as well, our poet? A small sketch like this?'

Rossel nodded. His chair was hard and uncomfortable. He stretched his shoulders and repositioned himself. 'Next to some photographs on the wall,' he said.

'What about the plaque she and this mystery man in the hat were staring at in the Hermitage?' asked Lipukhin.

'A missing picture, I think. I don't know whose, though,' said Rossel. 'It could have been Konev, or Timoshenko, or Marshal Zhukov. That room, that wall, is dedicated to some of the most illustrious and glorious military heroes of the Soviet Union.'

Lipukhin pushed an errant strand of hair out of his eyeline. 'But not *all* of them are still heroes,' he said.

They fell silent. Before the war, the papers had been full of headlines about the treachery of the officer corps – their incompetence, their collusion with the German military, their failure to prepare . . . And, after it, even Zhukov had fallen from grace. Glory on the battlefield was no guarantee of prosperity off it.

'Perhaps the poet Kovalyova has a famous military relative,' said Gerashvili, keeping her voice low. 'A relative whose past has further tainted her.'

Lipukhin tossed the cardboard butt of his *papirosa* towards the fire but missed.

'Fuck your mother, I am already so tired of photographs and drawings and paintings that tell us something without telling us anything,' he said.

'Agreed,' said Rossel. 'So let us concentrate on real people. For example, I would like to know who the man in the homburg was.'

'Did you get a good look at him?' asked Gerashvili.

'Not so good. Thin but with a paunch. A little unkempt, somewhat shabbily dressed. About a hundred and seventy-five centimetres. Early sixties, with a small grey beard and round glasses. I can go back and give Kovalyova a proper grilling, and I will, but before that, I want to do some research, undisturbed. And next to this fire seems to be the perfect location.'

Rossel hoisted a string bag from his feet and dangled it before them. He pulled out several large books.

'The complete works of Viktoria Kovalyova,' he said. 'I went to the House of Books last night. So, the task this morning is clear, comrades. What has she written, to whom, when and why?' He held the books out to Gerashvili and Lipukhin. 'With your permissions, of course?' he said.

Lipukhin hauled himself upright. 'Permission granted, comrade. Essential detective work.' He turned to Gerashvili. 'And what about our friend Abazi? Have you heard anything from Gori?'

She shook her head. 'No. Life moves at its own pace in the provincial towns of the Soviet Socialist Republic of Georgia. What's already yesterday here will still be tomorrow in Gori this time next week. I will contact them again to see if there has been progress.'

She got up and refilled their glasses with tea.

'Thank you, Lidia,' Rossel said. He clinked his glass against hers. 'Pushkin has a line about women and tea,' he added.

Gerashvili rolled her eyes.

'Pushkin has a line about everything,' she said.

*

Ashtrays were full, tea glasses cold, open books strewn in front of them – half of the complete works of Kovalyova. Uninterested in esoteric stanzas, Lipukhin had gone downstairs to rummage through the files.

Rossel glanced across his desk at Gerashvili, saw her engrossed in the poetry and felt a pang of pleasure at this stolen moment of contentment – fireplace, literature, companionship, peace. For a moment, it was like old times, or not-so-old times, when Rossel had been a senior lieutenant and Gerashvili a promising, sharp-eyed junior who took the job seriously and had difficulty disguising her contempt for those who didn't. Their roles may have been reversed – indeed, he was more junior to her than she had been to him – but Gerashvili seemed, for the most part, oblivious of the fact. He admired her all the more for it.

He returned to the poetry, marvelling at Kovalyova's work. What verbal dexterity – such assurance, what wit, zeal, daring . . .

And their collection was, in fact, far from being complete. A nervous bookseller at Dom Knigi had told Rossel that much of Kovalyova's poetry had been withdrawn from publication. In other words, as she herself had implied, the poet had fallen out of favour with the Party. Nevertheless, she still had several earlier collections on the shelves, such as *Pushkin's Ghost*, *Fever Leaves* and *The Drowned Mountain*.

The poems had something unique and haunting about them – a creeping, insidious melancholia – that Rossel found unsettling. Like a man who'd put his ear to the wall of a graveyard and overheard whispering among the corpses. One of them, 'Harvest Time', contained lines he seemed to remember, though he was certain he had not read this poem before:

Lies bud, knives blossom, scythes bloom.
And out on the blood-red plain only bones grow.

Gerashvili looked up.

'Interesting,' she said. She turned the book she was reading around so Rossel could see the pages and pointed to a poem: 'A Man of Steel'. 'It's dedicated to Comrade Stalin. And in the notes, it says Kovalyova read it aloud in his presence at the Historical and Cultural Forum at the Seventeenth All-Party Congress in Moscow. A great honour.'

Rossel sat up. 'The Seventeenth?'

He stared at the pages Gerashvili was showing him, the words plain before his eyes but somehow not reaching his brain.

'Yes,' she said. 'Does that mean something to you?'

He didn't answer.

Born in the citadel of mountains,
Marx's seer, Lenin's heir
You are our Revolution's one true voice . . .

The rest of 'Man of Steel' continued in the same pompous vein. It was a hack piece, a muddle of words that had been filtered through numerous committees at the Union of Writers before being given the final stamp of Bolshevik approval.

'The Seventeenth, Revol?' Gerashvili pressed him.

Before Rossel could answer, the door to the senior officers' room opened and Lipukhin was back.

'You were right about Viktoria Kovalyova and Anna Orlova. They knew each other for years,' he said with a look of triumph. 'Senior Militiaman Fateyev – the smug bore with the wooden leg who sits in the records room all day picking his nose – he turned it up. Both women were born and bred in Ukraine – not the same town, but the same region, and very close. They came to Leningrad after the war, within a year of each other.'

'Two Ukrainians come to Leningrad after the war,' said Gerashvili. 'So what?'

'But still friends,' replied Lipukhin. 'And still in touch, according to Comrade Professor Lapshin, or why else would he have given us the poet's name?'

Rossel jumped up, his chair scraping on the floor. 'I'm off,' he said. He stopped himself. 'With your permission?'

'Off where?' asked Gerashvili.

'The State Library.'

'Yes, of course. But why there?'

'For a history lesson,' Rossel shouted over his shoulder.

24

Crinkled copies of *Pravda*, *Izvestia* and *Trud* lay in heaps alongside the faded editions of magazines like *Bolshevik* and *Bezbozhnik*.

All dated from the days before, during and just after 26 January to 10 February 1934. The 17th Congress of the All-Union Communist Party, held in Moscow, in the savage theatre that was the Great Hall of the Kremlin. The Bolshevik Grand Guignol.

Rossel puffed on his cigarette and turned another page, sifting through the brittle sheafs of paper in another lonely corner of the State Public Library – one that collated the papers and periodicals that charted the history of the Communist Party.

The 1934 Congress was, of course, extensively covered – fawning articles punctuated with grainy images of Stalin speaking, of Kirov, the First Secretary of the Leningrad Regional Committee and darling of the Party, with his brawny fists clenched and his arms in the air as he bellowed into the microphone. Pictures of cheering delegates waving their ballot cards as they voted to give Stalin yet more control, more of the power that, before long, would send many to their graves. For hours, Rossel stared at them, even though he knew they were not the real focus of his investigation.

Names. Like an MGB interrogator charged with weeding out a conspiracy, he wanted names.

One photograph, an overview of all 1,225 delegates taken from above, showed balconies bursting and slogan-daubed banners everywhere. Kirov was speaking. Adoring delegates were stamping and cheering, declaring their raucous devotion to the Party that would soon devour them.

As it had devoured two delegates to the 17th he knew personally.

Their faces were not discernible. Like the rest, they were only smudges on the page.

But they're there, I know it.

Proud Communists, lifelong Bolsheviks.

Lev and Tamara Rossel, his parents.

When he was a child, his father had once told him that he had visited Kirov's apartment on Kamennoostrovsky Prospekt and in the great man's study was a full-sized polar bear hide that he used as a rug.

The detail had stuck in his head. It came back to him after Kirov was assassinated in December 1934, months after the Congress. If only he had wrapped himself in the bearskin and taken refuge in the nearby Leningrad Zoo, Rossel had thought, then Kirov might have survived. Such were the hallucinatory, fairy-tale thoughts that had assailed his mind as a teenager, and especially in the days and weeks after his parents had been dragged out of their apartment and into a waiting NKVD truck.

Rossel turned the faded page.

Another picture. More smiling delegates, happy faces. A group of twenty men standing outside the Kremlin, arms around each other. In the immediate years following the 17th All-Party Congress, more than half the delegates had been arrested, his parents among them. If what people said was true, every second face in the photographs was now either in a camp or in a grave.

Because their parents had been among the first of the delegates to be arrested, he and Galya had presumed it was their surnames that had done the damage. A descendant of Volga Germans who came to Russia in the eighteenth century by invitation of Catherine the Great, Rossel's father had shed everything Germanic about him except his name. He would wave his battered copy of *The Communist Manifesto* at his children, extolling the virtues of the 'brilliant German philosophers' who had penned it and insisting that they must read it, absorb it, learn it by heart. But the foreign taint of the name could not be so easily eradicated.

Rossel placed the copy of *Pravda* he had been reading to one side and picked up a copy of *Izvestia,* dated 8 February 1934. On the front was a picture of Stalin, with Kirov and a few more Party dignitaries standing next to him. A headline proclaimed: 'This is our Socialist Century! says First Secretary Kirov'.

Rossel picked up another *Pravda* and began half-heartedly flicking through it. More names, dozens of them. None he recognised.

He stretched his arms and yawned. He looked at his watch. It was nearly seven. He had been trawling through old newspapers for almost eight hours. He stood and gathered the newspapers and magazines into a bundle so he could return them to the library clerk.

As he turned, a copy of *Pravda* fell to the floor. He picked it up. The front page had crumpled, and he noticed yet another collection of delegate photographs on the first inside page.

One of them made him sit back down.

The fourth picture from the top, on the right-hand side, was one of three men. 'A Meeting of Old Friends', stated the headline, picked out in a smaller font than the grand proclamations of the front pages.

A caption read: 'Members of Lenin's Guard share memories of the Revolution.' Lenin's Guard was the term for those in and around the revolutionary leader's inner circle.

One of the men was Kirov.

The second was identified as Comrade Baikalin, Deputy Chairman of the State Planning Committee. He was younger and thinner, but thanks to that neat beard, Rossel recognised him immediately as the man whom the poet Kovalyova had met at the Hermitage.

The third man was tall and ungainly, flabby around the waist but exuding physical strength. According to the caption, his name was Tamas Abazi.

25

He had got here as fast as he could, excited at long last to be able to share some facts in their flailing investigation. Rossel banged his fist on Lipukhin's apartment front door for a third time.

This time, he heard footsteps in the hall.

Lipukhin opened the door. Even though it was only 8 p.m. he looked as if he had fallen asleep in his clothes some time ago.

'You do not look so well, Comrade Captain,' suggested Rossel.

Lipukhin shrugged. 'These days, for me, "not so well" is better than normal.' The words caught in his throat halfway through the sentence and he needed a bout of coughing before he could make it to the end. He held the door open. 'Why are you here?'

'A social call,' replied Rossel. Then, in a lower voice: 'Is Dasha here?'

Lipukhin shook his head. 'But the walls are thin, and I have one or two new neighbours,' he said.

The captain sloped off to the kitchen as Rossel wiped his boots and hung up his coat. Lipukhin turned on the radio and stuck the kettle on the hob.

'Well?' he asked.

Rossel opened his bag. 'Tamas Abazi was a Party member who had sufficient connections to be invited to the Seventeenth Congress of the All-Union Communist Party,' he said. He held up the page of the newspaper with the photograph of the three smiling men. 'And also seems to have known a certain Comrade Baikalin.'

'I remember that name from the papers years ago. A coming man in the Party back then,' said Lipukhin. 'Is he still alive?'

Rossel nodded. 'Not only is he alive, he is the man I saw in the Hermitage with Vika Kovalyova.'

On the kitchen's plastic radio, which was stuck to the wall, the Red Army Ensemble, or one of its many imitators, began a rousing version of 'Song of the Volga Boatman'. As the chorus swelled, the radio's tinny speaker distorted. Lipukhin stared at the photograph.

'So Abazi knew Baikalin, who knows the poet Kovalyova, who knew our dead woman Orlova,' he said, mouthing the words almost without voicing them, tapping his forefingers along the edge of the kitchen table. 'And two were present at the Seventeenth All-Party Congress.'

Rossel nodded. 'A Congress where hundreds of delegates are subsequently regarded as unworthy of their Party membership and face the consequences. But Abazi and Baikalin survive.'

The kettle began to hiss and gurgle.

Secrets were funny things, Rossel thought. Here he was, bending every sinew to unearth those of people he had never met, and at the same time being careful to conceal his own.

Better not to mention his parents' fate. It was safer not to reveal such things, and safer still not to know them. There was no reason to endanger his closest comrades by saddling them with the knowledge that he was the son of two enemies of the people.

'Where is Dasha?' Rossel asked.

'She has Pioneers after school. She's still an *Oktyabrina* but can hardly wait to be a real Pioneer.'

160

There was a lull in the music.

'She had some friends over last night,' Lipukhin continued. 'They chatted and played just like girls her age should. *Rezinochki, Kolechko.* "Ring, ring, go out to the porch!" and all that. I gave them a button in place of the ring. They were laughing like idiots. Dasha seemed like an innocent child again.'

The captain smiled, and in that instant Rossel saw the family man his friend might have been if not for his weakness for alcohol.

Another military anthem struck up. Lipukhin sighed.

'But?' said Rossel.

'I walked the other two girls down the street to where their mothers were picking them up. We introduced ourselves and parted. But on the way back I caught up with them again – without knowing it, we were headed to the same shop. One was telling the other that she didn't believe it.'

'Believe what?'

'That such a nice man could be the counter-revolutionary capitalist sympathiser that Dasha had told her little friends I was. They were wondering if it was a good idea to let their children play with her again . . .' Lipukhin's voice trailed away.

Rossel knew what he was thinking: if Dasha had been saying that to two of her friends, what might she have been saying to the teachers at school?

Rossel took out his *papirosy* and tossed the pack on the kitchen table.

Lipukhin reached out for one. 'A joke,' he said.

'I'm sorry?'

'At the Finland Station, when we were staring at those two broken souls. You said you had a good joke. I need to hear one.'

Rossel leaned forward.

The doorbell rang.

'That's her. Back from school,' said the captain.

Rossel stood. 'It can wait.'

He strode down the hall and opened the front door.

Dasha, wearing her *Oktyabrina* uniform, was standing there. A man in uniform was standing next to her.

'How good to see you again, Comrade Rossel,' said Colonel Vishensky.

*

Lipukhin must have recognised the voice or been alerted by the change in mood. As Dasha, followed by Vishensky and then Rossel, walked into the kitchen, the captain was on his feet, standing to attention.

'No need, comrade, no need,' said Vishensky. He was all kindness and bonhomie as he placed his hat, with its blue rim, on the table. The MGB colonel pointed to Lipukhin's chair and the captain sat.

Dasha gave her uncle a blank look.

'Dashenka, I promised you this,' said Vishensky, pulling a small book from his pocket and handing it to her.

He turned to Lipukhin.

'I ran into this adorable child as we made our way back home after our respective dutiful days in the service of the motherland. She has been regaling me with stories, haven't you, my brave *Oktyabrina*? Of Pavlik Morozov, hero and patriot. And some other interesting tales.' The colonel held out the book towards her. 'This, Dashenka, is the Pioneer's handbook that belonged to young Pavlik himself,' he said. 'It has been in the archives of state security, and because of your dedication, I have decided that you should have it. Take very good care of it. Its preservation is a great responsibility, just as your vigilance against traitors and saboteurs and wreckers is, too.'

Dasha's eyes widened. The child took the book and started leafing through the pages.

Lipukhin picked up a mug and held it out. 'Tea, Comrade Colonel,' he said, stepping towards the kettle. 'I trust you will stay – I'm sure Dasha will insist upon it.'

He tried to stroke the child's hair. But she stepped away from him.

Colonel Vishensky glanced at the unwashed pots, the plate of half-eaten food on the draining board and the empty bottles on the table.

'Regrettably, I must decline, Comrade Captain Lipukhin,' he said. 'Matters of state security demand my presence.'

Rossel opened his mouth, but a look from Lipukhin closed it again.

Vishensky picked up his hat from the table. He walked towards the hall door. As he reached it, he turned and pointed at his eyes with both hands.

'Ever vigilant, Dasha. Ever vigilant.'

The little girl held up his gift.

'I will be, Comrade Colonel,' she said. 'Just like Pavlik.'

26

The nose was bulbous and pockmarked with gaping pores, like the craters of a distant moon. And his breath . . . it stank of the sourness of *rassolnik*.

'Your mother is a traitor, yes, boy? Your father, too?'

In the dream, his interrogator was asking the question over and over.

Rossel ran the four fingers of his left hand across the desk. Like he was practising a scale.

Four fingers?

'They are enemies of the people, is this not so?'

Rassolnik grinned – pink gums, yellowing teeth. Except for the jagged front two, which were stained a dirty brown.

'Just like you,' he said, 'they have a traitor's heart.'

Rossel wanted to nod. All he had to do was give in and this would end.

'No,' he said, staring at a thick bloodstain on the concrete, urging himself to have courage. 'They are not traitors. I am not.'

No shoes?

Mr Rassolnik here isn't wearing shoes?

White feet. Grimy, black toenails. Like the keys of a piano. You could play a little Tchaikovsky on them.

What is our life? A game!
Good and evil are merely dreams . . .

Galya's favourite aria.
Water, he's ankle-deep in water . . .
Swirling, gurgling, it slowly drowned the desk between them.
'Your mother is a traitor, yes, boy? Your father, too?' Rassolnik bellowed.
Nod. Just nod . . .
He placed the two fingers of his left hand on his chin to stop his jaw from betraying him.
Two fingers?
Water covering his face, forcing itself into his windpipe.
I'm choking.
A light far above. A hypnotic fluorescent rippling on the surface.
Ten metres more. Five. Two . . .
Gasping for air, his head pushed through the waves.
And saw . . . a drowning boy.
A breathless front crawl, arms windmilling, waves slapping into Rossel's face.
Dark eyes, pupils unnaturally shrunken into tiny bullets of shrill certainty. But frightened now.
Pavlik Morozov . . .
Morozov slipped beneath the waves.
A gulp of air. Rossel dived into the darkness.
A white face slipping away into the depths.
He gripped one of the Young Pioneer's outstretched arms, but . . .

... Galya's face stared back at him. Then it dissolved. Disappeared.

Replaced by another. A child's. A boy's. The features blurred. Indistinguishable. But light playing in a circle around his head.

His mouth opens, he's trying to sing. To say something.

Air, I need ...

He broke the surface.

A broken steamship, lights shining through its portholes, slipping beneath the waves. Bodies in the water. 'Who is the boy who should not exist?' chanted the drowning philosophers.

Another sound – an ugly, repetitive beat.

Anna's calligraphic pen, divining ancient secrets from Glagolitic texts? Or Lipukhin tapping out his mangled rhythm?

'Who is the boy who should not exist? Who is the boy ...'

* * *

On an easel in one corner of the room was the outline of Iosif Vissarionovich Dzhugashvili, a humble old man from the Caucasus Mountains. Iosif sat dressed in simple Georgian peasant garb – a woollen chokha *with a high neck. Pockmarks speckled his cheeks. His head was bowed. His slumped shoulders carried the weight of the recent small stroke the kitchen staff at the dacha whispered about. The figure seemed to be staring at a spot in the middle of the table. It was impossible to say exactly where, as the painter had not yet applied any colour to his eyes.*

And the bastard's right, it is all about them.

Zlata Sidorenko and Stalin sat face to face again, as they had for the last ten days. The painter breathed in his scent, now familiar – Troinoi, mixed with the stink of pipe tobacco and the brandy on his breath.

On one wall was a white screen. Behind Stalin, the flickering light of a projector cast a black-and-white French film – Katia. *The story of a love affair. Zlata had been at the dacha for three weeks and this was the fourth night in a row they had watched it together. It was, Zlata thought, a somewhat tawdry romance. Nothing more.*

So why does he like it?

Stalin glanced at the canvas. Then back to her.

'Tell me about the poet Yesenin, Zlata? His portrait was what made you famous. Tell me why you painted it.'

Zlata.

It was the first time he had called her that.

Around him, she was every bit as careful with her gestures as her words. But Zlata allowed herself a small shrug.

'When I was young, I was a girl like any other. Everyone, at least in my artistic circles, loved Sergei Yesenin. So when he killed himself . . . well, you must remember, there was a spate of girls who did the same thing. Copycat suicides. Perhaps there is something about poets, something tragic that . . . Why, I even thought about it myself, very briefly. I was seventeen. At that age, love and death are often confused, equally alluring. Later, by the time I painted him, I was a committed Bolshevik. The portrait was a way of atoning for my childish romantic stupidity. All that fool Yesenin discovered was that putting a rope around your neck is easy. But writing a great stanza is difficult. Or, for that matter, painting a great painting.'

As she had done for the past three nights, Danielle Darrieux appeared on screen. She was Katia, the princess with whom a Tsar, Alexander II, fell in love.

Stalin took another drink of brandy and nodded at the film star.

'She looks like my Nadezhda,' he said.

'Your wife?'

Another nod.

'Lenin was too soft on her. When Nadezhda was his clerk, he let her off with little things. Her spelling, for instance, was always terrible. When she was my clerk, I did not.' He chuckled. 'She once misspelled "communism". Gave it one "m" only. Can you believe it? I pointed it out to Beria in front of her. We both laughed. He blamed it on the shortages. Said we'd have to double production at the consonant factories. She hated him for that. Me, too, I suspect.'

Another sip of brandy.

'Four-eyed Mingrelian bastard, that's what my sweet little Nadezhda was thinking about him.'

He squeezed the top of his left arm – the one he held awkwardly and seemed to avoid using.

'A childhood accident,' he said. 'She would sometimes look at me and think, "To hell with you too, you crippled Georgian cunt." I could read it . . .'

Zlata turned to him and stared. She could do that now. He was growing more relaxed in her company. This was the first time she had heard him use profanities.

She finished his sentence for him: '. . . in her eyes.'

Returning her gaze, Stalin nodded again. 'You look a little like my wife, too.'

Zlata, laughing, pointed at the actress on the screen. 'I'm nothing like that French piece.'

'Not Nadezhda,' said Stalin. He leaned closer and winked. 'Kato, my first wife. She was a real Georgian beauty.'

His eyes moistened. A moment passed. Then, as if forcing himself to break the spell, Stalin stood.

'I have something for you, Mkhat'vari.' He had started calling her that – the Georgian word for painter.

He left the room.

A minute passed.

One minute more and the doorknob twisted. Swaying slightly, Stalin walked in and placed something on the table.

A very small German pistol.

He pointed at it.

'This is a Walther PP,' he said. His voice was soft now, almost childlike. A Leshi in the forest, tempting a traveller from the path.

'Tell me who you are without speaking. You asked me that, Comrade Mkhat'vari. With this, I have done.'

Zlata Sidorenko stared at the pistol on the table and – just as Sergei Yesenin must have done in his final moments – thought about death.

27

'Fuck your mother, gun dog. Fuck yours, too – in fact, fuck them both twice.'

A skeletal, hard-faced street urchin, a *besprizornik* for whom the militia and a spell in jail held no fear, was shouting out insults to anyone in uniform.

This included the three officers who were dragging the boy – no more than fourteen, shaven-headed, dead-eyed, like all the other children who lived on the street, doing their apprenticeship for the criminal gangs – through the station and down the corridor towards the cells.

'Fuck them three times, fuck them four . . .'

His chants sounded not unlike a religious incantation, Rossel thought, though a little more profane than the kind his grandmother used to whisper at Lent to the forbidden saints she kept in a hidden ikon cupboard in her room. 'Set a watch, O Lord, before my mouth and keep the door of my lips. Incline not my heart to any evil thing, nor to practise wicked deeds. Let my prayer arise in Thy sight as incense . . .'

Incline not my heart to any evil thing.

As a child, those words had terrified him.

A thin-faced corporal was following the boy's bumpy progress with amusement.

'What's he in for, Comrade Corporal?' Rossel asked him.

'He's been dipping wallets near Pevchesky Bridge. Got the little bastard early this morning when he ran straight into one of our sergeants.'

'Fuck your mothers five times . . .' sang the boy, as he went head-first through another set of doors.

'No need to beat him up,' said someone behind them. 'Especially when he is so fond of everyone's mothers.'

Rossel and the corporal straightened their backs. It was Gerashvili.

'Comrade Militiaman Rossel, I would like your report,' she added. With a flick of her head, she indicated that the two of them should find a better place to talk.

They pushed their way through the crowded station and down a short flight of stairs to the interview rooms and the cells.

'Comrade Senior Lieutenant,' said Rossel when they had found a quiet spot in a damp corridor. 'During the course of my research into the Party Congress of 1934, I established that Comrade Abazi was among those present at the Congress.'

'And?'

'It appears that Abazi was at that time an associate of senior Party officials.' He lowered his voice. 'Including the most senior.'

Gerashvili held his gaze. 'Go on,' she said.

'His exact role is unclear, but my guess would be that he provided personal security, given that he does not appear himself to have held a prominent political position, and the fact that he was, how can I say, well suited to physical tasks.'

'That makes sense.'

'I have further established that an Old Bolshevik with an illustrious record – until he was purged in 1937 – was also present, and probably associating with Comrade Abazi,' said Rossel. 'A Comrade Baikalin.'

Gerashvili stepped closer to him. 'Baikalin? You're sure?' she said. 'That name does sound familiar.'

Rossel nodded. 'Records show his real name is Vladimir Rusanov. He changed it before 1917, just as many young revolutionaries did,' said Rossel.

He did not need to say, just as Iosif Dzhugashvili had done when he called himself the Man of Steel – Stalin. Or Vyacheslav Skriabin, better known as Molotov. Or, for that matter, a certain Vladimir Ilyich Ulyanov, also known as Lenin.

Gerashvili's eyes remained impassive, but he could tell by the working of her jawbone that she was concerned.

'And where is Comrade Baikalin now?'

'He was given a second chance,' said Rossel. 'A spell in a corrective labour camp to atone for his sins, which he managed to survive. And now he has been restored to a position at Leningrad University as an economics professor.'

'How long in the Gulag?'

'He received a ten-year sentence, though it is not clear if he served all of it. He returned to Leningrad only recently.'

'Has he been readmitted to the Party?'

'With that history? Doubtful,' said Rossel. 'But I will check.'

'You have an address for him?'

'Yes,' Rossel replied. 'He lives in Lesnaya District.'

Gerashvili nodded. 'Good. Anything else?'

Nothing she would want to know about. Only a flood of memories about his mother and father. Photographs and newspaper reports, which they haunted by their absence. Only the thoughts of their son, scanning endless official records of the 1934 gathering of the Party's most loyal members as he tried, and at the same time tried not, to find evidence of their presence.

'No, Comrade Senior Lieutenant. Nothing else.'

Gerashvili nodded, turned on her heel and marched up the soot-stained, wooden stairs to her office.

Rossel headed for the street. As he did, a sergeant and his men were returning from the cells to the main hall.

'Twenty-seven times so far, with the "fuck your mothers",' one of them said to another. 'And the little bastard is still singing it now.'

*

The Titan was a sleek, modernist building, all concrete and metal. A neon sign picked out the cinema's name in red lights. Above it was a huge yellow-and-black poster of a hard-faced middle-aged man holding a test tube. A caption read: *Serebristaya Pyl* – Silvery Dust. The film starred Mikhail Bolduman and Valentina Ushakova.

Inside, another famous actor dominated the posters and photographs lining the walls: Mikheil Gelovani playing Stalin – for at least the third time – in a film called *The Vow*. Gelovani was wearing a white, gold-buttoned suit and standing in front of a cheering, flag-waving crowd. The actor's skin bore no sign of the smallpox scars with which the Great Leader himself was afflicted, and his eyes were soft, dewy and filled with love for the Soviet people.

The plot was well known: a man tries to deliver a letter to Lenin but is murdered by reactionary *kulaki*, oppressive landowners. His widow takes up his quest and sets out for Moscow, only to discover that the great Bolshevik leader has died. At the funeral, Stalin delivers a eulogy calling for all the people of the Soviet Union to vow to maintain Lenin's legacy. The film's message was unmistakable: just as the woman had taken up her husband's quest, Stalin had taken up Lenin's.

At ten in the morning, showings had not started. The Titan's café was almost empty, patronised by only two men, both on their own, and a thin woman with a well-fed young son. No one looked up as Rossel entered.

A man with a scruffy beard and scuffed, unpolished boots was sitting alone in a corner. Rossel walked towards him.

'Comrade Baikalin?'

Although he seemed startled to hear his name, the look on his face as he took in Rossel's militia uniform was merely one of puzzlement. He was not a man to be intimidated by authority.

'And you are?' the man enquired. His unkempt appearance was not confined to beard and battered boots; there was mud on the bottom of his trouser legs and his off-white shirt was half-hanging out.

Rossel did not answer. He pointed at the posters on the wall. 'You're a film buff?'

Baikalin shook his head. 'Not particularly, Comrade Officer. Before the Revolution, this place used to be the Palkin restaurant. Very grand. Gogol, Dostoyevsky, Chekhov, the painter Saltykov-Shchedrin, as well as Tchaikovsky, they all ate here. That's why I come, really. For the conversation. These walls can regale a man with great wit and grand erudition, if you know how to listen, comrade.' His eyes searched Rossel for clues, just as Rossel had scanned him. 'I sit here, eat cake, place my ear close to the satin wallpaper, and every now and then Gogol whispers, "In this world, people always find a way of doing what they want." Or Chekhov might observe: "What fine weather today. I can't decide whether to drink tea or hang myself." Back at my *kommunalka*, even though my room is right at the end of the hall, I can't avoid the others. And the most stimulating conversation I get to hear there is over which traitor to the motherland has used up the last sheet of toilet paper.'

Baikalin paused for breath. He sat back. 'How can I help you, officer?'

Rossel sat down opposite Baikalin. He took out two photographs of Anna Orlova and Tamas Abazi and placed them on the table. Bleak portraits, rather than images of their mangled bodies lying in the snow, but with death on their faces.

'Did you know these two citizens? Were they friends of yours?'

Baikalin looked around the room. Rossel followed his gaze. The thin woman was eating some cabbage soup, while her son nibbled at a sweet. Baikalin picked up a serviette and waved it at them. Both tried their hardest to ignore him.

'Friends, comrade?' said Baikalin. 'These days, I try so hard to make new ones and look what happens. Perhaps it's for the best. Friendship is such a bourgeois notion – based on time spent together, shared interests, other trivialities. I have only comrades. Old Bolsheviks, those who shared the true spirit, rigours and disciplines of our glorious movement.' He glanced at the photographs. 'No. I do not know who they are,' he said.

Rossel took out a torn sheet of newsprint and placed it on the table. On it was the picture of Kirov, Baikalin and Abazi at the 1934 Congress.

'Are you sure about that, Comrade Baikalin?' he said.

Baikalin snorted. 'When was this? A long time ago, I can tell. I recognise Comrade Kirov, naturally. But the other one? No. He could have been any hanger-on, an autograph hunter, a driver, a delegate from a far-flung district, like Siberia. Do you have any idea how many people took pictures of Kirov? Everybody loved the man.' Baikalin tapped a finger on Abazi. 'Who is he?' he asked.

'A coincidence,' said Rossel.

'A coincidence?'

'In many ways. For one thing, just like Comrade Kirov, he is now dead.'

The academic scratched at a small blemish on his lip. Then waved an arm in the air and began to laugh.

'Everyone knows how Kirov died and who his killer was,' he said. 'That deluded dwarf Nikolayev shot him because the foolish little man had convinced himself the dashing Sergei had been making the beast with two backs with his darling wife.'

He picked up the photographs.

'You seem like a pleasant enough man. Hard-working, helping to maintain Soviet order. A plodding policeman in the diligent application of his duty. Although, no doubt, a stranger to the delights of Gogol, Chekhov and Tchaikovsky.'

Baikalin pushed his jaw forward.

'But I advise you to piss off, comrade,' he hissed. 'Leave me alone. Or it will end badly for you, Senior Militiaman. Very badly.'

Baikalin stood up, grabbed his hat and coat, flung some coins onto the table, and stalked out of the cinema.

28

After lunchtime, the Hermitage was quiet. It gave Rossel the space he needed to think. And he wanted to think about one puzzle in particular.

Having made some enquiries of the attendant, who had scuttled off in search of an answer, Rossel sat in the same place where Baikalin and Vika Kovalyova had jointly contemplated the pantheon of Russian military heroes. A host of square-jawed men looked back at him. On one, an avuncular smile played around the lips; on another, the eyes creased with bonhomie.

Which one had the poet and the Old Bolshevik come to see?

A small voice came from behind him. 'Comrade Rossel?'

The man greeting him was keen to please – respectful, a little anxious. He pushed his round glasses up on his nose and then clasped his hands together.

'Are you Comrade Chasovytin?' Rossel asked.

'Yes,' Chasovytin replied. 'I am the curator of this wing. I understand you had a question about some of the art?'

'Not exactly,' said Rossel, getting to his feet and giving a small bow. 'You will find my question curious, but, alas, I am interested in such details.'

He led Chasovytin to the brass plaque on the wall that did not seem to relate to any of the paintings, the one with a few letters that had survived the abrasion of time.

The curator bent down, a finger on his errant spectacles. 'Ah yes, this thing.' He poked it and scratched at it with a fingernail. 'It is an oddity,' he said, smiling as if recounting a favourite anecdote. 'No one has ever been able to remove it. Even when the Hermitage was cleared out during the war and the paintings sent east for safekeeping, it clung on like a limpet.' He straightened up. 'We redecorated after the Blockade, but the workers couldn't shift it. The screws won't budge. A chisel just takes lumps out of the plaster. After a while, it was left there. As if it was meant to be.'

'Do you know whose painting it refers to?' asked Rossel.

Chasovytin's smile vanished. 'I do not recall, comrade, forgive me.'

'A general?'

The curator hesitated. 'It seems likely,' he said.

Rossel glared at him. 'Well, perhaps we should spend the rest of the afternoon in your archive going through the records of every painting that has been displayed in' – he checked a number on the wall – 'room 316. And tomorrow and the next day, if need be.'

Chasovytin led Rossel to the window.

'Perhaps I could save us the time, comrade,' he murmured. 'It was a general who was once compared to Napoleon. And like Napoleon, he fell from grace. Unlike Napoleon, his name is no longer mentioned much.'

Rossel nodded. He leaned over to speak into the curator's ear. 'I understand, comrade. And perhaps you could, in a most discreet manner, remind me of this Napoleonic figure. It would make the wheels of Soviet justice turn more efficiently.'

Chasovytin swallowed. 'Marshal Tukhachevsky,' he said in a voice so low, Rossel could hardly hear him.

Rossel patted him on the back. 'The People's Militia is grateful for your co-operation, Comrade Curator Chasovytin,' he said. 'If it makes you feel better, you could always glue another plaque over the top of that one. But I think you should leave it. I greatly admire the tenacity of this Soviet Napoleon.'

29

Slapping his gloved hands together to warm them, Rossel walked from the bank of the frozen Neva towards the Twelve Collegia of Leningrad State University. The massive edifice comprised twelve buildings, once housing separate imperial ministries, now united in the cause of scholarship. In the gathering darkness of the winter afternoon, it was an inspiring sight.

Comrade Baikalin, it turned out, was an authority on the origin of economic value, the impact of class, and of class struggle, on economic and political processes. When not communing with the ghosts of Russia's intellectual and cultural titans, he was to be found fulfilling his duties to the education of Soviet youth at the university.

No Soviet citizen would dare to defy a militia officer, no matter how lowly, unless they were sure of their ground. Rossel had returned to Station 17 and made some calls, including to the membership department of the Leningrad Communist Party on the pretext that the militia wanted to give out a public service award for outstanding community service, provided the recipients were politically reliable. It turned out that Comrade Baikalin had indeed recently had his Party card restored – a remarkable comeback for a man who had been expelled almost two decades ago and hurled into the Gulag system. The Party did not forgive lightly.

So he must have a protector.

If so, it followed that harassing him was unwise.

But the Tchaikovsky jibe had touched a nerve.

Only one of us has the talent to have made it through the Tchaikovsky Violin Concerto from beginning to end, Comrade Baikalin. And it isn't you.

Rossel's boots, still wet with snow, squeaked on the parquet as he walked down the endless corridor of the Twelve Collegia. This time, Baikalin would not escape so easily.

His father had once brought him and Galya to the university when they were teenagers. He had been visiting an old friend, a professor of mathematics, who taught there. Rossel remembered how disorientated they'd felt when first stepping into this magnificent corridor. Standing at one end, the doors on the other side appeared to be in miniature. Galya had run the entire length before turning and shouting to him, 'Come on, Revol, walk towards me.' He had done. They had passed each other in the middle, and she'd turned and opened her mouth, striking a pose as if to sing.

With the intuition of a twin brother, he knew what was coming – a line from her new favourite opera.

What is our life? A game!

But she had wrongfooted him, snapping her mouth shut at the last minute and fixing him with a look so hostile it had frightened him. Her way of telling him that although they were siblings, they were different. That he could not predict her.

On one side, prestigious members of the university looked out from their paintings or plinths, as if still engaged in some endless intellectual quest. To his right were wooden bookcases filled with books and manuscripts no one had read for decades. Small groups of chattering students, along with a few solitary

academics, patrolled the vast hall, following in the spectral footsteps of the nation's great scientific minds of the past. Von Baer,
embryology pioneer and the first person to observe the mysteries
of the human ovum in the laboratory; Lomonosov, who mapped
the transit of Venus and discovered its atmosphere; and Borodin,
to Rossel the most tantalising presence, a pioneering chemist
whose brilliance was acknowledged by Darwin – as well as being
a celebrated composer. His mother had taken them to see Borodin's opera *Prince Igor,* and he and Galya had loved it.

This late in the day, student lectures and studies were almost
over. But adult education was considered a key part of the university's obligations, particularly political education.

A lone woman in the administrative office pointed him in
what she thought was the right direction. Without breaking into
a smile, she made clear her approval of Rossel's attempts to
better himself and deepen his knowledge of Marxist-Leninist
theory.

It was, she said, the duty of them all.

*

About halfway down the huge hall was an open door into a
small lecture theatre. A little creased white card stuck to its glass
pane had the academic's name on it.

Rossel walked in.

The front row was half full; he counted nine people listening
to the words of Professor Baikalin. In the second row were four
more adult students, and another two in the third. The theatre's
other seven rows were empty.

Standing at a wooden lectern and on a small platform, the
economist was in full flow. He pressed a red button and a new

slide appeared on a screen behind him – a table of three boxes, each with a caption: 'State Farms', 'Collective Farms', 'Individual Peasant Farms'. The title read: 'The Process of Collectivisation, 1932–33'.

'What do these tables show?' Baikalin said, turning a page in his notes. 'That this period of reorganisation in Soviet agriculture, during which the number of collective farms and the number of their members increased at a tempestuous pace, ended in triumph in 1932 . . .'

Rossel slid into a seat in the back row on his own. Baikalin looked up and noticed him for the first time. He removed his glasses and cleaned them with a handkerchief. Then took a drink of water and turned a page.

'The process of collectivisation was one of gradual absorption and re-education of the remaining individual peasant farms and farmers by the collective farms.'

A new slide appeared.

'By 1933, all across the USSR, eighty-four point five per cent of the total area under grain came from the heroic process of collectivisation. As Stalin himself said at the Seventeenth All-Party Congress, "It must be admitted that the labouring peasantry, our Soviet peasantry, has completely and irrevocably taken its stand under the Red Banner of Socialism." A Five-Year Plan achieved in just four years, a testament to the collective will and shared strength of Bolshevism.'

There was more of it. Much more – endless statistics, unanimous in their support of the destruction of traditional peasant agriculture and the process of collectivisation, juxtaposed with the usual ideological homilies by which the policy was justified. Baikalin was a reasonable speaker, but his words were so clearly meant to be taken without fear of contradiction that when the students were asked if they had any questions, nobody had. Lectures like this were to be endured rather than enjoyed. A supplement to correspondence courses popular among adults seeking to improve their employment chances.

As Baikalin began to place his notes in his briefcase, Rossel raised his hand.

'I have a question for you, Comrade Professor,' he said.

Everyone in the lecture theatre turned towards him.

Baikalin glanced in Rossel's direction. The overhead light, glinting on his glasses, concealed his eyes. 'Yes?'

'These admirable achievements are, as you say, almost unbelievable,' Rossel began. 'And yet we all know them to be true. But, of course, they were not achieved without considerable heroic sacrifice. How can we be sure that the scale of this sacrifice did not outweigh the benefits that collectivisation has brought to the Soviet state?'

Baikalin pulled at his ragged beard, giving the impression this was an issue of great significance, deserving of a considered reply. He had not bothered to smarten up for his lecture, and his boots still looked like something a collective farmer would wear.

'As Lenin often told his vanguard of Bolshevik revolutionaries, sacrifices have to be made in order to follow the correct course,' said the professor. 'The answer to your question lies in part in taking the longer-term view – the undoubted benefits of collectivisation, not only to this generation but to many generations to come. It is a pity only that this process was delayed, when I personally believe it could and should have been pursued with much greater vigour.'

'Were the sacrifices not sufficient for you?' said Rossel.

The others in the lecture hall began to shuffle towards the exit. The exchange had taken an uncomfortable turn.

Baikalin removed his spectacles and blew on them hard. 'Fifth columnists, enemies of the people, saboteurs . . .' he said. 'Those were the terms Comrade Stalin used to describe the majority of the delegates who attended the Seventeenth All-Party Congress, and, in my opinion, he was right to do so. Even if some loyal Party members . . .' He tapped his chest twice with his glasses. 'If some loyal Party members were caught up in the purges, well . . .'

Baikalin replaced his spectacles.

'To cut down weeds one must sometimes run a scythe through the stalks of corn that surround them.'

30

Baikalin was waiting outside his office, looking up and down the corridor in an agitated manner.

'Not here,' snapped the economist as Rossel approached. He walked off without another word.

Rossel followed.

Baikalin led them out of the building, but instead of making for an open space outside, as Rossel expected, he doubled back and set off down a side street.

The professor paused at the opening to a grimy courtyard, making way for a small car which braked and swerved into the road, its wheels fighting for purchase in the snow and slush.

Then he darted into the courtyard and through the other side, across another side street and into a second courtyard. He looked over his shoulder to check that Rossel had kept up and pointed to a small set of steps leading to a wooden basement door.

Outside, a big man wrapped from head to foot in a mixture of coat, hat and filthy rags sat smoking on a wooden chair. He held up a tin mug.

'A few kopeks, comrade, to help buy a little winter sun. There's no sadder sight than an empty cup.'

Ignoring him, Rossel ducked his head and stepped inside.

Even by the normal standards of Leningrad's illegal drinking dens, the stench of raw alcohol, cigarettes and body odour was intense.

The basement room was three metres by three, or thereabouts, and had only two other men in it, both practically comatose.

'It might be unorthodox, Comrade Militiaman, but the university is not a place to speak about the past,' said Baikalin. 'Here is somewhere a little more Dostoevskyan. A place more suited to . . . personal stories.'

Baikalin banged a fist on a small counter in one corner. Without a word, a hatch opened, and a hand appeared, sliding over an unmarked bottle.

The professor held up two fingers; two shot glasses were passed across. The hatch slammed shut.

*

Rossel and Baikalin were sitting around a little wooden table in a dingy corner, as far away from the other two drinkers as was possible.

'I know full well what you are about, Militiaman,' said Baikalin. 'And, yes, there are aspects of the past that should remain . . .' he groped for the word, 'buried. I presume you have something else to show me? Something that would undermine my position at the university were it to come to light?'

Rossel opened his leather case and took out the newspaper photograph of Baikalin, Kirov and Abazi.

'You told me there were thousands of pictures taken like this at the 1934 Congress,' he said to the professor. 'So one of my comrades contacted *Pravda* and *Izvestia* and asked for a selection.'

Rossel placed a second photograph on the table. Then a third.

'It took less than three hours to find eleven photographs of yourself, given your position in the Party hierarchy at that time. Three of them also featured Tamas Abazi. This one, in particular, makes me think you remember Comrade Abazi well enough.'

Baikalin stared at the photograph.

Three men again. But with one big difference. Baikalin was on the left, Abazi on the right, and the man in the middle was the most famous person in the entire Soviet Union.

Rossel tapped a finger on Stalin's jocular, pockmarked face. 'I can bring you in for questioning and we can start to write everything down,' he said. 'But I can also give you the option of remaining an *informal* advisor.'

He poured them two more measures of vodka. The spirit smelled of petrol and there were black flecks swimming in it. But he had drunk worse.

Baikalin ran a hand through his hair and straightened his tie. Then sighed. 'Yes, I remember him, this Abazi. But I didn't *know* him, not really.'

The professor exhaled, driving the air from his lungs, before throwing his vodka back. Rossel did the same. Then the two men sniffed at their elbows, searching for the stench of the street to distract and deceive their senses from the shock of the rank spirit. Before inhaling and grimacing in unison.

'*Yob tvoyu mat*',' cursed Baikalin, his eyes watering. 'All right, all right. Try this for *informal* advice.'

He pinched the bridge of his nose, breathed in and out. He began to speak.

'The Seventeenth All-Party Congress brought down a biblical plague on all its delegates. Within three years, hundreds had been arrested, and many of them shot in the back of the head, buried in shallow graves in the wilds of Karelia. I was lucky, I suppose. I was spared execution but not exile. I went into the camps but got out three years ago – that's a lot of years, comrade. Now I have my job back. Piece by piece, I have been gathering the shreds of my reputation and stitching it back together. I have no desire to be dragged into your investigation into a Georgian buffoon who thought he was a big shot. A fool. So you have five more minutes for questions and not a second more.'

Baikalin's voice trailed away. Even he sounded unconvinced by the threat.

Rossel refilled their glasses. They repeated the masochistic ritual – getting the liquid from glass to stomach without having to taste it.

'A fool, how?' Rossel asked.

Baikalin wiped his lips. 'I met this Abazi on the second day of the Congress. Kirov introduced us. It was early in the morning, but this fat Georgian with a nose like a freshly peeled potato was already a bit pissed. Then he collared me that evening. I couldn't get away from him. A beaming idiot who kept talking in his barely comprehensible Georgian accent to anyone who would listen about how he was a great friend of Stalin. Of course, nobody believed him.'

A friend of Stalin.

Rossel felt another twist in his gut. This time, it wasn't the vodka.

'And how was this unlikely friendship supposed to have come about?' he asked.

'Abazi claimed they were young comrades together. That they had fought the Tsar's secret police in the streets of their hometown. All utter nonsense, of course. Can you imagine?'

The smaller of the two other men in the basement slumped forward and began to be sick.

Baikalin took out a handkerchief and wiped at his nose.

'Anything else?' Rossel pressed him.

Baikalin threw back more vodka and indicated to Rossel that he should do the same.

'Even taller tales,' said the professor, patting Rossel on the back as he grappled with the effects of the rank spirit. 'How Stalin invited him to attend secret workers' meetings and introduced him to Georgian revolutionaries. Endless exaggerations. Each one bigger than the next. How he was with Stalin's men on their bank raids. Gori, Baku, Tbilisi – smuggling, robbery, protection rackets. All to fund Lenin and his revolution.'

Rossel's cheeks were glowing, the vodka already fuzzing his brain. But he swilled more of it into their glasses. Baikalin was in the mood for confession.

'Bank raids?' Rossel asked.

'Don't you know anything? It was what Stalin was famous for. Dashing brigand, partisan, rabble-rouser, organiser. It's why Lenin promoted him. Anyway, this halfwit Abazi rambled on and on about how the two of them and a gang of others robbed banks and sent money to Lenin. If I hadn't managed to shake him off by going for a piss, I suspect the fool would also have claimed to have dined on foie gras with Marx and Engels at The Swan in Brussels while all three wrote *The Communist Manifesto* together.' Baikalin tugged at his beard again. 'Who do you really work for, comrade? Am I to be allowed to know that, at least? You're no ordinary militiaman.'

'Lenin?' Rossel said, shrugging the comment aside. 'Abazi claimed to know *Lenin*?'

Baikalin began to laugh. 'If you're claiming to be Stalin's best friend, why not Lenin's to boot?' The professor reached for the bottle again and refilled his glass. 'The braggart claimed to have been a bodyguard when Stalin met Lenin at their celebrated first encounter, in Finland in 1905,' he said. 'He even had some fanciful story about how the Okhrana, the Tsar's secret police, had infiltrated their group – some great secret he might reveal if I only bought him another bottle of *chacha*. If I'd been stupid enough to do that, he would, at that point, no doubt have confided that he was the very sailor who fired the first shot from the battleship *Potemkin*.'

Rossel thought for a moment. 'Fanciful, you say, but he's standing next to you and Stalin in the picture?'

Baikalin shrugged. His tone was mocking. 'Stalin didn't say a word to him. Which proves my point. Stalin was lauding the success of the first Five-Year Plan and Abazi just appeared. Stepped behind us into the shot. As soon as the photographer took that, Kirov whisked Stalin away and that was that.'

'And you have not seen Abazi since then?' said Rossel.

Baikalin shook his head. 'Not once. If I ever wasted a second's thought on him, I would have assumed he had been sent to the camps. Like the rest of us.'

Rossel examined the dregs of the grimy bottle. He poured them into the glasses and drained his.

'As far as I know, he was not,' he said.

Baikalin drank his vodka and slammed his glass on the table. 'Slunk off back to his mountain cave in Gori, I'll be bound,' he muttered. 'Bastard Georgians, they all stick tight together, like leeches on a wound.'

Rossel staggered to his feet.

'My surname is Rossel, Comrade Baikalin,' he said. 'I have a personal interest in the 1934 Congress. My parents were among the delegates. Lev and Tamara Rossel. Perhaps you knew them?'

He watched Baikalin's face. The Old Bolshevik's eyes misted over, but otherwise his expression did not change.

'Sorry, I didn't,' he said. 'I do not recognise the name. There were many delegates, many good people.'

Rossel sighed. It had, at least, been worth asking. He began to gather the photographs and replace them in his case, doing so with exaggerated, inebriated care.

Perhaps Abazi had indeed slunk off to a cave, he thought. But how odd that he had resurfaced now.

And so very quickly wound up dead.

31

The loudspeaker in the Finland Station was crackling with static. The announcer was listing distant, mysterious places – Vyborg, Vainikkala, Kouvola, Lahti . . . After the previous evening's generous vodka quota, each name went through Rossel's head like a hammer.

With impatience, he tapped his finger on the two pictures of Abazi and Orlova and asked another question to the ticket clerk in the booth.

'You say you were working last Tuesday, comrade. Are you sure neither of them bought a ticket from you or any of your colleagues?'

She shook her head. 'No, Comrade Officer, and I have shown them to everyone in the back office, but no one did.'

He thanked the clerk anyway and put the pictures back in his pocket. He had hoped somebody else might have seen them. But ten days after their deaths, no one had.

Rossel began to pick his way through the evening commuters towards the main entrance to the station.

Still no luck. Perhaps Gerashvili will do better?

The lieutenant was following up on the activities of Comrade Baikalin. Despite the economist's drunken verbosity at the back-street *ryumochnaya*, Rossel was certain he was hiding something. He was also still berating himself for failing to ask about Baikalin's tryst with the poet Kovalyova, and their possible interest in a picture that was no longer on show. But the rank vodka, along with memories of his mother and father, had addled his mind. A line of questioning for another day, he told himself.

Movement caught Rossel's eye and he stopped. A man and a woman were standing near a small hut between two of the railway lines. The woman was gesticulating at the man and shouting into his face.

'No more, I can't take another week there, not another day . . .'

The man was grimacing, digging his little finger into a broken front tooth.

Rossel shrugged. There was no harm in asking again.

He walked up to them and tapped the railwayman on the shoulder. Belov turned towards him. The woman stopped shouting.

'A moment of your time, comrade?' asked Rossel. 'I just want to go through your story again. See if there's anything you forgot.'

*

Inside the untidy hut, Belov introduced the woman as his wife. She was a tall, middle-aged redhead with hard eyes and a long, thin nose.

'He told you everything last time, comrade. He tells me everything, so I know exactly what he told you,' she said.

Rossel ran through the details of Belov's original story with them both – the night was dark, two men in the car, a dark blue or possibly black GAZ Pobeda, or an 11-80.

The Belovs nodded along.

'And the car just hit them and then drove on?' Rossel addressed Belov. 'That's what you told me.'

Belov nodded again. His wife joined in. Rossel turned to her.

'Is that what he told you as well, comrade?'

Mrs Belov stared at him. She took a pack of cigarettes out of her handbag, lit one and sat on an old packing case next to Belov's workbench.

'I can't take another week there, not another day,' she said to Rossel.

'You can't take another week *where*?'

'Our apartment in Primorsky. It's a shithole. I've got stockings with fewer holes in them than the ceiling. I asked for another one in Petrogradsky, but that smug bastard Golubev, the local Party man there, he won't help us.'

'I'm a militia officer,' said Rossel, as his hangover sent a flash of pain across his eyeballs. 'Not a housing officer.'

She glanced at her husband. 'The gun dog says he can't help us, Belov.'

Belov dug his finger into his tooth. 'Like I say, the car hit them and drove away.'

Rossel understood. He turned to the wife. 'I have a friend, a Major Nikitin, on the Kremlin's staff,' he said. 'He has the ear of Comrade Khrushchev himself these days, I'm told. I am sure the major will be willing to talk to this Golubev for you.'

He was sure Nikitin would have Golubev, the Belovs and Rossel shot on the spot rather than spend a second on such a petty issue, but if dangling the bait got these two to co-operate . . .

Mrs Belov took a puff on her cigarette and considered this. Dropping the cigarette on the floor and stubbing it out with the heel of her boot, she nodded to Belov.

The railwayman dug at his tooth and spat out a gobbet of

blood-specked phlegm. 'It was no accident,' he said. 'The two of them were standing together talking. The car swerved towards them deliberately.'

'And then it drove on?'

'No. It stopped and backed right over them. A proper job, it was. I think the woman was still alive at that point. I could hear her groaning. But not after they did that.'

'So why didn't you tell me this initially, Comrade Belov?' Rossel demanded.

Belov took a moment to think about this. 'This Major Nikitin, is he *really* close to the high-ups? To Comrade Khrushchev?'

'They're like two pickled herrings inside a tin.'

The little finger picking at the tooth again. A reflective nod of the head. 'Because they turned left.'

'Left?'

The railwayman pointed at his wife again. '"Don't ask questions. Don't answer any, either. That's how we'll get through all this." That's what you always say to me. Isn't that right, Irina?'

She shrugged.

'Khrushchev,' she said to Rossel. 'This Major Nikitin really knows him?'

Rossel nodded.

'Tell him,' she ordered her husband. 'I can't stand one more week in bloody Primorsky.'

Belov scratched his chin and spat on the floor again. 'A black GAZ Pobeda, as black as a *raven,* and they turned *left* across the Liteyny Bridge towards . . .' He made a fist of his left hand and clutched the lapel of his coat. Then he held the palm of his right hand stretching out in front of him. 'Lenin knows,' said the railwayman.

Rossel smiled.

'And now me,' he said.

*

As the last rays of a bleak winter sun dropped behind the horizon, the Finland Station was engulfed in shadow.

Rossel stood next to the towering statue of Lenin. The revolutionary leader's giant frame and heroic pose seemed designed to intimidate even the encroaching darkness.

His huge right arm was pointing directly at something on the opposite bank of the Neva – the flat roof of a squat, brown piece of Constructivist 1930s architecture on Liteiny Prospekt.

Every Leningrader knew its name – Bolshoi Dom, the Big House. The MGB's main headquarters in the city. For those, like Rossel, who had visited its cells, just speaking the name out loud tightened the throat.

He glanced up at Vladimir Ilyich, who, he half-imagined, was smiling mischievously down at him. This was a scene Stravinsky might have scored as part of one of his comic operas.

At last, I have an irreproachable key witness who can identify the murderers, he thought. *But I'd need a truck and a builder's crane to bring him in for questioning.*

32

Lipukhin's eyes were shut and his face was pale, almost white. A thin, sticky trail of vomit stretched from one corner of his mouth, across the white sheets and onto a worn red carpet, on which were two empty vodka bottles.

Rossel shook him again. The captain stirred and mumbled something unintelligible.

'Get me a jug of water from the sink, Dasha,' said Rossel.

The little girl got up off her knees and left the room. After a moment, she returned with a chipped tin jug. Rossel took it and threw the water into the captain's face.

Lipukhin's eyes blinked open.

'Fuck your mo . . .' His voice trailed away as he saw his niece. 'Sorry. Sorry. I . . .'

He sat up, put his hand to his temple and groaned.

'Dasha says you're supposed to be taking her to a performance at the Kirov this afternoon,' said Rossel. He pointed to the girl, spotless in her Little Octobrists uniform, hair pinned back, as if ready to be painted into a poster standing alongside her hero, Pavel Morozov.

'The concert . . .' Lipukhin said.

'Yes, the concert,' said Rossel.

'Sorry. Dasha, forgive me, my darling. What time is it?'

Dasha looked at her watch. 'Five past twelve,' she said, her voice flat. 'The performance starts at one, but our group is sup-posed to be there half an hour early. After it's finished, we are to be presented on stage.'

Lipukhin rubbed his eyes. 'That's nice,' he said. 'Who are you being presented to?'

'Comrade Beria,' she replied.

The two men froze.

Rossel knelt and looked into the girl's eyes.

'Are you sure?' he said. 'Comrade Beria himself?'

'Yes.'

He and Lipukhin exchanged glances. The presence of the man who was feared almost as much as Stalin himself put a new perspective on their situation. For Dasha to miss this concert was now unthinkable. Lesser acts of indifference or carelessness had been construed as deliberate insults. And that put one foot into the realm of treason.

Lipukhin tried to stand. He reached out a hand to steady himself on a bedside table, but only succeeded in knocking over a lamp and a full ashtray.

The captain sat down on the bed again and put his head in his hands.

'I'll take her,' Rossel said. 'Dasha, put your coat and shoes on.'

The girl headed for the corridor. Lipukhin gave his niece a small, sad wave. She did not return it.

*

As the tram trundled down one side of the Moika, past the white columns of the Yusupov Palace, Dasha sat staring out of the small spots in the window that were not frosted over. They could see only snatches of the outside world – boots trudging through the snow, a barking dog, a glimpse of a pretty girl wearing an outsized white ushanka.

The snow was heavy, and the tram was travelling at a crawl. The lights flickered on and off and the carriage was often shrouded in gloom, reminding Rossel of journeys he had taken in the blackout during the city's terrible nine hundred-day blockade by Nazi forces. To make them harder for the Luftwaffe to hit, tram cars had been separated and all lights replaced with faint blue lamps, shielded to stop the light emerging through the windows.

Sitting opposite him had been a beautiful woman with dark red hair and a pinched, emaciated face, marked by months of unrelenting hunger that matched his own. Their eyes had met.

When she had got off, he had watched her walk across the road. The overhead wires on the line next to theirs were tangled and hanging down like cobwebs. As she had crossed the street, a gust of wind had blown off the canal and they had swung viciously, passing only centimetres from her head, throwing up a blizzard of sparks. But the woman didn't duck or run. She carried on walking. As the tram had started up again, she had turned back and looked at him. A small, resigned smile.

Death or life, it's all the same to her, he'd thought.

And all the same to me, too . . .

There had even been something about Lipukhin's melancholic wave as they shut the door behind them that had reminded him of the woman's fatalism. As though it were a final act of surrender.

But Rossel wasn't ready to give up yet.

Especially after his meeting with Comrade Baikalin. Once again, he went over recent revelations in his head as Dasha gazed through the gap in the frosted window at the streets and snow.

Tamas Abazi, an Old Bolshevik. A former acquaintance of Kirov, possibly even of Lenin, reappears in Leningrad after a long absence without warning or obvious motive. And is killed, probably by the MGB. Not arrested, nor sent to the camps, nor beaten to death in the interrogation cells of the Bolshoi Dom. Rammed by a large black car, whose driver ensured his death by running over him again.

Why did they need to do that – to pretend it was an accident? It's not their style. They arrest you, torture you, build the case against you, get your confession, try you, and then dispose of you, calling it justice.

Murdered alongside him is Anna Orlova, an academic and expert in defunct Slavic alphabets, particularly Glagolitic.

Orlova also knew Comrade Baikalin, another Old Bolshevik, who, at the very least, once got drunk with Abazi at the 17th All-Party Congress in January 1934. The academic had claimed this meeting was fleeting, inconsequential, hard to recall, but was probably lying. A day on which you spend time with both Kirov and Stalin is not one you forget easily.

Baikalin knows the famous poet Vika Kovalyova and enjoys going to art galleries with her to look at portraits of military heroes. In turn, Kovalyova knew Orlova.

But Orlova is not the key to this. That's where I've been going wrong. I'm certain of it. The key is Abazi.

Why did he leave his mountain home? Why did he travel all the way to Leningrad? And who wanted him dead?

Rossel patted his breast pocket. He took out the long-distance train ticket he had bought that morning, looked at it, then replaced it. The key to Tamas Abazi most likely lay nearly three thousand kilometres away in his hometown of Gori: a cold, cloudy Georgian mountain redoubt famous throughout the USSR as the birthplace of Comrade Stalin. A place where the locals might not appreciate a low-ranking Leningrad militiaman poking around and asking questions.

Tomorrow, he would set off on a journey to pursue it.

He reached out and patted Dasha on the head. To his surprise, she smiled up at him.

'*Peter and the Wolf*,' she said.

'I'm sorry?'

'*Peter and the Wolf*. By Sergei Prokofiev. That's the piece we are going to hear today. Do you know it, Uncle Revol? You used to play the violin, yes?'

'That's right, Dasha, I did. I know of Prokofiev, the composer. But I don't know this piece.'

'They say it is wonderful,' she said. 'A bit frightening, but I'm not scared. Not one bit.'

He smiled back. 'Uncle Ilya would be with you, Dasha. If he could, I mean.'

The little girl turned away and wiped at the window with her mitten. 'He isn't though, is he?'

33

The Kirov was crammed and noisy.

Everywhere he looked around the great opera and ballet theatre, parents and relatives of Young Pioneers, many clutching bouquets, were making their way into the auditorium. Dasha had been a little late but escaped with a mild scolding. She was shepherded away by a young woman in an olive-green skirt who had been waiting for stragglers in the foyer.

Rossel found a seat, at the end of a near-full aisle towards the front of the stalls. He felt immediately at home beneath Douzy's painted blue sky filled with cupids and cherubs dancing around a spectacular chandelier.

The theatre, renamed in 1935 to honour Kirov after his early death, was full. Some of the smaller children were seated on stage, around and behind the ensemble; the musicians had escaped from the orchestra pit for the occasion. Rossel scanned the lines of young faces for Dasha but could not find her.

In two golden boxes closest to the stage, groups of Party dignitaries were taking their seats, greeting each other with much backslapping and exaggerated bonhomie.

With a lurch in the pit of his stomach, Rossel caught sight of a gleaming head on top of a grey uniform belonging to a short squat figure. The man turned, and he saw a face he knew. That of Lavrentiy Beria, First Deputy Chairman of the Council of Ministers.

Let's hope the malevolent bastard doesn't see me.

*

Peter and the Wolf was 'a symphonic fairy tale for children', according to the posters in the theatre foyer, by 'our great Russian composer Sergei Prokofiev'.

The orchestra was small – he counted just over thirty musicians as they marched on stage to deafening applause and excited juvenile cheering. In front of the musicians were two microphones, one at adult height, the other lower.

At last, he caught sight of Dasha, sitting second from the end of a long line of smartly dressed Pioneers and Octobrists, on the far side of the stage, closer to Beria than to himself. She looked solemn, in awe, indifferent to the hubbub of the children around her and the shushing of their adult guardians.

As a few final stragglers were taking their seats in the hall, the lights dimmed and the orchestra began to tune up – first the oboe giving the A, then the wind and brass, and finally the strings. The last to arrive – a plump woman in a red dress waving at her own child on stage – squeezed past Rossel and sat a couple of seats away from him.

A woman, small, dark-haired with a quiet, intelligent air, walked from the wings and took her place at the tallest microphone. As her name was announced to the audience as 'Natalya Surkova', she bowed.

The director of the Moscow Children's Theatre. The one who has commissioned Vika's new libretto and Prokofiev's original score of *Peter and the Wolf*, Rossel remembered.

He recollected that there had been a lot of gossip about her in the musical circles he used to frequent. It had been rumoured she was once the lover of Marshal Tukhachevsky – the 'Red Napoleon'. Tukhachevsky was a great hero of the civil war and, later, had played a major part in reforming the Red Army. He was also a music lover; a close friend of Dmitri Shostakovich and often seen at concerts and recitals in the composer's company.

But during the terror of the thirties, Tukhachevsky had been arrested, tortured and shot by the secret police for plotting a 'right-wing Trotskyist' military conspiracy, and unlikely accusations of being a Nazi spy. And, now Rossel came to think of it, the marshal had also been excised from the Hermitage's pantheon of military heroes.

If the rumours had been true, Surkova had done well to survive the entanglement.

*

Natalya Surkova leaned into the microphone. 'This is the story of Peter and the wolf,' she said. 'Each character in the tale is going to be represented by a different instrument. The bird will be played by the flute . . .'

She half-turned and pointed to one of the musicians. The flautist played a short, skittish motif – a bird that was flitting from branch to branch, looping the loop, exulting in its freedom.

'The duck, by the oboe . . .'

This time, she picked out a grey-haired oboist, who put the instrument to his lips. A low, mournful lament floated across the theatre, hushing the children more surely than any grown-up admonitions.

'The cat, by the clarinet,' said Surkova. A clarinet hopped lightly over the grass, graceful and poised.

Then came Peter's grandfather, represented by the bassoon – a low, grumpy character, limping along, wagging a bony forefinger as he grumbled about his arthritis and the recklessness of today's youth.

'The wolf, by the horns.'

A trio of French horns sounded a series of low, menacing chords. Rossel thought he could see Dasha's eyes widen.

'Hunters, by the drums.'

The timpani thundered out a long volley of shots.

'And our young hero, Peter,' said the narrator, 'by the strings. A boy not unlike our own hero, children, our very own Pavlik Morozov.'

Rossel bit his lip.

Even Prokofiev isn't safe from that little shit.

The violins, violas, cellos and double basses raised their bows and struck up a simple melody, depicting a boy strolling along in the countryside, full of hope and adventure.

Natalya Surkova paused for effect, looked out across the sea of expectant young faces, then spoke again. 'Are you ready, children?' she said.

As she did so, a blond boy of about ten years took his place at the smaller microphone next to her.

'Then we shall begin,' whispered the narrator as the conductor raised his baton again.

*

As the performance unfolded, Rossel realised Prokofiev's deceptively simple scoring was perfect.

The rasping horns got louder and louder as the snarling wolf skulked back and forth before slinking behind the trees. He glanced around him. The younger children clutched at their parents, or at each other, some even putting their hands over their ears. In their imaginations, they could see the story. Peter stepping out into a meadow, greeting his friends the bird and the duck, who both narrowly escaped the claws of the cat. Grandfather scolding Peter for venturing so far from the house in case a wolf was on the prowl. Insisting his grandson go home – and then, gasps, as the wolf emerged from the forest.

Rossel saw movement out of the corner of his eye. A small gold door in the wall of the auditorium to his left opened, and a dishevelled figure stepped into the aisle.

Lipukhin had obviously tried to smarten himself up for his niece but had hardly succeeded. His hair was untidy, his suit crumpled, his boots mud-spattered. His forehead and cheeks were ruddy, pimpled and covered with a sheen of sweat.

The captain glanced around him. Every seat was taken, but there were two empty wooden stools usually used by ushers. He picked one up and plonked himself down on it, about two metres away from the row Rossel was sitting in.

A few heads in the audience turned towards him. A Party official in one of the boxes glared down at him. The plump woman in the red dress tutted.

Rossel stared at the stage, hoping Dasha hadn't seen her uncle arrive.

'No matter how hard the duck tried to run, she couldn't escape the wolf,' said the narrator.

'He was getting nearer, nearer, catching up with her,' said the blond boy standing next to her.

The eyes of the Pioneers and Octobrists on stage widened and they sat forward.

'The wolf caught the duck in its jaws and ate it,' said the narrator.

'But fearless Peter snared the wolf by its tail,' declaimed the boy.

On stage and in the auditorium, children tried and failed to suppress their cheers. All except Dasha, who Rossel could see sitting motionless, staring at her uncle, her cheeks flushed.

As they reached the fable's climax, with the conductor puffing out his chest and waving his baton in sharp, stiff motions through the air, the orchestra began a rousing, triumphant final march, based on Peter's own theme, in which the characters paraded towards the zoo with the captured wolf.

Rossel heard a sharp intake of breath.

He turned to his left. Lipukhin was gesturing to him, pointing to the orchestra, his face agitated. The captain put his left hand to his ear and used his right to make a dialling motion.

Rossel immediately understood.

The music at Anna Orlova's kommunalka – the music someone had played down the phone in her room . . . it was Peter's theme.

Lipukhin had just heard it again.

Surkova's voice softened as she recounted the bird's boasting. 'My, what brave fellows we are, Peter, and look what we have caught!'

But there was another twist in the tale, said the blond boy, waiting for silence to descend once more. It turned out that the wolf, in his haste and greed, had swallowed the duck alive. And if you listened very carefully, you could hear the creature's lonely, plaintive song coming from within the belly of the beast.

A rumbling began – pulsating strings, *accelerando*, until in a final *tutti* burst, the triumphant procession was over, ending in a joyous celebration of Peter's – or Pavlik's – exemplary revolutionary zeal.

For a fraction of a second, there was silence. Then the hall erupted.

Lipukhin, clapping and smiling with everyone else, rose from his chair. The captain's eyes fixed upon his niece.

'Bravo,' he shouted. 'Bravo!'

The applause lasted for several minutes, fuelled by the cheers of the children, while a train of girls and boys brought flowers onto the stage for the narrators and the conductor.

As the audience started to take their seats again, a man walked towards the centre of the stage. He was small, wearing his usual pince-nez glasses and a black suit that was too big for him, and flanked by two pretty blonde girls of about fourteen years old.

Minister Beria glanced around the auditorium. Then raised a hand.

34

If Prokofiev were to compose a leitmotif for Lavrentiy Beria, Rossel thought, he might take his inspiration from the chant of a Dies irae, as Berlioz had in *Symphonie fantastique* or Liszt's *Dance of the Dead*.

The two narrators bowed nervously to Beria and stood back.

The man many believed would be Stalin's heir stepped towards the microphone. A Party stooge in one of the gold boxes stood up and began clapping, soon followed by another man. In a moment, the entire audience was furiously applauding.

The plump woman was staring at Rossel. A little too late, he got to his feet and began clapping along with everybody else.

After three minutes or more, Beria nodded – a reluctant emperor acknowledging the dutiful, if by now wearisome, flatteries of his court.

As one, everybody sat.

Beria tapped the microphone. Static echoed around the hall. As it subsided, the minister began to speak.

'What a wonderful performance we have witnessed here today,' he said.

He reached out with both arms and affectionately patted the two girls standing to his right and left on their heads.

'For what else is a revolution's future shaped from if not its children? It is their noble innocence which must constantly replenish the Marxist purity of our cause. Did not Lenin himself say, "Give me four years to teach the children and the seed I have sown will never be uprooted"? And what a lesson Sergei Sergeyevich Prokofiev has created for you Young Pioneers and Little Octobrists here today. Its message is plain. The hearts of the young are always more valiant than those of the old. Peter's grandfather scolds him, warns him to stay away from the fearsome capitalist wolf, but the boy, a brave Young Pioneer, just like our glorious martyr for Bolshevism Pavlik Morozov, puts the Revolution first!'

Beria stared at the audience and then half-turned towards the Pioneers and Octobrists behind him.

'Never in the history of Socialism has your loyalty been needed like it is now,' he continued, his thin voice carrying into the auditorium. 'For Bolshevism's struggle against rootless cosmopolitanists and anti-revolutionary metropolitan elements is eternal. As evidenced by this recent Doctors' Plot. Only their defeat will allow our Party to remain the intellect, honour and conscience of the modern age, the Bolshevik age. You must, children, all be ever vigilant; like your famous motto, be "always prepared". For reactionaries and fifth columnists are all around us . . . in the factories, in Leningrad's streets, inside our own homes even . . .'

Beria removed his glasses, took a small, white handkerchief from his pocket and ostentatiously cleaned them. He blinked three times and put a finger to his temple, as if trying to recall some long-forgotten secret, then replaced them.

'Yes,' he said, his voice dropping to a whisper. 'Even here, inside this very Kirov Theatre. Named, as it is, after one of our great revolutionary heroes, he, himself, murdered by reactionary traitors.'

The minister glanced around the auditorium. Rossel noticed

the plump woman to his right turn her eyes down and begin fishing for something in her handbag. All around the theatre, people shifted uncomfortably in their seats. As if Beria, simply by willing it so, had the power to conduct an inventory of their souls.

The minister finished surveying the stalls, then glanced mischievously up at the nervous faces in the gold boxes, clearly enjoying his game.

'He's one,' said a small voice behind him.

The fidgeting stopped.

Beria turned. 'One what?' he said.

Dasha stepped out from her row of Young Pioneers.

'A reactionary element, an anti-revolutionary,' she said. Eyes blazing, the little girl took another step forward. 'He gets drunk every night and disrespects the Party and Comrade Stalin.'

Her right arm stretched out. The index finger pointed past Rossel, at Lipukhin.

Every head in the Kirov turned towards the bedraggled object of the girl's contempt.

The minister adjusted his pince-nez and smiled at Dasha. 'Well done, child,' he said. 'What a good little girl you are.'

Beria looked triumphant. As if Prokofiev had indeed written him his own leitmotif and he was just about to whistle it.

4

ОХОТНИКИ

Hunters

35

The rhythmic rattle of the train muffled the moans and snores of about sixty people. Some were clustered in quartets: two bunks opposite two more, with another couple on the other side of the narrow aisle and at a right angle to their neighbours, running the full length of the wagon.

Leningrad to Moscow. Then a series of towns, many of which Rossel had never heard of. Six hours into the journey to Tbilisi, most of the passengers had fallen asleep, sprawled across their bunks, defended by starched sheets, threadbare blankets and hastily built fortifications made of parcels, boots and bags. It was a long journey to the Georgian capital, and still further to Gori, Stalin's birthplace.

Rossel closed his eyes and tried to rest. But he could still see Lipukhin's stunned expression as he sat in an ever-expanding circle of empty seats – seats that flipped upwards with an echoing *thunk* as horrified citizens got up and left as fast as they could.

Beria had patted Dasha on the head and murmured into her ear. The child had listened intently. She had nodded once before retreating to her seat.

The Kirov had emptied and no one had come forward to arrest Lipukhin, even though the captain had not moved, but simply sat staring blankly at the stage as if hypnotised.

But they would before too long. They knew where to find him.

Will it snow, Soselo? Will it rain? Is there a storm coming?

Rossel thought of Tamas Abazi, of Galya's curious expression as she passed him in the long hall of the Twelve Collegia, and of Dasha's accusatory finger.

As the train rumbled on, he stared blankly into the darkness.

*

He opened his eyes; daylight was creeping around the edges of ragged pink curtains tinged with nicotine. Rossel wiped the condensation from the windows but could see only massed ranks of pine trees freighted with snow.

Mother Russia, vast, walled off, seemingly unreachable.

A steady stream of travellers rubbed their hands together and stamped their feet as they tramped to the toilets, or to the samovar, or to find a brief perch between two carriages where they could have some fresh air and a morning smoke as the unseen land thundered by.

Gerashvili had agreed that Rossel should make this journey at once. It would get him out of Leningrad. Which, at a time when Dasha might be enlightening a fatherly MGB interrogator about Uncle Ilya's closest associates, seemed a prudent move.

As both a militia officer and a former resident of the labour camp system, Rossel knew key tenets of Article 58 of the penal code by heart: 'A counter-revolutionary action is any action aimed at overthrowing, undermining or weakening of the power of workers' and peasants' Soviets ...' It was vague enough to catch anything. Section 58-12 – 'Non-reporting of a "counter-revolutionary activity".' If Dasha told them just some of the things her uncle had said, including opinions stated in Rossel's presence, that alone might mean imprisonment.

Give me four years to teach the children and the seed I have sown will never be uprooted. Lenin's words came back to him. In little Dasha's case, it had taken longer – nine. But now the child belonged to the Revolution. How, he wondered, might she be saved from it?

By mid-morning, people began pulling out travelling chessboards. Three cubicles down, a contest between an old man and a collective farmer who was carrying two chickens with him in a crate became so hard-fought it attracted a small crowd.

'Who do you think you are – Mikhail Botvinnik?' said the old man as the farmer took his bishop. Botvinnik and Taimanov were facing off to decide the Soviet Chess Championship. The papers were full of it.

From a creaking bunk two down from where Rossel sat, a moon-faced Muscovite with an open smile and a wispy moustache took advantage of a quiet moment to introduce himself as Misha. He hoisted himself into a position from which he could converse and asked Rossel if he was travelling for work or for family. It was a chance to try out his cover story, and Rossel began to explain. But Misha was not interested in others, only in his forthcoming challenge – a piano competition in Tbilisi.

'I will play Bach's Prelude and Fugue number sixteen. Do you know it?' Then he would give them Schumann's *Carnaval*, Beethoven's 'Waldstein' Sonata and three Scriabin studies. There was a chamber music component to the competition, a trio by Mendelssohn or by Dvorak. 'I chose the Dvorak – I can't stand Mendelssohn. Sentimental nonsense. Have you any familiarity with music?'

Rossel decided to change the subject. He nodded at the chess players.

'Who do you think will win?'

'The red-faced farmer, I suspect. They're always two steps ahead, planting grain in the spring, harvesting in the summer, and so on.'

'No, I mean, in the Soviet Championships, between Botvinnik and Taimanov?'

'Taimanov. He's a real killer. No holds barred with that shit-kicking Sicilian Defence of his. And you?'

'Botvinnik,' Rossel said. 'He's already been champion, after all. And he's clever.' He stifled a yawn and closed his eyes. 'He is prepared to give up a significant sacrifice, a castle, or a rook, in the middle of the game. Lets them think he's done. Lets them think they've won. But then—'

'Botvinnik? No, I don't think so,' said Misha, shaking his head.

But this time he did not sound so convinced.

*

Night.

A screech of brakes as the train began to pull into a station.

'Where the hell are we?' Misha called out from his bunk.

For a moment, no one was sure.

'Novocherkassk,' came a woman's voice.

'Not Rostov yet?'

'Next stop.'

The farmer's chickens began to cluck in their crate. Rossel reached for his *papirosa* and headed for the end of the carriage.

Midnight. Finally, he fell asleep again. Only to be awakened a few hours later – he had no idea when – by a light peeping through a crack in the curtains, straight into his eyes. Not sun, but a fierce lamp illuminating a rusting sign saying Mineralnye Vodi. Around ten people left the train. No one got on to replace them.

Dawn. More places he didn't know: Kotlyarevskaya, Beslan, Vladikavkaz.

He lit another cigarette.

Will this journey ever end?

*

A change of trains mid-morning and a change of passengers – from grim-faced Russians shuffling along the platform, hobbled by the stiffness of a journey that had taken almost forty hours, to cheerier southerners, Georgians, Armenians and Azeris, or Chechens, Ingush, Dagestanis and others heading east.

Soon, Rossel thought, he would need that cover story. At least Gerashvili had not dismissed it out of hand. It had a personal touch, if he was capable of being convincing enough. And a family photograph would make it seem authentic.

'Oh, they'll be welcoming,' she'd said in parting words at the railway station in Leningrad. 'The Georgians will stuff you with *khinkali* until you burst, ply you with *chacha*, slap you on the back and declare eternal friendship. But in the mountains, they never trust an outsider, even one claiming to be what you are claiming to be. A family friend. And *you* should never trust *them*.'

Rossel rolled the little stone in his pocket and smiled to himself.

If Lidia's right, he thought, *at least before the Georgians kill me, they're going to feed me first.*

*

Tbilisi. A city of red-roofed houses, mosques and churches, surrounded by mountains.

He was the last out of his carriage. The rest of the passengers had poured onto the platform of the shabby main station to hurl themselves into the embrace of loved ones or to hurry on to the next leg of their journey. Once this human tide had gone, Rossel stood alone, rubbing sleep from his eyes. Yawning. It was cold, yes, but warmer than Leningrad.

At the far end of the platform, near the main station building, stood two men in black suits. Perhaps watching him, perhaps not – viewed through his befuddled brain, it was hard to tell. As he picked up his bag and began to walk towards the men, a rabble of taxi drivers and porters, working in teams, intercepted and assailed him with demands that he follow them.

'I need a hostel,' Rossel said. Of course – a young man with a thin moustache who had latched on to him knew the best hostel in the city. By the time a price had been established and the hubbub had dissipated, the two black-suited men were gone.

Twenty minutes later, the moustache deposited Rossel outside a long, two-storey brick building in the north of the city, close to the Mtkvari River and a vast builder's yard.

Rossel paid in advance for two nights. Once in his room, he slit open the lumpy mattress and secreted his service pistol inside – off-duty, out of uniform and in another country, it would be hard to explain it away if he was stopped by local police or MGB officers. Then he grabbed a couple of hours' sleep, too tired to care about the stained sheets or the skittering of insects around him.

*

Another cramped train, creaking its way along the river valley. The wheels grinding, carriages shuddering, moving painstakingly towards Stalin's birthplace. Gori.

As they made their way out of Tbilisi, Rossel looked up at an ants' nest of buildings, some snow-dotted, tilting and jumbled, clinging to the slopes. Georgia was like a secret kingdom, he thought, a world away from both the classical elegance of Leningrad's centre and the brutalist uniformity of its gritty suburbs.

The city began to recede and the terrain rose higher. The steam engine, one of the new P36s but already feeling its age, wove a route through it, hauling the carriages and struggling upwards towards the northwest. Through an iced-up window, Rossel glimpsed the Caucasus Mountains, the snow masking their barren blackness, clouds circling the peaks. Through the other window was only the frozen smear of the river.

Tbilisi was behind him. It was time, he thought.

Time for Revol Rossel to become Zurab Ivannikov, a bookkeeper at the Lomonosov Porcelain Factory, come to Gori at the tearful request of Tamas Abazi's dear, grief-stricken niece to impart the tragic news of his death.

36

Rossel paused to let the crowd of upturned, mournful faces take in his words. Then repeated them to make sure everyone understood.

'A car accident. A driver who lost control in the snow. The *militsiya* say he panicked, drove away to evade responsibility for . . .'

He did not say 'the deaths'. He was Zurab Ivannikov from Leningrad, after all, unaccustomed to imparting distressing personal news.

Gathered around the hearth of a crumbling Gori house were the red-eyed relatives of Tamas Abazi – nieces and nephews, cousins and second cousins, school friends. Behind them, an endless line of sad old men who were toasting him with Eniseli brandy, claiming to have run with Tamas in the gutters of Gori way back when, and to have played *gorodki* with him – 'Yes,' said a man with a long, thin nose and shadows around his eyes, 'Tamas loved the game. Loved his skittles. We all did. Still do.'

They were perched on anything they could find. And leaning in close, some weeping into grimy handkerchiefs, others watching on, hands behind their backs, listening in silence.

'The *militsiya* are searching for the coward who was responsible,' said Rossel. 'They tell me . . .'

A collective sigh, punctuated by a few angry voices – what

good would the Leningrad militia do? When had Russians ever cared about the spilling of Georgian blood?

An elderly man with black, bushy sideburns who had needed several minutes to travel from one end of the shadowy, lamplit room to sit on a rickety stool vowed in broken Russian to travel to Leningrad to 'hunt the bastard down and feed him his own balls. Like they were dumplings'.

More angry voices matched his bloody pledge.

Some in Russian, some in Georgian – words Rossel could not understand but spoken at an intensity that made translation redundant. In front of him, a fat *babushka* with wet eyeliner running down both cheeks broke down. Two other women hugged her and began to rock her gently back and forth.

'I'm sorry,' he said. He reached out and patted her on the back. 'Sorry to be the bearer of such bad news.'

Among the faces, two stood out.

One belonged to the local undertaker, introduced as Levan Abakelia, who himself never took his eyes off this unexpected visitor from a far-off land – as if he was listening to every word and at the same time measuring him up for the right-sized coffin. In his late fifties, maybe. Immaculate, from his gleaming white teeth to his black suit, his dark, slicked-back hair, smooth finger-nails on the end of slender fingers. Buffed and polished to perfection, Rossel noticed, ever ready to fasten up the last button on a dead man's shirt.

The other, bigger man hung over Rossel like a winter cloud. He was grey-haired and doleful, with a large mole on his left cheek. He had shaken Rossel's hand roughly, holding on to it for a little longer than was polite. He was about Abazi's age and claimed to be an old friend. Nikoloz something-or-other – in the hubbub, Rossel hadn't caught the surname.

Both, he realised, were not entirely convinced by his tale, and prepared to push a knife into it until they met bone. They asked him to repeat the details several times. What make of car, again? What colour did you say? Where did this happen, again? How long had Elene worked with you at this factory where you are a book-keeper?

'Elene fainted away at the news,' Rossel told the crowd. 'She hit her head on the floor and split open her scalp. She begged her doctors to let her travel, but they refused.'

Murmurs of approval greeted this sensible decision.

'So she asked me to come ahead of her and speak to you all,' Rossel said.

Abakelia, the undertaker, took a step forward.

'All you Muscovites and Leningraders are the same. You think Russia ends outside your precious city walls. That we are all dumb peasants out here in the Caucasus, burning horseshit on our fires, sewing spring wheat when we should be planting the autumn corn. We have telephones in Gori, friend,' said Abakelia. 'Telegrams, too.'

Rossel nodded. He had expected the question.

'Of course,' he said. 'Of course. But she felt that news of such a family tragedy should be conveyed in person.'

'She was right to,' shouted a scrawny middle-aged woman wearing a faded red headscarf. Heads nodded furiously.

What is our life? A game!
A three? A seven? An . . .

Time to play his ace.

Rossel reached inside his jacket and took out a photograph.

'Elene gave me this – a picture of her as a young girl with

Uncle Tamas. A happy, smiling niece visiting a lake in summer with her beloved uncle.'

He held the image, which he had stolen from her apartment, above his head. Many hands reached out for it, but Abakelia was quicker than the rest.

Half the room crowded round the photograph, the other half around Rossel, pulling at his sleeves and praising him. Some older women blessed him. Even the undertaker's dark, restless eyes seemed to soften.

Rossel looked up to see the older man, Nikoloz, crying. Embarrassed, the tall Georgian wiped at his eyes with his wrinkled fingers.

'At my age, when old friends go, we weep for them and for ourselves, too, comrade,' he said. 'For their death is a portent of our own.'

*

It took a few hours, but eventually the room began to empty.

Some women were still singing an impromptu Georgian funeral chant. But other people were talking and gesticulating as if the topic of conversation was already moving on. Among them, Rossel thought, Tamas Abazi was already becoming a memory.

He made a show of buttoning up his coat and preparing to depart. But he had no intention of going. After a moment, Abakelia approached him.

'Where are you going, Comrade Ivannikov? And so soon,' he said.

'To the station, comrade,' replied Rossel. 'I'm a long way from Leningrad.'

227

Abakelia touched Rossel lightly on the arm with his buffed fingertips. 'I will not hear of it. It would dishonour this humble town. First, let us show you some Georgian hospitality. You can stay overnight at my house.' He pointed at the old man. 'Nikoloz will cook for us. He is a master.'

Nikoloz opened his hands. 'I make the kind of *khachapuri* they serve in heaven,' he said.

'Besides,' said the undertaker, producing the photograph of Tamas and Elene from between his fingers in a deft movement, 'Nikoloz is one of Tamas's oldest friends. I'm sure he would like to hear a little more about his final hours.'

Rossel politely protested but had no thought of passing up the offer. The chance to interrogate men like Abakelia and Nikoloz was why he had come here. The two village elders almost certainly knew every family in Gori because they would make it their business to. And they were men not unlike Tamas Abazi, he thought, unable to resist the chance to take a long gaze into history through the bottom of a glass.

Rossel looked from one man to the other. Then smiled softly at Nikoloz.

'The kind they serve in heaven, you say? Then how could I refuse you?'

37

The bread in Nikoloz's *khachapuri* was stuffed with so much cheese it had to be sliced and then scraped, almost poured, onto the plates.

Rossel loosened his belt, suspecting this was only an appetiser. Sure enough, steaming *khinkali*, dumplings the size of a man's fist, were next, accompanied by small cucumbers sliced from end to end and drizzled with a home-made *adjika* that made the eyes water.

The undertaker's back room made an unorthodox kitchen. It was warmed by a heap of coals in an open brazier and, next to that, a glowing stove. In between two framed photographs, one of Stalin, the other of Lenin, a long line of coffins were propped against a wall.

On the stove were two or three pots and a sheet of battered metal that Nikoloz cooked on while the undertaker cross-examined Rossel again as to the factory in which Elene worked, her health, her prospects, her intentions . . .

Gerashvili had drilled him well and the train journey had given him plenty of time to rehearse his story. But he needed to keep his wits about him – and concentrating was not easy, for around them were not just photos of Stalin but also a sinister display of *khanjali*, traditional Georgian daggers.

Rossel licked his lips. The dumplings were delicious, their

dough pinched into ornate domes that could have graced a Muscovite church, the stems long, round and robust enough to hold up the parcel of minced pork, spices and the scalding juices inside.

'Let them cool or they'll take the skin off your tongue,' the undertaker said.

Catching a string of cheese hanging from his jaw, Abakelia stood, disappeared for a few moments and returned with two clay jars filled with wine – his own, he said, from vines that grew in his garden and a few acres behind his house.

Rossel picked up a glass and drank. The quality of Georgian wine was famed throughout the Soviet Union. Sweet. Dark. Comforting.

Rossel pointed at the coffins. 'Has there been a plague in these parts?'

The undertaker laughed. A little too loudly. 'I have regular custom from every village for thirty miles around,' he slurred.

Rossel nodded. 'Business is good, then.'

'Not as good as in your hometown in forty-two, eh, during the Blockade?' asked Nikoloz.

Rossel took out a *papirosa* and lit it.

'No,' he said. He nodded at Abakelia. 'A corpse on every corner. For a man in your profession, Leningrad's streets were paved with gold.'

The undertaker showed his perfect teeth. He stood and raised his glass. 'A toast,' he declared.

'To what?' said Rossel.

'To good health, of course.'

The three men clinked their glasses.

More toasts followed, each more traditional than the last – to Stalin, to the Second Five-Year Plan, to the teachings of Marx and the leadership of Lenin, to the Politburo and its

Georgian-born members in particular – may Comrades Beria and Stalin be ever guided by the wisdom of Lenin to victory over the capitalist West . . . To women, to friendship among nations . . .

Rossel raised his glass a final time.

'To Tamas Abazi,' he said, slurring the name.

Nikoloz stared into the fire. 'Poor bastard,' he said.

'Poor bastard.' Abakelia nodded.

'A real *muzhik*,' said Rossel, 'strong, proud and—'

'Yes, a proper *muzhik*,' roared Nikoloz. 'Raised in the gutter. A fighter. Never gave an inch. In those days, we told the Tsar's snitches to go fuck themselves and we took what we needed to survive, and to keep our families alive. We did the bank jobs, and we did the—'

'Nikoloz,' said the undertaker, an unsteady finger pressed to his lips.

'I'm just telling it like it was,' Nikoloz protested, his eyebrows raised.

'In any case, it was a long time ago,' said Rossel, reaching for and missing his glass.

They all gazed into the dimming stove for a moment. Then Abakelia stood.

'*Chacha*,' he declared. 'I have a bottle in the back room.'

Nikoloz started clapping his hands together.

'*Chacha, chacha*,' he chanted. '*Chacha, chacha* . . .'

*

Abakelia uncorked the bottle, poured each of them a glass of the brandy and sat down.

The three men clinked glasses again and drained them.

Rossel felt the alcohol burn the back of his throat. It felt rougher than gravel – he would only be able to cope with a couple of glasses.

It's time . . .

He pushed his glass away.

Abakelia began to refill it.

'*Will it snow, Soselo? Will it rain? Is there a storm coming?*' Rossel said. 'Elene told me those were her uncle's last words – his very last.'

The undertaker paused mid-pour. He fixed Rossel with a look that was part fear, part malevolence.

'Soselo,' he whispered. 'That's a name I have not heard for a while.'

Rossel tried to focus his eyes on Abakelia. 'It is not one I know, either – a friend of Tamas, I had assumed?' He turned to Nikoloz. 'Perhaps someone you also know, comrade?'

Nikoloz sat up, pulling himself back from the brink of stupor. He looked as if he was trying to sober up quickly.

'That's a name not many know outside Gori, friend,' he said.

Rossel looked from one man to the other. A coal popped in the grate.

'Who is he, this Soselo?' he said, pushing himself up in his chair. He could feel his temples throbbing. 'Elene said her uncle would say the name in his sleep, over and over, when he was staying with her.'

'We were comrades,' mumbled the undertaker. 'We robbed banks, sent money to the Bolsheviks, sent money to Lenin.'

Rossel threw back his *chacha*. The spirit burned his lips and nostrils.

'Tamas Abazi and you robbed banks for *Lenin*? I don't believe you.'

Nikoloz thought for a moment. Then nodded. 'Tamas Abazi always did exactly what Soselo told him to do,' he said. 'We stole the money, gave it to Soselo, who then sent it to Lenin.'

The flames in the stove were going out, but in the brazier the coals were still glowing. Nikoloz yawned; the old man was flagging. Abakelia's eyes closed for a second.

'And where is this Soselo now?' asked Rossel.

Nikoloz got to his feet. 'Do you want to tell him or should I?' he said to the undertaker.

Abakelia spat into the coals, his spittle hissing, but didn't answer.

Nikoloz clapped his hands together and laughed. 'Why, he's right here with us in this room, comrade,' he slurred.

Swaying as he struggled to his feet, Rossel pointed at Nikoloz.

'You,' he said. 'You're Soselo?'

The old man grinned, staggered towards the wall, and took down one of the two pictures that was hanging above the empty coffins. He propped it up against the half-full *chacha* bottle.

Then he tapped a finger on Stalin's moustached, enigmatic face.

'Not me,' he said, 'him. Koba, Soso, Soselo . . . *Iosif.* A man of many names.'

Rossel slumped back into his chair, nearly missing it, his mind reeling, barely able to remember what his own name was supposed to be.

Abakelia lifted his glass and waved it at him, as if to toast the news. Then he leaned forward and bared his perfect teeth. 'You're not from any porcelain factory, friend. I'm certain of that. So, exactly who are you?'

Nikoloz pulled the nearest *khanjali* down from the wall and took a step towards Rossel. But then, in a quick, precise, almost balletic movement, he reached down and slit the undertaker's throat.

'An informer,' he said as Abakelia slumped to the floor, his hands pawing at his neck, his feet thrashing. 'I've wanted to do that for some time. And in Gori, we say no wine tastes sweeter than a traitor's blood.'

38

Rossel's head was still thick, but the cold was sharp enough to help him recover some of his senses.

The moon lay below the silhouette of the mountains, though the snow reflected a little light from flickering gas lamps that always seemed to appear around each corner as they stole through the alleys of Gori. Above them was the hunchbacked shadow of the mediaeval fortress on the hill that dominated the town. The backstreets, some no more than stony paths, were deserted. Whenever they came to a window where light glimmered through curtain edges or the slats of shutters, they moved as quietly as their heavy burden would permit, trying to stop the thin ice covering the pavements creaking and crunching underfoot.

Rossel and the old man lumbered onwards, supporting the body of Abakelia between them as if he was a hopeless drunk. Moving beyond a row of houses that appeared to mark the edge of the town, they came to the gate of the undertaker's yard. On the other side was a battered, ancient ZIS truck, painted black; on occasion, Nikoloz said, Abakelia had pressed it into service as a rudimentary hearse. It was a dented hulk with one headlight smashed, one footplate missing and its huge, sweeping front mudguards riddled with rust.

Nikoloz clanked the chain on a rusty padlock, turned a key

and heaved at the gate. 'Let's get him in,' he said, pointing at the hearse.

They pulled open the back doors. There were two coffins inside, of rough and unpainted wood. Rossel and Nikoloz threw the undertaker into one of them and pushed down the lid.

'A hearse with a body in it,' the old man said. 'If we get stopped, at least we've got a perfect alibi.'

Rossel climbed into the passenger seat of the hearse as the old man got behind the wheel. He pulled at a rusty spring that was sticking out of the faded brown leather seat and gave the car door a thump.

'I was worried you wanted to kill me, Nikoloz,' Rossel said. 'Looking at this pile of junk, I still am.'

*

As the hearse reached the edge of the town, the Georgian pulled the steering wheel to the right and the vehicle slewed off the road and onto a mountain track.

Nikoloz pumped the brakes with a heavy boot as the gradient got steeper. Soon, the track was nothing but gravel and stones and snow, with a cliff on one side and a drop on the other, the bottom of which was shrouded in darkness. The old man swore as he wrestled with the steering wheel. Behind them, the coffins smacked and crunched against each other. As they picked up speed, Rossel gripped the door handle, fighting the instinct that told him to leap to safety. They were metres away from a steep, icy ravine. The front tyres spat up slush, mud and gravel.

'Shit!'

The old man yanked the wheel to the left. Rossel could feel

the back end slipping away. The Georgian spun the wheel one more time and the front wheels thumped into a rocky ledge, the back doors burst open and, out of the corner of his eye, Rossel saw the coffins shooting out of the back and over the edge of the ravine, the undertaker's body still inside one of them. They hurtled down the snowy mountainside.

Nikoloz wrestled the wheel to the right.

Somehow, the hearse bounced back onto the road. Accompanied by the sound of a small avalanche, the rear end of the truck slid across the icy stones, slammed into something hard and came to a halt.

The two men sat in silence.

Rossel was still clutching the door handle. One leg was braced against the floor of the truck, the other jammed against the dashboard. Nikoloz was slumped forward over the wheel. He lifted himself and stared after the coffin into the dark. Then he reached back, found a bottle, took a drink and handed it to Rossel.

'If the bastard wasn't dead before, he is now,' said Nikoloz.

Rossel began to laugh. Soon, the laughter had gripped him until he could barely breathe, and tears sprang to his eyes. It took him a while to calm down. But Nikoloz never mustered so much as a smile.

Finally, Rossel's bout of uncontrollable relief subsided. 'Perhaps I should drive?' he said.

Nikoloz shook his head. He fumbled for the ignition and turned the key. The engine gave five throaty coughs, a bang and a brief firework display before starting. The one functioning headlight came back on.

'No chance,' said the old man, patting the dashboard. 'She's my little bitch.'

Nikoloz stuck the truck back into gear and it rolled forward again.

*

At last, the moon rose. Nikoloz, now more certain of the road ahead, turned to Rossel.

'So, who are you really, Comrade Ivannikov?' he said. 'Maybe you're screwing Elene? That might bring you out here. Or maybe you just *want* to screw her. Is that it? So you've come all this way, a knight on a quest, pursuing the Holy Grail that lies between those long, long legs of hers. You're no factory manager. That's for certain. When I dealt with Comrade Abakelia back there, you hardly blinked. You've seen plenty of death in your time, comrade.'

Rossel stared into the darkness and remembered a man he'd met in the labour camps who could shoot and butcher any animal – bear, elk, wolf, sable. One of the other prisoners had tried to steal his buckwheat porridge and he had gutted him, too. But, other than that one incident, the man – in his former life a clerk in the Ministry of Engineering – had been kind, polite, quiet. Something of a gentleman.

Suffering, tragedy, grief, violence, murder – it had become part of so many lives. Maybe once, he thought, there was a world where you could tell, just by looking at someone, if they were capable of violence.

Not any more.

Besides, he already knew what Nikoloz was. But what did it matter now?

Tell him . . .

'I'm a militia officer,' Rossel said. 'They were murdered – Abazi and the woman he was found with.'

Nikoloz fumbled for a cigarette packet that was jammed between the dashboard and windscreen. He slowed to negotiate a bend, then changed gear, fighting with the protesting engine, and sped up again. He scratched at the mole on his cheek with a dirty fingernail.

'The Leningrad militia means nothing out here, friend. I can push you out, leave you to freeze by the side of the road, and no one in Gori will lose a wink of sleep.'

'Of course. But you still brought me along with you?' said Rossel.

Nikoloz stared ahead. The headlights played across deep potholes in the road. The cliff face on one side and the river on the other were partially obscured by a thick line of trees.

'How did Abazi and Stalin meet?' said Rossel.

'Let's keep calling him Soselo. I'll feel a lot safer if we call him that.'

Rossel stared down at a sheer wall of ice and rock as they rounded another bend. 'Safety first,' he muttered. 'I'm all for it.'

The truck hit another pothole and shuddered.

'How *did* they meet, Nikoloz?'

'All right,' said Nikoloz. '*Ruka ruku moyet.* One hand washes the other. Let's start with Abakelia. The only funeral an undertaker doesn't celebrate is his own because he can't collect the fee. You want to know why he made so many coffins for such a small population? It's because he got good business from the local MGB. There's a lot of loose talk at funerals. Grief and *chacha*, a potent mix. Abakelia reported them all. That's why he extended his hospitality to you so readily, and got me to come along. An outsider, a Leningrader, appearing out of nowhere? Your story didn't fool him. And me, an old-timer who knew Tamas and his past better than anyone. Ply us with *chacha* and let us condemn

ourselves with loose talk and drunken confessions. Easy pick-
ings for the bastard – report us to the Chekists in the morning.
But he didn't know I was on to him.' Nikoloz spat on the floor.

Rossel rubbed his eyes. He needed sleep, but Nikoloz had
secrets to tell. He needed to prise them out.

'As far as I can tell, Tamas Abazi arrived in Leningrad on the
twelfth of February,' Rossel said. 'He was in Moscow for three
days before that. His niece claimed he'd never met Soselo. But I
could tell she was lying. I think he met him there.'

'I believe you,' Nikoloz said.

'But how can you be certain?'

As the truck took a sharp bend, Nikoloz pressed his foot on
the accelerator.

'Milk soup and dumplings,' he said.

'Milk soup and dumplings? I don't understand.'

The old man grinned. 'Tamas had been to see Soselo in
Moscow before,' said Nikoloz. 'Not at the Kremlin but at his
dacha outside the city, at a place called Kuntsevo. He would brag
about it. Tell anyone who would listen. People didn't believe
him. But I did. Those two were close, many years ago. Very
close. First as boys in Gori. When we were children, we used to
run up the hill to the castle there. Sometimes, Tamas would
carry Soselo on his shoulders like he was a Cossack riding a
horse. Later, when Soselo was working at the meteorological station, he got Tamas a job there. And when Soselo started making
trouble, proper trouble, they were Bolshevik brigands together,
doing bank raids in Gori, Baku, Tbilisi, a few other places.'

Rossel pictured it – two youngsters, born with nothing, side
by side in the gutter. Growing up, picking fights, looking for a
cause in life. Finding it in revolution.

'Tamas was one of Soselo's bodyguards when he first met

Lenin in Finland. This was in 1905, at some kind of revolutionary assembly. The story goes that Tamas is told to organise a
meal. He hears that Lenin loves milk soup and dumplings – some
German crap he got a taste for in exile.'

'Sounds disgusting.'

'It sounds like a bowl of piss is what it sounds like,' said
Nikoloz. 'Anyway, Tamas didn't know the Finnish for milk, so he
turns to the cook, points at a picture of a cow and makes like he's
pulling its udders. Lenin sees this and the whole room falls silent.
Then Lenin starts laughing and so does everyone else. Afterwards, Soselo asks Tamas, "What were you going to do for the
dumplings – pull down your pants and point at your bollocks?"
They were close before that, even closer after.'

Rossel smiled to himself. *And thirty years later, at the 17th
All-Party Congress, Tamas is still telling people he's best friends
with Lenin.*

He held on to his seat as the truck tore around another corner.

'A meteorological office,' he said. 'You say the two worked
together there?'

'Yes, the old observatory in Tbilisi. Not what you might call
academic work, though. Soselo checked the instruments were
working properly, Tamas was the night guard. And they weren't
there for long. But they remembered it. Soselo used to ironi-
cally call Tamas "the Weathervane". He had a point. Tamas
was never a great one for understanding politics and revolutionary ideology. Never knew which way the Party winds were
blowing.'

Thick wet snowflakes were swirling towards the truck's
windscreen.

'*Will it snow, Soselo? Will it rain? Is there a storm coming?*'
Rossel muttered.

Nikoloz nodded. 'Now you're getting somewhere, comrade,' he said.

*

The road had dipped into a ravine, leading them into a world of fantasy and folklore. On one side, ice floes in the river fought each other to be the first to Tbilisi. On the other, black shards of rock rose into the night sky.

Unimpressed by the scenery, Nikoloz had parked the truck at the side of the road so he could relieve himself.

Rossel got down from the cab, away from the stench of the diesel engine, to fill his lungs with air.

The old man stepped out from the back of the truck and zipped up his fly. 'Ahh,' he said, 'that's better. I had a bladder the size of a watermelon.'

Rossel put one foot on the stairwell of the truck and grabbed the door handle to hoist himself back up. Then paused, half-turned and stepped back down again.

'You slit the undertaker's throat,' he said.

Nikoloz sniffed. 'I did.'

'That means you can't go back.'

'Yes.'

'And you knew that,' said Rossel. 'It wasn't just a drunken impulse. You have a plan, perhaps one you've had for some time?'

In the distance, an owl fluttered from a tree branch and took flight. Nikoloz pulled out his flask, took a long drink and nodded.

'I kept on telling Tamas, don't go to Moscow,' he said. 'Don't go looking for Soselo, don't draw his attention. Don't go reminiscing about the good old days, because that's just dragging up stuff everyone wants to forget. Don't make him jealous, don't make him suspicious, don't make him paranoid. But Tamas wouldn't listen. He was in love with the past. In love with the man he thought he had been back then. And now he's dead.'

Nikoloz burst into a fit of coughing as whatever liquid was in his flask went down the wrong way.

Rossel thought some more. 'And now you are afraid that Soselo will remember you, and send someone for you,' he said.

Nikoloz wiped his mouth. '"To run away is not glorious but good for one's health." I always did like that old saying. Half of Gori is loyal to Stalin, half would like to kill him themselves,' he said. 'That man is the devil and the world he has created is his Hell. Man against man, woman against woman. And in the Kremlin, wolf against wolf. Now Tamas is dead, he will come for me. Come for all of us who knew him back then. But I will not be there simply waiting to die.'

Rossel nudged a small lump of snow with his boot. It rolled a couple of times, before stopping.

'Then I'm a danger to you. As you would not want anyone to bear witness to your bloody departure,' said Rossel. 'And still less to know where you headed once you left Gori. Which means you must have a purpose for me. You need me for something. That's why I'm still alive.'

Nikoloz handed him the flask.

'Here's to you, gun dog,' he said. 'There's someone I'd like you to meet. A man who can help you in your quest. And now that Tamas is dead, I think *you* might be able to help *him*.'

39

They glimpsed the twinkling lights of the outskirts of Tbilisi just after four. They stopped at Rossel's hostel, despite Nikoloz's protests. Rossel went inside to pick up the few things he had left there – a spare shirt, a thin bar of soap and a razor. He felt for the slit he had made in the mattress, reached inside and recovered his pistol.

Next, they stopped in a run-down district Nikoloz seemed to know well. The two of them walked a few hundred metres to a fenced-off stretch of wasteland half-filled with lorries and populated with rank, unshaven drivers.

The first two men who Rossel and Nikoloz approached shook their heads and turned away, but the third man, a surly individual with a flat, broken nose, took their roubles and vodka and listened to their instructions with an inscrutable expression.

Nikoloz smiled at him, patting the cab of his huge KAMAZ lorry.

'*Is mshvenieria*,' he said, then translated for Rossel: 'She's a beauty.'

He slapped the man on the back, embraced him as a proud peasant and a true Soviet hero, and palmed him a pack of cigarettes and a few more roubles.

The truck driver twisted his lips. Blinked. Looked from Rossel to Nikoloz, and made a decision. Yes, he'd take the two of them north. But the snow was heavy and there was no guarantee the road would not be blocked.

'Only a *q'lishvili* would go up there,' he said in a tangle of broken Russian and Georgian.

Rossel turned to Nikoloz

'*Q'lishvili?*' he asked.

The old man shrugged. 'Not a compliment,' he said.

A few truckers had made it through from Vladikavkaz two days earlier, but that meant nothing – the avalanches could happen at any time; no one gave a shit whether the driver and his comrades lived or died. It was true, though, that no one had been forced back in the past few days; maybe their luck was in. Sometimes you could only get halfway before turning round and coming all the way back to Tbilisi. The truck driver had loaded up at the factory depot yesterday, no rest – a cargo of chemicals for use in the construction industry, so mind where you smoke.

Nikoloz and Rossel looked at each other. The Georgian gave a nod.

Halfway would be fine. 'I'll get rid of our own vehicle,' Nikoloz said.

*

'Where did you leave the hearse?' said Rossel.

He was on the right side of the KAMAZ's cabin. Nikoloz took the middle seat, next to the broken-nosed driver – Gosha, his new best friend.

Somehow, the cabin seemed colder than the air outside. Rossel hoped the tiny, spluttering heater and their bodies would warm it up.

'On the other side of the river,' Nikoloz said. 'I wanted to go further, but we didn't have time. It'll take them a while to find it.'

'Them?' said Gosha to Nikoloz.

Rossel pointed at the cigarettes Nikoloz had given the driver.

'Smoke those, comrade, and keep your eyes on the road,' he said. 'Let us worry about "them".'

Gosha pressed the accelerator and spat on the floor.

He glanced at Rossel and nodded to Nikoloz. 'A real *q'lishvili*,' he muttered. 'Like I said.'

*

Tbilisi was already fifty kilometres behind them. But Rossel didn't feel like celebrating. He had pressed Nikoloz as to who it was he wanted him to meet. But the old man wouldn't be drawn. Simply tapping his nose with a finger, he had said, 'Wait and see, gun dog, wait and see.'

All Rossel could think about was the swaying and thumping of the lorry as Gosha nosed his way north along the Aragvi River. The jerking motion of the KAMAZ was making him sick.

In winter, only the truckers dared travel along the Military Highway. So, checks on internal borders were few and cursory. Even better, lorries and their cargos offered plenty of places to hide.

Another bend. Another giddy incline.

The lorry's engine whined in response. Nikoloz and Gosha began yelling at each other again to keep their conversation going. None of that would have prevented Rossel from dozing off if he'd chosen to. But he didn't trust Nikoloz, and he needed to keep an eye on where they were headed. He needed to stay awake.

'I have a joke to tell,' he said to Nikoloz. 'You like jokes?'

The old man gave a non-committal grunt.

'A man goes to buy a copy of *Pravda*, and says to the shop-keeper, "What page are the obituaries on today?" The shopkeeper shrugs and says, "Page forty-seven, same as they always are, comrade." So, the man turns and leaves without buying the paper. But next day he's back—'

Nikoloz waved a dismissive hand at him. 'Heard it. Every-one's heard it. Here's a good one. Who built the White Sea Canal?'

'Everyone's heard that one too, comrade,' said Rossel. 'The left bank was made by the people who told the jokes, and the right bank by the people who listened to them.'

Gosha snorted. Rossel began to laugh. Nikoloz joined in.

After that, Rossel fought the urge to sink into a blissful black-ness, fuelled by the nicotine hits of his *papirosy*, Nikoloz's magic flask of hooch and the relentless cold.

As the hours passed, fewer and fewer vehicles followed them into the mountains. The roads were too dangerous at this time of year. And it was the wrong season to transport fruit or flowers, two staple Georgian exports. But the Military Highway stayed open for heavy goods deemed vital to the Soviet state.

As they struggled higher, they were entering a strange, alter-native realm. Churches clung to vertiginous cliffs, miraculous limpets fashioned from stone and faith. Small fortresses looking like miniature versions of the Kremlin nestled in the bend of the Aragvi. Mysterious worlds set inside a giant snow globe. All of them bereft of life.

By the side of the road, the snow piled up in monstrous drifts; above the drifts, Rossel could see black trees poking out of the ice in patches, scrawny sticks stuck into the mountainside.

'In summertime, this is a green and beautiful land,' said Nikoloz.

'This isn't summertime,' grunted Gosha.

Past Pasanauri and past a few nondescript wooden buildings that might have been homes or garages or storage facilities. Mists rolled down into the ravine and began to coalesce. Rossel, already staring at the landscape through bleary eyes, began to suspect he was hallucinating from fatigue, for once or twice he thought he glimpsed statues of stern and outsized saints glowering at him from unreachable stony platforms.

40

Nikoloz elbowed him in the ribs.

'Wakey, wakey, comrade,' he said. 'We're here.'

Rossel sat up. 'How long have I been . . .?'

'About forty minutes.'

Rossel checked for the pistol inside his coat

Still there.

He rubbed at the misted window. They had reached the highest point, he presumed – the mountains still loomed above, but the road stretched flat before them. Over the horizon, the only way was down, and into Russia. Through the drifting, dancing blizzard, both distance and height were all-encompassing, impossible to comprehend.

'This will do, friend.'

Gosha looked sideways at Nikoloz, bemused. 'Here?'

Nikoloz nodded. Gosha shrugged. The KAMAZ rumbled to a halt.

From within his huge fur coat, the old man pulled out a bottle of *chacha*. He offered it to Gosha.

'If anyone asks, my comrade and I had an argument. We were drunk. We fought. We opened the door and fell into the snow and down the mountain and out of sight. You looked for us, but the mist came down and you had your own life to think of. Is that understood?'

Gosha shrugged. 'That's what wise men always do – think of themselves,' he said. He reached out, took the bottle, and waited for them to climb down.

Rossel's leg sank up to the knee in a drift. The lorry's chugging engine was muffled by the wail of the wind, which was stirring the endless field of snow in front of them into frenzied, swirling flurries. Already feeling nostalgic for the tinny heater in its cab, Rossel watched as the KAMAZ pulled away in the direction of Vladikavkaz.

'Where are we now?' Rossel said.

'The Jvari Pass.' Nikoloz pointed due west. 'Now we go that way.'

Pulling up his coat around his neck and the flaps of his hat around his ears, Rossel followed the older man's outstretched arm.

Nothing to see. Only a howling, angry whiteness.

'Do you think our friend Gosha will sell us out?' asked Rossel as the two men began to tramp slowly forwards.

Nikoloz shrugged. 'Almost certainly,' he replied. 'But no need to worry. The mountains will likely kill us first.'

* * *

A flat handle like a Luger. Small. A woman's gun. The Walther PP was now in the portrait.

Normally, Zlata would not have introduced an object brought by a sitter into the image. But Stalin – Iosif – had not objected.

Brush in hand, she stepped back from the canvas. It was nearly complete.

The woollen chokha *painted black, the pockmarked cheeks tainted yellow, the moustache mottled grey and brown, a ghostly glint of silver on the barrel of the gun that still sat exactly where Iosif had placed it one week ago. In the middle of the table.*

She still hadn't dared to touch it. Not once.

Is it loaded?

The question hung in the air between them. Every now and then, Iosif's eyes sought out hers to ask it again.

Zlata worked the oil into the canvas, trying to give one of the pockmarks a little more definition.

Who is Stalin?

Who is Koba? Another name he had once used.

Who is Iosif?

He had said he'd had many more.

A poet from Gori. Yes, he had written poems. Celebrated ones about the mountains and woodlands. An atheist who had studied to be a priest. A meteorologist. A bandit. A robber. An Old Bolshevik. Lenin's lackey. Lenin's friend. Lenin's enemy? Perhaps. Something more than a man. A revolution. Something more than a god now. The embodiment of an eternal creed.

The Leshi, too, she thought.

Yes, exactly that. A shape-shifter. A master of this game.

But she already knew her portrait of Stalin was going to be a failure. No one, not even a Titian or a Repin, could truly capture him.

To check the Walther's magazine would be a declaration of intent. That, she was certain, was the trap that he'd set her.

Zlata was allowed to read the papers that were in Stalin's study. 'Vicious Spies and Killers under the Mask of Academic Physicians' had been the headline in Pravda. They continually denounced the vrachi-vrediteli, vermin doctors, and their 'Doctors' Plot'. In the cloying atmosphere of paranoia that permeated the dacha, the pistol, she knew, was intended to undo her.

Draw her from the path.

Tell me who you are without speaking. She and Stalin shared that subtle skill.

Dr Vinogradov, his own physician, had been arrested in January.

So, if he's frightened of a stethoscope, why give me a gun? Me, with my history?

Perhaps he really doesn't know it?

Stalin shifted in the chair.

'That's enough for tonight, Mkhat'vari. My back is aching,' he said.

She rested the brush on the easel, put a hand to her brow and pushed back her hair.

He gazed at her with the yearning intensity of a younger man.

'Kato,' he said. 'You do look like her. Twenty-two when she went. Typhus took her, back in Tbilisi.'

His eyes lingered. His voice was distant, nostalgic.

'With her died my last warm human feelings.'

'For yourself?'

Stalin's voice returned. The one Iosif used for the masses.

'For everybody.'

'But what about Nadezhda, your second wife? Surely, you had love for her too . . . Iosif?'

He looked at the small pistol.

'It wasn't appendicitis that did for Nadezhda. That was just the official tale.'

'What, then?'

Stalin stretched out his right arm and pointed at the gun. Then put two fingers to his temple, made a popping sound.

'Murdered?' she said.

An imperious shake of the head. 'She was weak.' Spitting out the word. 'Like your poet – Yesenin.'

A despairing blackness in his eyes. So bleak it made her think of Yesenin's line: 'I wanted to marry a white rose to a black toad.' Made her heart break for Kato and Nadezhda.

Iosif kept staring. Until she felt giddy. Until the room began to spin. Until she was not sure where Zlata Sidorenko ended and Iosif Vissarionovich Dzhugashvili began.

Finally, he spoke. His radio intonation again.

'What would you bring?' he asked.

'Bring, Comrade Stalin?'

'What object would you bring to me to reveal your true self?'

Tell me who you are without speaking.

For the first time, she thought she knew.

41

The mountains first appeared to Rossel a long way in the distance. Then, seemingly without warning, they were before him. Colossal. Intimidating. Impenetrable.

Nikoloz ploughed on, through the snow and ice, pausing at times, looking and listening. The old Georgian was alert and apprehensive, yet also invigorated. Even joyful. As if each step was taking him back towards the days of his youth.

The light began to die. A suffocating darkness fell. The wind rose again, whipping into their faces.

Rossel's boots sank into the snow and he stumbled, banging his temple on the frozen stump of a tree.

He hauled himself to his feet and touched his face – grazed but no blood.

He peered ahead.

Where is . . .

Nikoloz gesturing. Waving him forward.

'Look,' shouted the Georgian, raising his voice to make himself heard above the wind. He stamped on the ground and scuffed the snow away with his boot.

Steps. Crooked and uneven, hacked into the stone and ice.

They began to walk up them. After about fifty, Nikoloz stopped and pointed again.

A wall, a pile of stones. Some kind of shelter. A hut for a

shepherd? Then more, and barns, and houses – most crumbled into ruins.

Was it a village? A town?

Or perhaps, Rossel thought, an entire hidden kingdom.

*

Threading their way through abandoned stone buildings, ducking under sagging wooden beams, Rossel and Nikoloz moved into what he could see was a village. Or had been, before everyone left.

After ten minutes, Nikoloz stopped in a tiny square.

He cupped his hands and put them to his mouth. 'Tariel,' he shouted. 'It's me, Nikoloz. I know you recognise me or you would have shot us by now.'

'Tariel?' said Rossel.

Nikoloz did not reply. He turned full circle, peering as he did so into the snow and shadows. Apart from the howling wind, they heard nothing.

'Tamas is dead,' he shouted.

Rossel strained to hear, but if anyone was answering, the wind was taking their words away.

There was no sign of life. Not even a clump of snow tumbling from a rooftop.

Without warning, the wind subsided, leaving silence behind it.

'We are the last now, Tariel.' Nikoloz's defiant voice echoed around the abandoned buildings.

Another voice. From behind Rossel. To his left.

'Nikoloz,' it said in greeting. 'You must be in big trouble to come up here.'

Keeping his body motionless, Rossel moved his head a fraction to stare into the shadows.

As if a spectre haunting the heart of the blizzard, a tall man stepped out from behind the cover of a mound of stones that still had its roof in place. The darkness shrouded his face, but Rossel could see something of his silhouette – an enormous woollen *papakha* on his head, a long coat down to his ankles, a rifle cradled in his arms.

The man called Tariel took another couple of paces and stared at Rossel. His beard was pure white, his nose like an eagle's beak. He said something in Georgian, words that did not seem to demand a response; rather, they sounded melodic, like poetry.

'You do not speak our language?' Tariel said, switching to Russian. 'Well then. "A narrow road cannot keep back Death, nor a rocky one; by him, all are levelled, weak and strong-hearted . . . Better a glorious death than a shameful life." So says our great poet Rustaveli.' He spat on the ground. 'But shame brought me to this place,' the apparition said. 'What about you?'

Rossel thought for a moment. 'In a way, the same thing,' he replied.

42

After searching Rossel and Nikoloz and taking Rossel's pistol, Tariel guided them further up the mountain, into the labyrinth of broken buildings and icy, overgrown paths. Always keeping his distance, always keeping his rifle at the ready.

Finally, he showed them into a small house and sat them on the floor around a low wooden table. The room was lit by a grubby hurricane lamp in one corner and by the soft glow of a wood burner in another. The interior was lined with old rugs, tarpaulin, the skins of sheep, cows, goats and whatever else Tariel had been able to lay his hands on over however many years he had been living in this eyrie.

Tariel levered open the door of the wood burner and shoved in another log.

'How did you know we were coming?' said Nikoloz.

'I didn't. I watch the trucks. They've been getting through since the new year. That's bad – it means the snow is piling up somewhere. You have to hope the avalanches hit during the night. When no one is stupid enough to make the journey.'

Tariel's voice was hesitant, stumbling. As though it was so long since he had spoken to another human being, he was out of practice. He sat down on the floor and pointed at Rossel.

'Who's your friend?'

'A man from Leningrad who knows how Tamas died.'

'He saw it?'

Rossel shook his head. 'I did not,' he said. 'My name is Revol Rossel. I'm an officer of the militia. I have been looking into Abazi's death.'

Tariel stared at Nikoloz. 'You brought the Leningrad militia here?'

Nikoloz raised the palms of his hands. 'I don't believe he's a threat. I think he can help us. Hear him out.'

Tariel picked up a poker, opened the burner door and poked at a log.

'Your rank?' he said to Rossel. 'Colonel? General? This must be an important case for a Leningrad militia officer to come all this way.'

'Senior militiaman,' Rossel answered.

'What is this, a joke? You are asking me to believe that they sent the cleaner, the coffee maker, all the way to Georgia to investigate . . .?'

'Nobody sent me,' said Rossel.

Tariel put the poker down. He picked at his beard. 'Then why are you here?'

'My motives are personal.'

'Personal?'

'Family,' said Rossel.

'Mother? Father?'

'Both killed.'

The two Georgians exchanged glances.

'And my sister, too,' Rossel added. 'She's been missing for many years.'

He removed his gloves, holding his hands towards the fire. The other men stared at his twisted fingers or, where he had none, the stumps.

'I believe the same man who took my parents' lives also took the life of Tamas Abazi.'

'And who is that?' said Tariel.

Rossel glanced around the room. 'What brought you here, Tariel? To this lonely place.'

Tariel smiled. 'I am used to it, comrade. I've spent the best part of twenty years alone up here. Since the thirties, when the Chekists began knocking on doors every night. So I'm used to my own thoughts, passing the time with little else to do than listen to your own heart beating. But sometimes, out on the ravines and passes, there's a bird, a snowcock, that has a distinctive call . . .' His voice dropped almost to a whisper – '*Sooo-looo-leeee, sooo-looo-leeee* . . . Everything seems to vanish – the snow, the mountains, even the bird itself. As if there's nothing left in the entire world, just me and that sound.'

He patted the butt of the rifle.

'When I feel like that, I want to go back to my old life, back to Gori. Go back to the world. Instead, I hunt the bird down just to stop it calling out.'

He poked at the fire again.

'How did Tamas die?'

Nikoloz leaned forward. 'He was murdered,' he said.

'By whom?' asked Tariel.

'Soselo,' replied Rossel.

Tariel tapped two fingers on the table. A slow, rhythmic beat. Under his breath, he crooned the bird's call. '*Sooo-looo-leeee, sooo-looo-leeee* . . .'

He sat still, staring at Rossel. The militia officer held his gaze. Neither man moved.

At last, Tariel got up, as if having reached a decision. He walked to the hurricane lamp, lifted it and set it on the floor.

He kicked back a section of carpet and dust shimmered in the weak, orange light. Tariel scraped away some stones before bending over and lifting away a plank of wood. He reached down, pulled out something wrapped in oilskins and resumed his seat.

'When we were all young together, Soselo delighted in winding people up. He was always taking the piss,' said Tariel. 'Good at it, too. If you had a weak spot, he'd find it. Me, I turned up one day in an old, outsized leather jacket with patches on it my grandfather had given me. "Look who it is," he says straight away, a glint in his eye – "the Knight in the Panther's Skin." The poem is Georgia's national epic. Its hero is called Tariel.'

'I have heard of it,' said Rossel. 'A great work. And, according to Nikoloz, he called Tamas the Weathervane?'

Tariel nodded. 'Yes, he did that when they worked together after Soselo got kicked out of the seminary.'

'The seminary?' said Rossel.

The two Georgians laughed.

'Yes, Soselo, destroyer of churches, executioner of Christians. That same man once trained to be a priest,' said Nikoloz. 'Can you believe it?'

Rossel tried to picture Stalin, leader of the atheist paradise, in a priest's black robes and funnel hat. Impossible.

Unless?

An inquisitor, he thought. One hand on the Bible. The other on the handle of a rack.

Tariel ran his fingers through his white hair. 'He got thrown out, of course. Following the orders of a just God was never his natural vocation. After that, he became a revolutionary and left the seminary for ever. But Soselo still needed a job for a while. He got one at the Meteorological Observatory in Tbilisi. Checking instruments, recording readings. Tamas was already employed as a nightwatchman there. Perhaps he put in a word for him, I don't know.'

'The two definitely worked together there?' said Rossel.

Tariel nodded. 'The bastard would do Tamas's voice, standing in the street with the snow coming down, laughing at the poor fool. Or he'd point at a blazing summer sun and declare that the "Weathervane" had just forecast a thunderstorm. He was merciless.'

Tariel began to unravel the package on his lap, peeling away the oilskin. Underneath was an ammunition box. It was dented in places, but otherwise still in good condition. He reached inside his coat and pulled out a key, fitted it into the box and turned it. The mechanism caught at the first attempt, but after a second sharp twist of the key, it gave.

Tariel opened the lid. He glanced at Rossel.

'Now Tamas is dead, Stalin will come for all of us. He always tidies up loose ends. Like I said, I never really was Tariel. But you, comrade, have something of the knight errant about you. So, let me furnish you with a weapon.'

With care, Tariel lifted out a yellowing document. A photograph was pinned to the top right-hand corner. Nikoloz stared at it, transfixed, as if the mountain had just given up the tablets of Moses.

'Read this,' said Tariel to Rossel.

Rossel took the document. Even though it was old, it was instantly familiar. A notice of arrest.

Dated 23 November 1901, it recorded a detention by the local police, as well as the grounds for arrest: sedition, banditry, armed robbery, organisation of illegal public gatherings, incitement of public disorder. The notice had three photographs attached to it, all the same man. Handsome, imposing, with narrowed eyes above a short, thick beard. A dappling of smallpox scars on the cheeks. For some reason, the entries for height, weight, eye colour and distinguishing marks were left blank, but at the bottom was a line of smudged fingerprints. And a name, scrawled in Russian, was Iosif Vissarionovich Dzhugashvili. The birth name of Joseph Stalin.

Rossel stared at the fingerprints.

If we dusted every street in Leningrad, every oblast in Russia, every Soviet city, every labour camp, every graveyard, we'd find them everywhere.

He turned it over to see if there was more. The back was blank.

'So what?' he said. 'Stalin was a revolutionary. This is not a secret.'

Tariel shook his head in irritation. 'Read the date again, and remember it,' he said. 'Now look at this.'

The second item was a thin brown notebook, wider than it was long. Opening it, Rossel saw that it was an accounts book. It recorded roughly fifty entries, beginning on 4 February 1902 and continuing until the final entry of 26 November 1907. The recorded amounts at the end of each line varied from ten to twenty-four roubles.

He went back to the beginning and flicked through it again. On each page was the imprint of a rectangular stamp, faded but still identifiable as belonging to the State Treasury of Imperial Russia. A smaller, circular stamp, erratically yet regularly applied, identified the bank's Tbilisi division – or Tiflis, as the city had been known.

Rossel returned to the first two pages. Typed and handwritten words declared the accounts book to be a record of payments to an informant of the Department for the Protection of Public Security and Order – better known as the Okhrana, the Tsarist secret police. This informant operated in Tiflis, as well as the Azerbaijani capital of Baku, 'and other places in Georgia and the Russian Caucasus'. The informant was identified as Comrade DZh.

At first, he was unable to take in the information he had been given or interpret the expressions on the faces of Tariel and Nikoloz.

Now Tariel passed over a third piece of paper.

Rossel took it and began to read.

Most everyday Soviet official documents, even those that ruled on the lives and deaths of its citizens, were printed on flimsy, near-translucent paper. This one was different. It had been pulled out of the drawer containing the best-quality paper, the stuff with the two-headed imperial eagle emblazoned at the top. Paper meant to survive decades in the files and archives of officialdom. Tariel had preserved it with care, of course, but even so – this was no ordinary piece of bureaucratic flotsam, a fill-in-name-here record of someone's employment, execution, birth, application for leave, medical record . . .

The paper was thick, the ink still dark.

It began with a formal salutation from a certain Major Ablomatov to an unnamed superior in the Okhrana. The major was reporting on a meeting of Russian Socialist revolutionaries, dominated by a small group known as 'the Bolshevik faction', that took place on 24 December 1905 in the Finnish town of Tampere. Of particular interest, wrote Major Ablomatov, was a meeting between two men, and the consequences of that meeting for future surveillance activities.

*

Informant DZh recounted that he had met V. I. Ulyanov, who is known among his acolytes as Lenin, in person. He confirmed previous intelligence that Lenin is now indisputably the leader of the Bolshevik faction of revolutionaries, that he is in good health, and that he is a forceful, vigorous speaker able to galvanise those around him through force of personality as well as his eloquence and ideological fervour. On Lenin's strategy, all intelligence suggests that he favours participation in elections to the Imperial Duma as a way of weakening the authority of the Tsar – that is, it is his intention to undermine the imperial government from within.

According to the Informant, Lenin intends to remain in Finland for the next several months in order to encourage or personally direct further criminal acts of banditry, robbery and assassination as a way of meeting the increasing costs of his organisation, which is frequently short of funds for administration, travel, propaganda, etc. However, the informant has also provided us with known addresses for Lenin in London and Munich.

Rossel turned the paper over and read on. His own hand, he noticed, was trembling.

Informant DZh has indicated his intention to continue with his operations both in Georgia and Armenia (that is, Baku); such activities, as is well known, include the organisation of strikes, intimidation and violence against

opponents in the radical union movement, bank robber-
ies, the assassination of imperial officials, extortion from
businesses, the murder of his own political rivals in the
revolutionary movement, etc. Although such activities
will affect government employees, allies in business and
commerce, and other of our informants among the vari-
ous Socialist revolutionary factions, against that one
must consider the invaluable intelligence that Informant
DZh provides, the increasing trust placed in him by
Lenin, and the fact that the Department for the Protec-
tion of Public Security and Order will be able to control
and, where necessary, curtail the informant's excesses.

At the same time, acting on information provided by
the Informant, last month members of the Department
for the Protection of Public Security and Order, along
with the Gendarmes, were able to raid four residential
premises in Tiflis, Gori and other towns and apprehend
14 suspected seditionists and bandits believed to belong
to the so-called Menshevik faction and other factions of
Socialist revolutionaries. Shortly before the encounter in
Finland between Informant Iosif and Lenin, the Depart-
ment also staged a raid on premises in Tiflis that was
attended and led by Informant DZh; however, the fact
of the raid was leaked in advance to give the Informant
time to organise his escape.

In other words, Rossel thought, the Okhrana was happy to see
imperial officials, private businessmen and even some of its own
agents sacrificed to protect this intelligence asset, while the asset
was happy to betray his own comrades, especially from rival

factions, to maintain his standing with the secret police. Doubt-less, both sides believed they were one step ahead of the other.

> *In his guise as Socialist revolutionary, Informant DZh's activities are of a seriousness that allowing them to continue – as well as rewarding him financially – requires approval at the highest level. Major B. G. Ablomatov therefore requests such guidance from the Minister for Interior Affairs at his earliest convenience.*

Across the bottom of the report were two hastily scrawled signatures. A date next to them. One was Major Ablomatov's. The other was more difficult to read, but Rossel could just make out the surname.

Dzhugashvili.

Nikoloz and Tariel stared at Rossel, gauging every twitch, every blink.

Tariel tapped a finger on the second signature. 'Informant DZh is, I hardly need tell you, Informant Dzhugashvili. This Major Ablomatov made the bastard sign it to hold his balls to the fire if he ever tried to wriggle out of the deal,' Tariel said. 'Tamas was with Stalin when he first met Lenin. Which means Informant DZh and Comrade Stalin – and Soselo, Soso, Koba – are all one and the same man. All traitors.'

Rossel raised his head. 'A signed confession,' he said. 'That's what Abazi had always told everyone in the bars of Gori. How he knew both Lenin and Stalin. But nobody ever believed him.'

Tariel pulled an old knapsack down from a hook on the wall and began stuffing the documents inside it. In the lamplight,

Rossel could see the ingrained wrinkles around his eyes and cheeks.

'Our great Georgian soul, Rustaveli, said of his most famous poem that it was a Persian tale, translated into Georgian, like an orphaned pearl, like a toy passed from one hand to another.' He fastened the leather buckles on the knapsack and handed it to Rossel. 'An orphaned pearl,' he said. 'A story I could not bring myself to tell. Was always too afraid to. But you might?'

Rossel stared down at the knapsack.

'I need some air,' he said.

43

The freezing night air hurt his lungs as he breathed it in. But the cold was exhilarating, like the moment a drowning man bursts through the surface of a lake.

Rossel stumbled up the mountainside, losing his footing twice on shingle made treacherous by recent snow.

Think. I need to think.

At a bend in the path, there was nothing but a broken chunk of wall with a few scattered stones around it. With one hand, he gripped it to steady himself and with the other groped for his *papirosy*.

The wind had died away, making the silence of the deserted, desolate village even more oppressive.

A rising moon only served to emphasise its gap-toothed emptiness.

Cliffs twisted around him, but there was one clear opening in the mass of rock, a promontory, an observation point with a restricted view of the valley. This must be where Tariel kept watch on the distant road.

Rossel looked down the slope, losing sight of the ground only when it bent into the valley. Below him, an owl swooped out of the shadows and disappeared again. He found his matches and sparked up the cigarette.

He inhaled deeply and began to calm himself.

'Too many secrets for one night?'

Rossel swung around. It was Tariel.

'That must be velvet you have on the soles of your boots,' Rossel said.

Tariel ran a bony hand through his thick, white hair. 'Snowcock feathers,' he said. 'I know why you came outside. Because you don't believe it. Because you cannot let yourself believe it.'

Rossel felt giddy. Like a child with a fever, drifting away into an unreal world for the first time. Something else, too. Rising in his gut, a prickling, boiling anger. The hot tip of the *papirosa* hissed as he drew smoke into his lungs.

'Too many secrets?' he said. 'In Stalin's world, just one can be enough to kill you. After the Terror, everyone realised what he was capable of. And something else too – what *they* were capable of – what they would do to survive. His face is the mirror everyone is too scared to look into in case they glimpse their own.' He drew hard on the cigarette. 'But a traitor? A spy for the Tsar's Okhrana? A man who betrayed Lenin. I don't . . .'

The moon floated behind a cloud.

Tariel nodded. 'I know,' he said. 'It feels too great a weight to carry. You're already wishing you didn't know it. That is how I once felt.' He pointed up to the black sky. In the gaps in the cloud cover, a multitude of stars blazed. 'Like an angel in Heaven who discovers that even God sins. But who will believe me, he asks himself.'

'Nobody.'

Tariel nodded. 'But now you know, you will always know.'

Rossel looked straight at him. 'Stalin *is* the Party,' he said. 'Stalin is the Revolution. If he is a traitor to Bolshevism, then nothing has ever been real.'

Tariel pointed at the knapsack. 'Comrade Beria would give anything for those papers.' The Georgian stepped a little closer. 'Listen to me,' he said. 'Soselo has always been careful. He has covered his tracks, settled old scores. He shows no mercy. Mensheviks who wouldn't follow him, Bolsheviks who got in his way. Old friends soon became old enemies – Bukharin. Zinoviev. Yezhov. Kamenev. Trotsky. Members of his own family. Avel Yenukidze – blue-eyed Avel, as genial as they come. A true Georgian. Fuck your mother! One of his greatest comrades. And he scraped him away like dog shit off his shoe. First sent him to freeze his bollocks off supervising mineral extraction in the northern Caucasus, then had him denounced and executed. Do you know why?'

Rossel shook his head.

'Avel wrote a book, memoirs of the Revolution out here. Gave me a big write-up – praise for an underground press I set up in Baku to print propaganda leaflets. Unsurprisingly, no mention of Soselo, because Soselo had nothing to do with it.' Tariel clicked his tongue. 'Big mistake, as Soselo had told everyone he did. No one holds a grudge like that man does. He waits fifteen years and . . .' Tariel used his finger to draw a line across his own throat.

Rossel dropped his cigarette butt into the snow and ground his boot on it. 'You talk a lot, Tariel. Perhaps too much. How did you get hold of those documents? Maybe you were in the Okhrana, too?'

Tariel pointed at Rossel's pocket. Rossel took out the pack of cigarettes and gave him one. He lit it. He pointed to a large, flat, icy rock, only lightly dusted with snow.

'Take a seat,' he said. 'And I will tell you.'

*

Rossel and Tariel sat side by side on the rock smoking and drinking. The Georgian had taken out a flask of brandy and offered it to him.

'It was 1904, April or May, in Baku,' said Tariel. 'We had planned to kill the regional governor of the oblast. Toss a dozen bombs through his windows and machinegun any bastard who ran out. But it was a set-up. The Black Hundreds, the Tsar's thugs, were lying in wait. I got a bullet in the thigh and another in the arm. It was easy for them to capture me. I was lucky – half of us were killed, either then and there or later, made to swing from the gallows. I got seven years in internal exile. But before that, I had to wait in a jail cell for two months while they thought about what to do with me.'

Tariel exhaled some smoke. Rossel took another drink of *chacha*.

'That cell stank,' continued Tariel. 'It was packed with Mensheviks, Bolsheviks, Anarchists, Nationalists, plus the usual bandits and crooks. As well as Armenians, Turks, Jews. No matter a man's beliefs or how clean his conscience, after a few weeks together like that, everyone reeks. Almost all of them had a story about Soso, or Koba, or Dzhugashvili, or Soselo, or whatever name Stalin went by, depending on the company he kept. And almost all of them had been cheated. Got to hear of lies he'd been spreading about them. Or been on bank raids where he'd made off with their share. Secret meetings he'd called where the Black Hundreds jumped out from behind the curtains. It took a while, but finally my eyes were opened. The bastard was working for the other side.'

'The Okhrana?' Rossel said.

Tariel nodded. 'I did my exile. Seven years in Siberia. Every day I was there, I swore vengeance. But by the time I got back, Soselo was long gone.'

'What happened then?'

'1917 happened, that's what. The fucking Revolution happened. You ever heard of that, Leningrad?'

Rossel took another drink from the flask. 'It rings a bell,' he said.

Tariel held out a hand. Rossel gave him the flask. The Georgian grinned and tipped it back, wiping his mouth with the back of his hand when he had finished.

'That was my chance to get what I had sought for many years,' he said. 'I found an Okhrana captain pissing his pants in the basement of an Interior Ministry building we'd stormed and offered him a deal. If he got me Soselo's files, I'd stop my comrades from cutting his prick off. Yes, or no? That was the fastest fucking answer to a question anyone ever gave me.'

'Was it a yes?'

Tariel took another drink. He waved the flask at Rossel. 'You're funny, Leningrad. I like that. But he was nearly too late – most of the documents had gone. Soselo must have got someone to grab anything compromising they could find. Or done it himself. But my Okhrana friend found some they'd missed. And they're the documents you just read.'

Rossel finished his cigarette but used it to light another one. 'Why not produce it before?' he asked. 'You could have brought him down at any moment.'

Tariel looked away. The old man gazed into the darkness for a moment before giving his answer. 'Fear is the great tyrant all men eventually bow to. After the Revolution, he grew too powerful. I waited, thinking I was clever to bide my time, that he would stumble. Telling myself that was why I was waiting. But really it was because I was too afraid. Shitting myself. And while I waited, he had half the Georgian Bolsheviks executed and then took over the Kremlin. So I fled. Went to monasteries, hid in the old cave cities, ended up here, hoping that Soselo would forget about me.' Tariel blew out a long trail of smoke. 'Now Tamas, the fool, has ruined it. He should have let it all be, should have stayed at home. But now Tamas is dead, *he* will come for us all.'

Tariel sat up. The Georgian's hand darted out and whipped the burning *papirosa* from Rossel's lips, dropping it on the ground and grinding it under his boot.

'Listen,' he whispered.

Rossel peered into the darkness. He could see nothing, could hear nothing except the rise and fall of the wailing mountain winds. Not even the hoot of an owl or the scurry of a rat.

Tariel didn't move.

Then . . .

A faint rattle of scree. Irregular, but recurrent.

Boots on the ground, somewhere beneath them.

Tariel hissed something in Georgian and stared down the slope. In one fluid movement, he stood, hoisted himself onto the wall and knelt there, crouching.

From below, another faint sound. The hushed curse of someone slipping in the darkness.

For a moment, the moon edged from behind the clouds and half-illuminated the mountainside. Rossel stood.

There . . .

Perhaps three hundred metres away and a couple of hundred below.

Three, four, five . . . six men.

All armed. Two holding huge dogs, Nagazi, Georgian mountain dogs. Trained to hunt in silence. And to kill.

Tariel leapt from the wall. Rossel crouched beside him.

'You idiots,' he snarled in Rossel's face. 'You've led the bastards to me.'

44

Boots slipping on the loose stones, Tariel, Rossel and Nikoloz scrambled further up the mountain. Below them, they could hear the approaching soldiers and the occasional deep bark from one of the dogs.

The two Georgians were carrying submachineguns, wartime *papashas* with heavy drum magazines. Each drum held seventy-one rounds – every Red Army veteran like Rossel knew that.

A comforting thought.

'The truck driver,' Rossel said as they ran. 'He must have told them.'

Nikoloz spat on the icy ground. 'Bastard.'

After another thirty metres, Tariel gestured to a shooting position for Nikoloz: a ruin that had a hole in the wall. Good cover. The two Georgians exchanged a comradely embrace before Nikoloz took up position.

Rossel and Tariel raced on. Fifty paces more. They stopped, turning to look back down the path. But the moon was covered by cloud and nothing was visible.

'This way,' said Tariel.

A bend in the path. Tariel shot forward and Rossel ran after him.

The wind was rising again. Rossel glanced up at the first flakes of a fresh fall fluttering through the air.

He stumbled further up the path, stopping at a stone shack with a corrugated-iron roof. He looked left and right. No sign of Tariel.

Shit, I've lost him.

He stepped inside to get out of sight. Listening hard but hearing nothing, save the rise and fall of his own breath.

Then a whining – the dogs.

Closer.

Closer and more eager now. Picking up his scent.

'*Tikho!*' A commanding voice, speaking Russian, not Georgian.

A pause.

Another order. This time shouted. 'Let them go!'

Another sound. Paws pattering over the ice and loose stones.

If they were Nagazi, they would rip his throat out before their handlers could reach him.

In the dark, Rossel paced out the length of the shack, running his hands along the walls, prodding at gaps with his pistol. Apart from the door and one hole where a window might once have been, there was only one other exit – a gap at floor height.

He began to wriggle through it.

Then, one foot still on the floor, he stopped.

Even fifty metres away from his hideout, somewhere further down the slope, the thunder of Nikoloz's *papasha* was incredible.

Anyone, man or dog, within his field of fire would have been cut to pieces. But the old man was holding the trigger down for too long, wasting ammunition.

Bursts – it's basic training, fire in bursts . . .

More shots. The enemy firing back, single shots at first, then doubles, then emptying their own magazines, reloading, firing again.

276

After a minute, the firing stopped.

Silence.

A voice shouting.

'Did we kill the bastard?'

A single shot.

'He's done now.'

'Who have we lost?'

'Two. Grisha and . . .'

The wind swept away the second name.

'And the dogs?'

'One dead, the other . . .'

The wind drowned the rest. But, above it, Rossel could hear the anguished howling of a wounded animal.

'Forward, keep moving forward . . .'

The men, whoever they were, resumed the hunt.

*

All Rossel could see were outlines, blurred by the falling snow. But the men kept moving relentlessly forward. Like a troop of spectres.

Lying flat on the freezing ground, half in and half out of the shack, he waited, settling into position, hands out in front of him clasping the pistol. The first man – big, with hulking shoulders – appeared out of the gloom. Twenty-five, maybe twenty metres away.

A second man, then a third.

One covering the path as the other two crept along, ducking behind whatever cover they could find. Firing into empty houses.

Blood in their nostrils – after killing Nikoloz.

Eyes watering in the cold, he took aim.

And fired.

The bullet missed the big man but hit one of the others.

A shout: 'The bastard got me.'

Rossel rolled sideways and jumped to his feet.

All around him, bullets bit into the stone.

He stuck his hand through the shack's open window. Let off three more rounds, firing blind.

Boots crunching into the snow and gravel. The sound growing louder as the gunmen raced forward.

Rossel ducked inside the shack and crawled on hands and knees towards a gap in the back wall.

Maybe, I can just . . .

He looked behind.

A rifle muzzle, then the rest of the Kalashnikov, then the face of the man holding it appeared at the window. His eyes wide. His teeth bared.

Every muscle taut, anticipating the bullets about to tear into him, Rossel twisted onto his back and fired until the chamber was nearly empty.

The man slumped forward in the frame of the widow.

Rossel squirmed through the gap, forcing his way into the open air.

Two low buildings stood before him. On one side of them was a path that snaked into the night, but after only a few metres, it was completely exposed. On the other was a precipice.

Trapped, I'm trapped.

Another roar of gunfire revealing Tariel's rough position – close by but higher up. From nowhere, two coated figures, silhouetted at the far end of a path, came into Rossel's line of sight. Their backs were to him, firing in response to this new attack.

Steadying himself, Rossel raised his pistol and fired twice. One of the men lurched sideways. His finger clamped down on the trigger of his Kalashnikov, the action of the mechanism jerking his body back and forth. The other man tried to get out of the way but was too slow and took several bullets in the chest.

Rossel peered into the snow and wind. Heart pounding, he edged down the path, pistol raised.

The two men were motionless.

The ground was slippery in places – with their blood, he assumed. As Rossel got beyond the two houses, he risked a look down the slope before ducking back but saw nobody.

Up in front of him, a dark lump was hunched against a wall.

'Tariel.' Rossel's loud whisper elicited no response.

But it must be him.

Keeping as low as he could, Rossel scuttled over the icy ground to the mountain man's position.

As soon as he reached it and hid behind a pile of stones, he knew.

Tariel, still on his knees, clutching his *papasha*, was slumped forward. His left temple had a gaping exit wound.

The energy drained from Rossel's body as fast as the blood flowed out of Tariel's skull and into the ground. He sat back, despairing at the death of this unlikely ally, exhausted by the battle, by the journey before that, by the feeling of dread that he realised had haunted him for days, his battered body convulsing, tears flowing in silence down his cheeks.

Sleep would be bliss.

Out of the whipping wind came the crack of falling stones.

He'd counted as best he could. But one cunning bastard had stayed back. Somehow, he must have got above them before circling round to attack from the rear.

Rossel stayed slumped, letting his arms hang loose, playing dead.

More shingle shifted as the gunman made his way down the slope. In his efforts to get above and behind them, he must not have seen Rossel run to Tariel.

Or I'd already be a dead man.

The crunch of boots came closer. Rossel's eyes swivelled right. The hem of a military coat. Muddy toecaps. He held his breath.

No. Not here, not now . . .

The gunman had his back to him. His right shoulder was hunched, dusted with snow.

Rossel rolled left and raised his pistol. The gunman barely managed a half-turn before Rossel squeezed the trigger.

The man's head arched to the left. He dropped to his knees as if praying to the mountain gods who had already abandoned him.

*

With dawn came half an hour of weak sunlight before the clouds wreathed the mountains once again. It was enough time for Rossel to make his preparations.

Nikoloz had indeed accounted for two men and both dogs, though one lay several metres apart from the other, as if it had hauled itself further along the path in a last demonstration of loyalty and duty.

The ground was too hard to dig graves. He covered the bodies of Tariel and Nikoloz with stones as best he could. The others he left for the wolves.

Most had nothing to identify them, but they at least provided ammunition, extra layers of clothing, a better pair of boots, and keys to the vehicles that must have brought them into the mountains. Rossel's way back to civilisation. But one had something else. A letter sewn into the lining of his coat. It was written on the official paper of the office of the Deputy Chairman of the Council of Ministers and read: 'The bearer of this letter has my full authority and is to be given all assistance in his endeavours.' At the bottom was a scrawled signature: *L. P. Beria.*

Rossel scanned the horizon, looking and listening for the first trucks of the day. Tariel's words came back to him.

'Comrade Beria would give anything for those papers.'

5
KOT
Cat

45

Inside the reading room of the Leningrad State Public Library, the desk lamps, fat, green and inscrutable as toads, stared at Rossel.

After the interminably long journey back from Georgia, all he wanted was sleep. But he had to do something first. He waited until a dark-haired woman in a blue blouse packed up her notepad and pencil into a handbag, took a black fur coat from the back of her chair, draped it around her shoulders and left.

Finally alone, Rossel rose from his desk. He pulled out an A4 manilla envelope containing the documents Tariel had given him: the arrest record, the slim brown ledger of payments and, most damning of all, the document that detailed Stalin's traitorous activities for the Tsar's secret police as 'Informant DZh'. The one that bore his signature.

Rossel walked towards the dark bookcases on the opposite wall.

He moved a small, brass-handled stepladder to the right and used it to access the highest shelves. The most distant of those in the room which, on his last visit, the librarian had commented, 'nobody reads'.

Taking down a green-leather volume of old research papers titled *Time of Troubles* by von Adelung and others, he blew the dust from the jacket, took out the top two papers and replaced them with the envelope. He covered them with one of the original documents in case he was unlucky enough for someone to take a cursory glance.

After slipping the remaining papers into the volume next to it, he left the building.

The woman with the red headscarf who sold *chebureki* from her stall was outside.

'Still hungry, handsome?' she said.

'Always.'

Rossel bit into the deep-fried pastry with care, knowing from experience what the hot cheese could do to the roof of his mouth. He set off to find a bus that would take him south towards Pulkovo, in the direction of Lipukhin's apartment. The captain would want a thorough debriefing on his time in the mountains.

Assuming he had not been arrested yet.

46

The bus ride to Lipukhin's apartment was a dead straight line from the centre of the city. Rossel's stop was a few hundred metres from where the front line had been during the Siege of Leningrad.

As he turned into the captain's street and walked towards Lipukhin's block, he noticed three people standing in the street outside – two women in animated conversation with an older man wearing a worn, brown hat.

On instinct, Rossel stepped into a doorway and scanned the street.

No blue-hats, no militia. What's up, then?

Rossel walked down the street and showed his ID card. 'Is there a problem, comrades?'

The man pointed through the open front door and up the stairs. Rossel glanced inside; a few other residents were crowding the stairwell, about halfway up.

'Someone heard a noise, maybe a shot,' said the man.

'They banged on his door, but no answer,' added one of the women.

'Whose door?' Rossel asked.

The man shrugged. 'I don't know the name. I live two blocks down.' He turned to one of the women. 'Natashenka?'

She shook her head. 'Don't know his name, either, but he's always on the sauce. The one I feel sorry for is the little girl.'

Ilya . . .

Rossel took the steps three at a time. Holding his ID card high, he pushed through the group on the stairwell.

When he arrived at Lipukhin's door, two of the captain's neighbours, a small man wearing glasses and a woman in a yellow housecoat, were hammering on it.

The woman was shouting. 'Ilya, Dasha, it's me, Lyudmila. Is everything all right? Open up, please . . .'

Rossel pushed them aside. He took two steps backwards and kicked the door as hard as he could with the sole of his boot. It juddered in the frame. He gave it a second raking kick. Wood splintered. The cheap door handle shattered.

'He was very drunk last night, even worse than usual,' said the woman called Lyudmila. 'Someone said he'd been asked to report to Liteiny Prospekt this morning, to the Bolshoi Dom . . . I heard him shouting at little Dashenka.'

Rossel rammed the door with his right shoulder. It moved, but only a few centimetres. He stepped back and kicked again. A safety chain snapped. He pushed into the hallway and raced inside.

Before he got to the living room, its door opened.

Dasha was wearing her white shirt and Octobrist pins. She was pale and her eyes were fixed straight ahead, past Rossel, through him as if he did not exist.

'Dasha, it's me. Uncle Revol.'

He took the little girl by the shoulders.

After a moment, she nodded and said his name twice. But the words sounded odd, hard, strangulated.

She looked down at her hands.

Blood . . .

He knew now but asked anyway.

'Dasha? Where is your uncle?'

She raised her right hand and pointed back over her shoulder.

Rossel stepped past her and pushed at the door.

Lipukhin was slumped in a red armchair. His head was tipped back; behind him was a splattering of blood and brain. His right hand was nestling in his lap, his lifeless fingers curled around his service pistol.

The captain's eyes were open and seemed to be staring at the poster on the opposite wall. At the young hero he had once been, blond, handsome, triumphant – *Keep the motherland safe from capitalist elements! Join the militia.* Rossel reached out and closed them.

He took Dasha by the shoulders again and pushed her out of the room, shutting the living-room door behind him.

'It's an accident, Dasha, it's an accident, that's all,' he whispered. 'Your uncle didn't mean to hurt himself.'

Dasha looked at the blood on her hand. Then at him.

'Yes,' she said. 'I know.'

*

No tears . . .

Gerashvili, Rossel and Dasha were sitting in the tiny apartment of Lipukhin's nearest neighbour, Lyudmila – the woman in the yellow housecoat. Rossel had called the militia and asked them to contact the station in Vosstaniya Street. A desk sergeant had taken the call and immediately passed the news on to Gerashvili.

Lyudmila had made tea, including one for Dasha, who got extra sugar. The child was sitting at a table with both hands clasped around a chipped green cup. Every now and then, she took a small sip. But she had said nothing since she and Rossel had spoken. And even though he wanted her to cry, to bawl, to display heart-bursting grief, she had shed not a single tear.

Gerashvili sat on one side of her, Rossel on the other. The lieutenant was stroking her hair and singing to her in a voice so soft it was almost inaudible. A traditional lullaby, *'Bayu Bayushki Bayu'*, which Rossel remembered his mother singing to him.

'Baby, baby, rock-a-bye, On the edge you mustn't lie, Or the little grey wolf will come, And will nip you on the tum . . .'

Dasha leaned her head against Gerashvili's shoulder.

'When she sang this song to me, my mother would say it made a pool of tears – a pool of all the sadness we keep hidden inside us,' Gerashvili whispered to her.

Rossel squeezed the child's hand. 'Cry if you need to, Dashenka,' he said.

Dasha glanced at the hand covering hers. Then up at him.

'I'm not supposed to,' she said.

'Not supposed to?' said Rossel. 'But—'

'I'm not supposed to mourn the deaths of enemies of the people.'

Gerashvili gave Rossel a look. He shook his head. The lieutenant patted Dasha's shoulder and began singing again, but after only two lines, she stopped.

Rossel followed her gaze. Two hard-faced women were standing in the doorway.

'We're here for the girl,' asked the older of them.

'Here from where?' said Gerashvili.

'State Orphanage number 48, in the Smolny District. Her

uncle is dead, along with both parents. She will be well looked after until another relative comes forward. If one ever does.'

Rossel got to his feet. 'No,' he said, his voice breaking. 'I won't let that happen.'

'Says who?' retorted the older woman. She pointed at him. 'You? You're a nobody. A friend, that's all. A senior militiaman, the neighbours say.' She fished a letter from her inside pocket. 'I have all the necessary formalities here . . .'

Rossel took a step towards her. 'I don't care what you think you have. The child is in shock, she's not—'

Gerashvili stood. 'I have some room at home, Dasha can stay with me.'

The woman shook her head and waved the letter in front of them. 'That's not possible, lady. A decision has already been taken.'

Gerashvili coloured. 'Senior Lieutenant. I am a senior lieutenant in the militia; you should refer to me as that while we are conversing or—'

Rossel grabbed the letter from the woman's hand. 'Let me see that,' he snapped.

He held it out of reach as she tried to grab it back, protesting and cursing.

Gerashvili began yelling at the other woman, who shouted back.

'I want to,' said a quiet voice. 'I want to . . .'

Everyone stopped shouting and turned towards Dasha. The child stood.

'I want to go,' she said again, this time firmly. 'I want to go with them.'

'Are you sure?' said Gerashvili.

A tear began to roll down the girl's cheek. She nodded.

'We were arguing again,' she said to Rossel. 'Uncle Ilya and I were arguing. You are right, he didn't really want to hurt himself.'

She wiped her cheek with her sleeve, sniffed, and gave Rossel a look of contempt.

'Just before he did what he did, he was pointing the gun at me.'

47

Rossel needed to know more about Tamas Abazi's last visit to Leningrad. He could tell by her tone that Elene Dzagnidze had been expecting him to call.

Rossel was a little taken aback by her proposed meeting place: outside a public *banya* on a maze of streets off Kantemirovskaya Street – not the centre, not the outskirts. About half-past eight in the morning, she said. He presumed she didn't want to set tongues wagging in her *kommunalka* with another visit from the *militsiya*.

He arrived ten minutes early and sat smoking in the dark-panelled foyer until she came out. The *banya* reeked of soap, steam and birch branches, used by *banshchiki* to thrash each other to get the hot air flowing over the body, stimulate the circulation and (it was said) fight off every bug a Russian winter could throw at you. The pungent smell of his own *papirosa* mingled with this healthy aroma as the morning bathers meandered in and out, ignoring the pale militia officer lost in thought.

He was halfway through his second cigarette before the image of Dasha being driven away from her uncle's apartment became in any way tolerable. The child's small head, visible through the car's back window, framed by the women from the orphanage.

As for Ilya . . .

A line from *The Idiot* came to him: 'It is better to be unhappy and know the worst, than to be happy in a fool's paradise.' Lipukhin had on occasion liked to pepper his vodka with some of Dostoyevsky's more maudlin insights. Perhaps in the end, that's what his old friend had decided to do – refused to remain a fool. Even if, unlike so many of his fellow citizens, he had never been a happy one.

'Good morning, Comrade Officer.'

Rossel stood.

'Comrade Dzagnidze,' he said.

She was wearing no make-up, a faux-fur coat and big boots, and was towelling her wet hair, but Elene Dzagnidze still had something of Klara Luchko about her – an openness, tinged with amusement or aloofness, depending on the light. A tall man buying cigarettes from a vending machine on the wall was staring at her.

She stopped drying her hair and pushed the towel inside a small green duffel bag. She smiled at Rossel.

'They've shut the hot water off in my street,' she said. 'This place is halfway between home and work.' She sounded friendlier than she had been over the phone, her voice sing-song and soft. Her gaze was mildly flirtatious. She was sounding him out, he thought. Perhaps to see if pulling him a little closer might be a good tactic.

'*Slyogkim parom*,' he said, the traditional salutation to the *banya*-goer – a congratulations on their cleansing experience. Non-committal – it was a social obligation to make such a remark, but not necessarily a sign of warm relations.

She put her hands out by her sides and wiggled her fingers. '*Spasibo*. This is me. All buffed and polished, top to toe.'

Rossel gestured to the door. 'Let's go for a walk,' he said.

She picked her bag up and nodded. As they left, the man by the vending machine gave him a wink.

*

They walked southwest towards the city centre.

About halfway along the wide, tree-lined boulevard, Dzagnidze stopped in front of a small shop window. Three loaves were proudly arranged in it, each with its own shelf, as if they were golden tiaras or Fabergé eggs on display at the Hermitage.

She leaned into him purposefully. He could smell her scent – warm, heavy with birch and eucalyptus. He could feel the outline of her figure through her coat.

She pointed at the bread in the window. 'Imagine standing here during the Blockade,' she said. 'What exquisite torture.' She turned towards him. 'Nothing but a pane of glass between you and everything you could possibly desire.'

Rossel stared into her dark eyes. He leaned towards her until his mouth was almost touching hers. 'I know,' he whispered.

She had readied for the kiss. But now took a small step back. 'Know what?'

'About your uncle, and his old friend, Soselo,' murmured Rossel. 'And yet, when I first met you, you denied knowing the name. About their meetings at the dacha out at Kuntsevo. Including the most recent one, just before your uncle showed up in Leningrad.'

Dzagnidze emitted a short, nervous laugh. 'Surely you don't believe all that nonsense?' she said. 'My uncle said no one goes to the Kuntsevo dacha except . . .' She couldn't finish the sentence.

Except Stalin and his closest associates, he thought.

'I have just returned from Gori,' Rossel said. 'I spoke to some of the locals. They have long memories. They told me some old stories about your uncle.'

Emotions flitted across Elene Dzagnidze's face – anger, fear, astonishment, reproach.

'What exactly did your uncle tell you the last time you saw him?' he asked. 'And speak plainly. I want details.'

Dzagnidze glanced up and down the street.

'I don't want to get into trouble.'

'No one does.'

Another look about her. The traffic was picking up, heading towards the bridge and the islands of the Petrograd Side. A man and woman were walking a small dog. A half-empty tram trundled past. A queue was beginning to form at a butcher's shop on the other side of the street, next to a hand-painted sign that read: 'Liver in stock'.

Elene pushed a strand of damp hair out of her face. Exposed to the air, it had grown tiny white crystals where the moisture had frozen. She started to walk on and motioned for him to come with her, but Rossel stood his ground. She gave up.

'One old friend is worth two new, as the proverb has it,' she said. 'Uncle Tamas would say that to me and whisper, "My old friend in Kuntsevo is worth a thousand. I go there, we play *gorodki*, we smoke, drink *chacha*, sometimes we even eat milk soup and dumplings, just like we used to." He even had some unlikely tale, which involved Lenin, as to why they ate the milk soup. Uncle was not a clever man. The old fool's face lit up when he talked of Kuntsevo. He'd become giddy with it all.'

'So, you'd seen him before? After these trips? He would visit you in Leningrad?'

'Yes. At least twice.'

'And did he say how these invitations to Kuntsevo came about?'

She glanced across at the butcher's queue before answering.

'A call, every now and then, a call from someone in Moscow. Then they'd send money for the train ticket and he'd go.'

Another tram rattled by, snow billowing in its wake.

One last push . . .

Rossel stepped a little closer. 'Did he ever mention an arrest?'

'An arrest?'

'Back in the old days. In Gori.'

'I . . . I didn't know he was arrested.'

Rossel shook his head. 'I don't mean the arrest of Tamas Abazi.' He squeezed Dzagnidze's wrist. 'I mean the arrest of his old friend.'

She looked up and down the street again, now terrified. She pulled away from Rossel and began walking away.

'Enough!' she cried out.

Rossel quickened his pace and fell in beside her, but she hid her face from him.

'Please, please, leave me alone!'

'You said someone called to set up your uncle's last visit to Moscow and the dacha at Kuntsevo,' Rossel said. 'When was that last call, that last visit? Just tell me that, and I will let you go.'

She shook her head. 'No, I—'

Rossel grabbed her arm and stopped her. 'You have already admitted withholding evidence, Comrade Dzagnidze. I already have enough to arrest you. If you're worried about attracting attention now, how much more will you bring upon yourself languishing in a cell in Militia Station 17? It's not that far from here.'

She gripped his fingers and tried to prise his hand away.

'Please, let me go.'

'The last call, the last visit. Tell me that and I will.'

She clawed at his fingers again, but then gave in.

'The week before,' she said. 'The week before he came to see me in Leningrad, he'd been there. To see *him*. At first, he was full of it. How his "old friend" had been so happy to be reunited. But the next day, his mood changed. He became anxious, melancholic.'

'Anxious about what?'

A snowflake landed on the tip of her nose. Dzagnidze used a finger to push it away.

Her voice dropped to a whisper. 'He kept muttering in Georgian: "*It was a mistake.*" So I asked him – what was? He just shook his head and said: "I shouldn't have said what I said when we were playing *gorodki*, I shouldn't have said that." '

'Said what, exactly?'

'You know the game? The players set the skittles up in different formations: "arrow", "artillery", "sickle", "lobster" and so on. There are lots of different names. Uncle liked to place his skittles in the "well" symbol. He'd tell S . . . tell Soselo it was to honour him because he'd always been "so deep". But this time he said something else, too.'

'Something else?'

'A joke, that's all. A stupid joke. Uncle made some kind of remark about him being so deep he'd always suspected he'd been the informer in their midst when they were all young together back in Gori.'

A third tram rattled past, this one fuller than the others. Dzagnidze stared at it as it stopped on the other side of the street; she was desperate to escape. The river embankment was in sight – she could put the Neva between her and Rossel.

She began to weep. 'I haven't slept since you first came around, not one wink,' she sobbed. 'I'm so scared. What if I'm next?'

Rossel nodded towards the tram. Swinging her bag over one shoulder, she raced across the icy street, waving at the driver to wait for her.

Rossel pulled his collar tighter. He glanced at the grey sky. His hand dipped into his pocket, searching for the tiny round stone.

A week, he thought, *that's all.* Tamas Abazi had dined with Comrade Stalin one week before he was murdered.

48

Two hours later, Rossel and Gerashvili were parking a militia car on a side street near the university. Comrade Baikalin appeared to have gone to ground. He was not at his room in Lesnaya and, according to the woman they had met there on their previous visit, had not been for several days.

They had visited the Titan cinema's café, and shown his picture to a couple of the receptionists at the Hermitage. Both recognised him as a regular but said he had not been in for at least a week.

'Remind me why we are spending so much time on Baikalin, Senior Militiaman?' Gerashvili said.

'Because he knows much more about Tamas Abazi than he has told us so far. I'm certain of it. Principally because Baikalin and Abazi were hanging out with the Party hierarchy, way back in 1934. At the All-Party Congress, mind you, not any old buffet. Baikalin tried to dismiss him as all bluster, a Georgian braggart, a hanger-on. Yet it turns out that Abazi is one of Stalin's oldest comrades. Something he must have known.'

'You're sure Baikalin is lying?'

'Yes, Lieutenant, I am.'

Boots crunching into the packed snow, they began trudging from the car towards the Twelve Collegia of the university.

*

It was a Saturday, so the university was almost empty. Gerashvili showed her ID to a security guard on the front desk. The man checked his register.

'Not been in for at least a week, comrades.'

He pointed in the direction of the office Baikalin had been using and gave them a duplicate key.

*

Baikalin's office was small and cramped with untidy shelves and an ancient oak desk strewn with papers, on which a cold glass of tea sat next to a large metal pencil sharpener and a blackboard duster.

'Are we looking for anything in particular?' asked Gerashvili.

'I'm not sure,' said Rossel. 'An old photograph, a memento from the Seventeenth Congress? I don't want to waste time, but since we're here, we might as well be thorough.'

They searched for an hour. And found nothing.

Rossel slumped down in Baikalin's swivel chair. He rubbed his eyes.

'Another dead end.'

Gerashvili ran a hand through her hair and nodded.

Rossel swung around in the chair, scanning the walls from his new position. After a moment, he spotted something. A battered wooden box peeping out from behind some files on a high shelf. He reached up, grabbed it and placed it on the academic's desk. Rossel twisted the handle. It was locked.

'Here.'

Gerashvili took out a penknife. Rossel took it and forced the box open.

More academic papers, some old pens, a scattering of kopeks

and a ledger of some sort, or a large album. Rossel removed it and dropped it onto the desk with a thump. He opened the thick, dog-eared cover.

'What is it, Revol?'

For a moment, Rossel didn't speak, even though he knew exactly what it was. Page after page spilled out on the desk – facsimiles, reproduced on modern paper, of ancient manuscripts of the kind that Anna Orlova had possessed. Alien characters, as inscrutable to the average citizen as hieroglyphs. Hundreds of words without a break, almost without punctuation.

'Glagolitic,' he said.

Gerashvili riffled through the papers. 'You're sure? This is what the Glagolitic script you have seen already looks like?'

He nodded. 'Yes, the script here looks exactly like the writing we found in Anna Orlova's possession. The capt—' Rossel broke off and swallowed. 'Ilya and I went to her home and found similar documents, though those were more stylised. The words even formed shapes and patterns, I mean. A colleague of Orlova explained her work to me. She was an expert in Glagolitic and other ancient Slavic scripts. Old Permic was one.'

'Baikalin is an academic, too,' said Gerashvili. 'Perhaps it's not so strange that he would have—'

'An economic historian,' said Rossel. 'Numbers and charts. Tractor output, agricultural yields, quotas. No, this is too much of a coincidence. Baikalin knows the poet Kovalyova, who was friends with Orlova. And now he has these papers in a locked box in his office.'

The lieutenant jabbed at one of the papers with her finger. 'What do these symbols mean?'

'I have no idea. But Professor Lapshin should be able to decipher them for us.'

'Right then,' said Gerashvili. 'Let's go.'

The lieutenant began to button her coat. Rossel clambered to his feet.

'That's odd,' said Gerashvili, pointing at something on one of the grey metal filing cabinets.

Rossel tried to focus but could not see what had caught her eye.

'Look.' She reached across and picked up a flat tin – one of four piled on top of each other. 'I noticed the first time when we met him at the Titan that he was a typical academic, a little scruffy, with scuffed boots. So, why keep four tins of polish at work?'

Rossel picked up another one. 'A new girlfriend, maybe, who wants him to smarten up his act?'

Gerashvili held up a cloth for Rossel to inspect. 'No polish on the cloth,' she said.

Rossel unscrewed the lid of the tin he was holding and showed it to Gerashvili. 'Polish, that's all.'

She did the same. Rossel tried the third. More black polish.

'Might as well be thorough,' said Gerashvili.

Rossel smiled. 'This is the vital investigative work they pay us for,' he said, as the senior lieutenant wrestled with the lid, grumbling about a damaged thread.

Finally, she popped it open. A black discus flew out, sailing across the room, before bouncing off a wall.

Followed by something else. A small, circular portrait that landed on the parquet floor, shattering the wafer-thin glass that covered it.

Rossel picked up the miniature. A roughly sketched human figure, bent over and carrying a walking stick. He removed the canvas from the frame.

A word was scrawled in pencil on the back of it.

'*Dyedushka*,' said Gerashvili. 'What can it mean?'

*

Rossel and Gerashvili drove back to Vosstaniya Street, skirting frozen canals on which a few bedraggled crows were scavenging for food. Gerashvili, who was driving, put a hand up to shield her eyes from the low sun. There were a couple of hours of daylight left.

'*Dyedushka*. What does it mean, Revol?' she asked again. 'A group of some sort? Conspirators? What are they up to?'

'That's the third miniature in the same style we have found,' said Rossel. 'A duck, a bird and a *Dyedushka,* an old man – a grandfather. It might be nothing more than an in-joke, a piece of whimsy among intellectual acquaintances keen to keep their bourgeois affectations out of sight. But then there is the music that someone played down the phone at Orlova's apartment. Ilya didn't recognise it until he heard it again at the Kirov, but even though he was about as musical as this engine, he was certain it was the same.'

'*Peter and the Wolf*,' said Gerashvili. 'A work written for young ears.'

She beeped the horn at a motorcyclist who came out of a side street in front of them.

'Idiot!'

Rossel nodded. 'A piece that has several characters. Among them, a duck, a bird and a grandfather.'

'That can't be a coincidence,' said Gerashvili.

'No,' he said, 'it can't.'

'But what does it all add up to?'

Rossel shrugged. 'A shared secret of some kind? Orlova, an academic whose Ukrainian philosopher husband was exiled and killed at sea. Kovalyova, a poet whose works are banned. Baikalin, an Old Bolshevik who did time in the camps. All three ideologically suspect. All three have suffered. But until a few days ago, all three had survived.'

Gerashvili stared ahead through the partially frosted windscreen. 'And then a Georgian mountain peasant, if you're to be believed, a childhood friend of our Great Leader, rolls into town,' she said. 'He meets Orlova, and both are murdered – probably by the MGB.' Gerashvili turned the wheel and sat back, her face in shadow. 'How many parts like that in all?'

'Parts?'

'In *Peter and the Wolf*. How many characters?'

Rossel thought for a moment. 'Apart from those three, there is a cat, a wolf and Peter himself. Then there are some hunters . . .' He stopped, realising what she was implying.

'More, then,' said Gerashvili. 'There may be more of them. But how many?'

*

As Gerashvili pulled up in front of the station, the car juddered as the front wheel hit a pothole filled with slush. She stopped the engine.

Rossel turned to her. 'There is something else you should know, Lidia,' he said. 'I saw Abazi's niece today. She was very frightened. Petrified.'

'So?'

He gestured towards the weathered façade of the station. 'Maybe you should be, too. Maybe we all should.'

Gerashvili said nothing. But he knew she was thinking about the time she had spent submitting to the tender ministrations of the MGB. It had taken her months to recover.

'One week before he came to see his niece in Leningrad,' Rossel said, 'Tamas Abazi had visited ... a great hero of the Soviet Union – if the papers and radio stations are to be believed, our greatest – at his dacha at Kuntsevo.'

Gerashvili turned away and stared out of the passenger window. They sat for several minutes without saying anything, letting the cold seep under their clothes and skin; finding its way into their bones.

'I don't want to go back,' she said at last, her voice steady but speaking through a tight jaw.

'No. Me neither.'

'You know why,' she said, looking at him. 'You've been there yourself. I don't mean the place. I mean the state of existence. Of being completely in their power. Of them owning you.'

Rossel reached out and took her hand. 'That's why I am telling you this,' he said. 'So you can decide not to help me any more, decide you don't have to.'

Gerashvili thought for a moment. Then, without saying another word, the lieutenant got out of the car and walked the last few steps across the slippery pavement to Station 17.

49

As Lapshin turned and saw Rossel, the professor began to walk more quickly. But, realising the futility of the move, he stopped in his tracks.

'You again,' he said.

'Comrade Professor, I need your help deciphering some texts, that's all. It will only take a moment.'

Looking flustered, Lapshin glanced around the ornate corridor of the Menshikov Palace as if hoping someone might rescue him. But he took the papers Rossel pressed onto him and started to leaf through them.

'Anna was the real expert on Glagolitic. Not me. And believe me or not, I really am very busy,' Lapshin said. 'If you come back another time, perhaps I can find one of Anna's research students to help you. It may take me a while but—'

Rossel placed a hand on the academic's arm. He had not intended it to be a hostile gesture, but the look on Lapshin's face told him it had been taken as one.

'Alexander Menshikov, the man who built this gilded palace, rose high, but then fell from grace and was exiled to Siberia. I have no desire to follow him,' the professor said.

Rossel released Lapshin's arm.

'Please, Comrade Lapshin. Just tell me what you can. Your sense of the overall idea. Not exact details. Is it a religious text, say New Testament or Old Testament? Or a sermon? Or a saint's life?'

Lapshin pulled out a pair of spectacles and examined the sheaves of paper more closely.

For a few moments, he read in silence. Then the academic looked up.

'Is this some sort of a test?' he said. His lisp was more pronounced.

'A test? What do you mean?'

Lapshin held up one of the papers. 'Just names,' he said. 'That's all it is, a list of names. Some in Glagolitic, some in Old Permic. There is even some early Cyrillic in there. But it's not religious, or a chronicle, not even the life of a humble woodcutter.'

'Names?'

Lapshin scanned the papers again, turning a few more over.

'"Ananiyev, Pavlo Panteliovich. Bagnyukov, Pavlo Vasilovich. Baranovska, Nadya Andriyivna. Beshenko, Volodomir Kindratovich,"' he declaimed. 'You want me to go on?' He shuffled the papers, placing the last sheet on top of the pile. '"Nesvisha, Olha Antonovna. Prytula, Stepan, no patronymic for this one."' And so forth. I'd say . . . perhaps sixty or seventy names? Please don't ask me to read them all.'

Rossel frowned.

'Beshenko, Antonovna . . . those don't sound Russian,' he said. 'More like Ukrainian, or Belarusian?'

Lapshin shrugged. 'It depends how old this manuscript is, and where it's from. But yes, they could be Ukrainian.' He handed the sheaves of paper back. 'Lists of names,' the professor added. 'A chronicle of sorts, then.'

Rossel nodded.

'A tale of our times.'

At that, Lapshin turned and quickly walked away.

*

When they came for you, four in the morning was a standard time.

Their victims were always groggy – you could only lie awake trembling for so long before you had to sleep, and that was when they loved to hammer on your door.

I might as well drink this glass, and then another one. If I'm going back to hell, I don't want to know much about it . . .

The stylus stuck again.

Rossel put down his vodka glass. He heaved himself out of his chair and walked to the temperamental Sokol radio-gramophone. He picked the stylus up and placed it on the edge of the record.

A masterly voice began narrating – the calm, authoritative tones of the composer himself, Sergei Prokofiev, introducing the characters he had created. *Utka*, Duck. *Ptitsa*, Bird. *Dyedushka*, Grandfather, and so on, pausing each time so that the instruments depicting each one could play the relevant motif.

Utka, he thought, Anna Orlova; *Ptitsa*, Vika Kovalyova, most likely; and *Dyedushka*? Well, that had to be Comrade Baikalin.

All three were in possession of miniature illustrations – duck, bird and grandfather. But what if there were others? Perhaps four more, if you counted the Cat, the Wolf, Peter and the Hunter. Even more if, as the narrator of *Peter and the Wolf* at the Kirov had stated, there were hunters, plural.

Signals. Ciphers. Ancient scripts and musical motifs. It adds up to the same thing – I'm still groping around in the dark.

A firm knock at the door.

They're here.

If you wanted to live, you went quietly. But he didn't care any more.

Rossel let the music play on but picked up his gun before walking towards the door. He let his arm hang by his side, then turned the handle.

Ahh.

Gerashvili's face was pallid, with dark shadows under the eyes from lack of sleep. The lieutenant glanced behind her before stepping inside.

Rossel placed the gun back on the table. She eyed it as if its presence was a portent of their future. She marched to a chair in the corner of the room and sat, brushing snow from her coat as she did so.

She sat silently, seemingly composing herself. Then spoke. Her tone tense, reflective. 'When I was in the Bolshoi Dom, my MGB interrogators stripped me naked in my cell,' she said. 'Every now and then, two of them – a fat, old Cossack and an oily Ossetian with broken teeth – would come in and stare. But say nothing. Just let me think about all the disgusting things *they* were thinking about. By the end, I was so scared of my own thoughts, imagining what they might do, that I was praying for them to get on with it. Maybe, I reasoned, it wouldn't be as bad as I imagined.'

Rossel looked at her, not knowing how to respond, only understanding something of what she had been through.

'And did they?'

'They didn't need to,' she whispered. 'After a few days of that, I told them everything they wanted to know. Conspiracies, intent to sabotage, anti-Soviet sentiment . . . whatever they needed.'

Rossel took two steps, then knelt beside her.

'Lidia,' he began, 'I understand. You do not need to explain. I can do this on my ow—'

She reached out and touched him on the cheek.

'Why is it that you have never found your sister, Revol?' she said.

'My sister?'

'All those files, all that searching, all those lonely hours among the missing. Even if you're just a street officer, even if you're just an archivist, even if you don't work as a criminal investigator, you're still an exceptional detective. So how come you can't solve the case that's more important to you than any other? I have been asking myself that question for a long time.'

He tried to look away. But she would not let him.

'You don't really *want* to find her, do you?' she said. 'You prefer suicide to a reunion with your own sister. You'd rather investigate Stalin for murder. Because, like me, you're afraid. Ashamed of what those bastards made you do, and what they have done to you.'

Rossel turned his head away from her. He glanced at his left hand. It was shaking.

'She used to say I was the lucky one,' he said. He could hear the self-pity in his voice and hated himself for it. 'Because I was more technically gifted – I could play the virtuoso music. But she wanted it more. She felt everything more deeply, and could express it, too. Love, hope, melancholy . . . betrayal. When she played, it was . . .'

They looked at each other.

'What I mean is, the moment I find her, she will know.'

'Know what?' said Gerashvili.

'That it was me who betrayed our mother and father to the

NKVD. We were both questioned after their arrest. I was a teenager; I could not help myself. But, of the two of us, she was always braver. Mentally stronger. She will know I was weak and never forgive me. I think she already knew it. Sensed it. I'm certain of it. That's why she disappeared.'

His fingers, he noticed, were still trembling. Gerashvili reached out and stilled them.

A crackle of static from the gramophone. The first few notes of Peter's motif began repeating themselves as the stylus got stuck again.

He tried to ignore it. But then . . .

Taking three quick paces across the room, Rossel reached out to adjust the stylus. Then stayed his hand.

The same few notes, repeated over and over?

A signal, perhaps? Telling people to gather.

He stood in silence, his mind racing.

'What's the matter, Revol?' said Gerashvili. A note of exasperation in her voice.

He thought back to his search of Anna Orlova's room, when Lipukhin had picked up the phone and first heard an excerpt from *Peter and the Wolf.*

Rossel gave the stylus a nudge. Peter's tune played on, and the fearless young boy skipped into the world beyond his home.

He turned back to Gerashvili.

'I have an idea,' he said.

50

As darkness fell, along with a heavy sleet, Rossel looked from a doorway and saw the light go on in the kitchen of Vika Kovaly-ova's apartment on the opposite side of the street.

The poet had been home for an hour. He had followed her from Sennoi Market, where she had bought two cabbages and a shank of mutton. He felt his stomach rumble. *Not much chance of a dinner invitation*, he thought.

Now was as good a time as any.

He stepped out of the doorway and, avoiding a trough of slush, turned left down Zhukovskogo Street.

After a brisk two-minute walk, Rossel stopped at a public phone. He fished a token out of his pocket, picked up the handset and made the call.

*

He checked his watch for the third time: 8.50 p.m.

Perhaps I'm wrong?

He pulled up his coat collar and stepped back into the doorway.

If she'd done as agreed, Gerashvili – at her sister's house – should by now be ringing Kovalyova. Like Rossel, the lieutenant had no telephone at home, so it was the only place she could think of where they could play a gramophone down a phone line.

When the poet answered, Gerashvili was to say nothing. Simply let Kovalyova listen to the sound of the orchestra playing Peter's simple musical motif, and hang up.

He was about to check his watch again when Kovalyova's kitchen light went off.

A minute later, enveloped in a large coat and hat, the poet stepped into the street and hurried off, head bowed against the sleet, in the direction of the Fontanka. Rossel waited long enough for her to get a hundred metres ahead of him and set off in pursuit.

*

Kovalyova crossed the Fontanka at the Belinsky Bridge, then bore right up the embankment towards the green rooftops and golden spire of the Mikhailovsky Castle.

After another few minutes, she crossed the Moika at the Sadovy Bridge and skirted the edge of the snow-clad Field of Mars. Rossel had to keep well back on the long pavements and boulevards, occasionally taking shelter behind the trees, but she glanced over her shoulder only a couple of times and seemed more concerned with hastening to her destination.

Eventually, she stopped outside a shabby, two-storey building fronted with small Greek columns and covered in peeling yellow paint. It was dwarfed by the buildings around it, as if the city's planners had overlooked it or not decided if and how to rebuild. A broken sign fastened to the columns said: Children's Theatre. Whatever it was, it looked long closed, almost derelict.

Kovalyova was more cautious now, turning around and

scanning the streets, but he was in luck; a tram lumbered up the tracks at little more than walking pace and he was able to use it as cover until he reached a parked van.

The tram rattled on and the street fell silent.

The poet did not try the front door. Instead, she continued for another thirty metres or so until she was able to turn into a courtyard. She would have to find a back door, he assumed.

He followed, slipping into the darkness of the yard. The only light came through the windows of a few residents, passing between curtains and through windows made opaque by the grime of the Leningrad winter.

There she is . . .

The poet knocked twice on a rickety stage door.

After a pause, someone opened it and greeted her – a woman's voice. The two of them embraced. Rather than follow, Rossel crossed the courtyard and took up position in the shadow of a covered door to another building and waited.

Moments later, a man walked in off the main street with slow steps, hesitant, sniffing the air cautiously.

He looked around, then struck a match and lit a cigarette. His glasses and beard were illuminated for a second by the flickering flame.

Comrade Baikalin rapped twice on the stage door. A greeting, an embrace and he was in.

*

Rossel tried the brass handle of the stage door. Even through his gloves, he could feel how cold it was. As he'd expected, it was locked.

He looked about him. A fire-escape staircase curled upwards

at an angle, but the doors it led to on the three floors above him were metal and shut tight.

He inspected the door again. Tied to a rusting screw in the wooden frame, at about head height, a pencil was dangling from a piece of string. He peered at it in the gloom. Not a pencil – the same length but thicker, and with no lead. His heart gave a little kick as he manoeuvred it free and held it up, trying to make out some of the detail, his gloved fingers running over the object's rough face. A face he recognised – the half-morose, half-enraged visage of the Slavic god Perun. He pocketed it.

Rossel moved further along the building, mindful of a gap and a drop of about a metre, enough to store a couple of dustbins and a packing case in which he could see a few discarded props – a broken telephone, some latticework poles used for scenery, an old Petrushka doll with its lopsided jester's face smirking at him.

At the end of the building was a rectangle of plywood covered in chicken wire where a window should have been. It took a minute or two to lever it loose, but the wood gave way without a sound. Rossel heaved himself up, got his backside on the sill and swung himself inside.

*

Ahead of him was a dark passage littered with broken chairs and props. The theatre was almost pitch-black, but he could make out a thin glimmer of orange light up ahead. He thought he must be somewhere backstage. Pistol in hand, he picked his way past a pile of stacked paintings leaning against the wall, rolls of tape, tins of paint.

Voices.

Five metres in front of him was a door that was half ajar. Pressing himself against the wall, he edged towards it.

A man was talking. An anxious, hectoring voice. It was Baikalin.

'He's generally always here first. He usually makes the first call, and we pass the signal on. That's how it's always been. So, where is he?'

A woman's voice now, one that sounded familiar. But he could not place it. 'Be calm, comrade. Have patience. He will come.'

'Patience.' Baikalin repeated the word a few times. 'Perhaps you're right, Natalya. I have waited what seems like a lifetime, we all have. So why not wait a little more . . . I suppose, like you, I should be braver. Is that what you mean?'

Baikalin's voice dropped to a whisper. Rossel pressed his ear to the gap between the door and its post.

A third voice – rhythmic, sonorous and dignified. Vika Kovalyova.

'*Khrabrost*. Our great Russian word for courage. "Fit for the songs of our children's children, pure on their tongues and free". My dear friend Anna Akhmatova wrote that once. Until *he* arrives, let us show a little of it. Isn't that, after all, why we have been brave all along? For the child Peter? For all of Ukraine's children?'

'Akhmatova is suicidally brave,' said Baikalin. 'They have banned her poems and they sent her son to a labour camp. You may have a packed suitcase waiting in your hall, Vika. I have actually been to the camps. I tell you, I am not keen to return.'

Rossel had heard enough to know that he needed to hear more. To drag it out of them, if he had to.

Holding the pistol in his right hand, he stepped through the doorway.

51

Sitting in a small, cramped dressing room, around a table, the three conspirators – if that was what they were – jumped up in shock as Rossel entered.

As Kovalyova and Baikalin recognised him, their faces showed uncertainty, anguish, but not exactly fear.

The third person was dressed in a matching green jacket and skirt, with a brown coat. It was Natalya Surkova, the woman who had narrated *Peter and the Wolf* at the Kirov. She watched the others' reactions to this newcomer as much as she was keeping an eye on him.

Were they finished? Or was there still hope?

Without instruction, they all put up their hands.

'A fine sentiment, Comrade Kovalyova,' Rossel said to the poet. '*Khrabrost*, indeed. The greatest of Russian virtues. Although not all possess it.'

He pulled out a chair and sat at the table.

'A question for you, Comrade Baikalin. For all of you, perhaps.' He removed the miniature illustration of the grandfather figure from his pocket and placed it on the table. 'What is the significance of this? Anna Orlova had one, and so, I know, does Comrade Kovalyova.'

Surkova did not respond. But she looked, he noticed, a little braver, more self-assured than the others.

Rossel turned to the poet. 'Then, when we're done with that, perhaps you will tell me who else we're waiting for?'

Vika Kovalyova returned his gaze. But the poet's eyes seemed to look past him, through him, as if he was merely one of the lesser creatures of her imagination.

'"Terror fingers all things in the dark, leads moonlight to the axe",' she whispered. 'Dear Anna wrote that, too, after they executed her husband. So, which are you, Comrade Senior Militiaman?' She lowered her hands and leaned forward, angling her neck as if to observe him better. 'The moonlight, or the axe? I'm still not quite certain.'

Rossel pointed around the table. '*Ptitsa*,' he said, gesturing at Kovalyova. She nodded. '*Dyedushka*.' Baikalin gave a resigned shrug. 'Anna, I believe, was *Utka*.' He turned to Surkova. 'And you, Comrade Surkova? What is your code name?'

She looked a little unsettled on hearing her name but hooked a thumb under the chain around her neck. A large locket emerged from beneath her blouse. She snapped it open. It was too small for Rossel to make out much detail, but the sketch was a line drawing of a woman with a bow.

A hunter, he thought. Silent, waiting.

She snapped the locket shut. 'Is there anything you don't know?' she said.

Behind her eyes, he could see defiance. The creases round her mouth spoke of humour, or perhaps mockery. She had a high forehead, its olive skin furrowed with wrinkles, her short, dark hair speckled grey at the temples.

'I saw you on stage at the Kirov,' Rossel answered, 'narrating *Peter and the Wolf* with that little boy. I understand you even commissioned the piece – asking Vika Kovalyova to write the libretto, and thus resurrecting her career.'

She thought for a moment, then nodded. 'Prokofiev is very ill,' she said. 'They say he has only a few weeks left.'

Rossel let his sadness show. She looked at him with sympathy.

'It's a blessing, I think. I would not wish him to die knowing that his last completed orchestral work was destined to be a fawning paean in praise of a beast.'

Her candour, he thought, was a sign of fatalism. The *militsiya* are here, she reasoned. The blue-hats will follow. We are all dead. Unless this man is more than his uniform suggests . . .

Baikalin looked downcast. But Kovalyova was her usual haughty self.

'So you have uncovered our little group, Comrade Officer,' she said. The poet put her hands together in mocking applause. 'Well done. But where have you got to with the *real* crime? Have you solved the murder of our beloved Anna?'

Rossel rested his pistol on the table. But kept his hand over it.

'Not yet,' he said. 'Though I am beginning to see the outline. Even some of the detail. That's why I brought you here. I need you to tell me the rest. And one thing, in particular . . .'

He regarded each of them in turn. His voice dropped to a whisper.

'Who is Peter?' he said. 'Who is the boy who should not exist?'

*

As Kovalyova began the tale, she asked for, and took, one of Rossel's *papirosy*, a gesture that somehow changed the atmosphere in the room. It was as if by offering the cigarette he was being drawn into their shared secrets; shedding his uniform and becoming more like them.

Kovalyova closed her eyes, touched a blue vein in her temple.

'Out on the steppe, near Kharkov, where the summer wheat turns the Ukrainian fields into shields of burnished gold, are two villages,' she said. 'Krasa and Polye. Twenty years ago, during a great famine there, Bolsheviks from Moscow on horseback and in armoured cars arrived in Polye and declared the villagers traitors and enemies of the people for hoarding food. They emptied the barns and smashed down the walls of any building in which the peasants had tried to hide their last handfuls of grain. It was a story repeated all over Ukraine. Do you know what it is to feel hunger, comrade? True hunger?'

Rossel nodded. 'I do.' He drew on his *papirosa* and exhaled. 'In the Blockade,' he said, 'we in Leningrad endured these trials, too.'

Kovalyova shook her head. 'With Nazis at the gates, of course,' she replied. 'But this was different. This was the Party itself. This was communism in action. Chekists, yes, but ordinary Party members too, recruiting and deploying activists from the towns and cities. An entire people, an entire nation made to suffer. Countless dead. Maybe millions. No one even knows how many.'

The poet blew out a puff of smoke and looked at him with disdain. Baikalin remained distant and aloof.

Surkova leaned forward and spoke.

'In Ukraine, the Bolsheviks murdered their own people,' she said.

Kovalyova held up a hand to silence her. 'At Polye, they stayed for a month. No one could go in, no one could get out. When the Party cadres and NKVD troopers finally left, their neighbours from Krasa scoured the houses and the barns looking for food and survivors. There was no food, and no survivors.'

She sat forward.

'Save one.'

Rossel held her gaze. At last, he understood.

'The boy,' he said. 'Peter.'

Vika nodded.

'Petro Petrenko. Only ten years old. They found him lying inside the remains of a tiny Orthodox church. A little chapel with round walls. He was impossibly frail – emaciated, eyes as watery as gruel. But he was still alive. A miracle child.'

'The people gave him a name,' said Surkova. '*Khlopchyk, yakogo nye povinno isnuvati.*'

Kovalyova translated the Ukrainian. 'The boy who should not exist. Amid the horror, the villages and fields strewn with skeletons, the people of Krasa – who were themselves starving – saw him as a symbol of survival, of hope,' she said. 'They took him away and tended to him. A few even gave up a little of their own meagre rations to give to the boy. They couldn't bear for him to go. Have you ever lost someone you loved, Comrade Rossel?'

'Yes,' said Rossel, with more force than he had intended.

The poet nodded. 'I thought so. In time, Petro began to get a bit better,' she said. 'In thanks, they gathered in the broken remains of the chapel at Polye, with its charred round walls and shattered cross, chanting and declaiming what would become a regular prayer: Remember the boy who should not exist.'

Surkova dropped her own cigarette onto the floor and stamped on it.

'They all believed that, because he had stayed alive, somehow they would, too,' she said.

Rossel stubbed out his own.

'But?' he said. 'There's always a "but".'

Kovalyova did not answer. She ran a finger across the vein in her temple. Surkova rose and went to her, covering the poet's hand with her own.

'They came back,' Surkova said. 'A few months later, the armoured cars and men on horses came back. And this time they surrounded Krasa.'

A single tear ran down Kovalyova's cheek.

'And the boy?' asked Rossel.

Surkova bit her lip. 'Everyone died,' she replied. 'Including him.'

Baikalin cleared his throat as the two women embraced each other.

'But that wasn't the end of it,' he said. 'You know how superstitious peasants are. Word got around. In the years that followed the famine, people began to worship at the abandoned chapel. They'd travel miles across the steppe to get there. Others came. And so did we. That is where we all met. Even when circumstances meant we could not reunite at the chapel, our friendship, our bond, has remained unbreakable.'

Rossel found the story both mesmerising and appalling. How could he have known nothing of this? How could the Party have inflicted such an atrocity on their own people, on the same people who grew grain for the Soviet Union and, as Stalin boasted, the world?

He shook his head, trying to gather his thoughts.

'A chapel with round walls,' he said to Vika. '"Death stands outside the circle . . ." You wrote those lines there?'

The poet nodded and wrung her hands. '"And sings a silent song,"' she said. '"A song of bones."'

In an Arctic labour camp, and in the transit camps through which he had passed, Rossel had heard men say, over and over:

BEN CREED

'If only Stalin knew about this. If only he knew, he would put a stop to it.'

But how could he not know?

He looked at them, one after the other. Too late, he registered their fixation on a point in space behind him. Too late, he went for his pistol.

But in one deft movement, Colonel Vishensky picked it up and pressed the barrel of his own Nagant into Rossel's temple.

52

Vishensky tossed Rossel's weapon to Baikalin, who caught it and held it as if not knowing whether to throw it away or keep it trained on the militiaman.

Rossel looked at the others. Surkova was half-smiling in relief. Kovalyova's face hadn't altered.

Which could only mean one thing: they were all part of the same group.

'Our *Kot*, perhaps?' Rossel said to Vishensky. 'We have almost everyone else.'

The colonel removed the nose of his Nagant from Rossel's head. He moved around the table, pulled up a chair and sat, keeping the pistol pointing at him.

'As a *nom de guerre* it sits a little uneasily with me,' he said. 'But Natalya and Anna were already using the names and I went along with it. I've known spies who had more ridiculous ones.'

With the pistol no longer at his head, Rossel's mind unfroze and began to work.

'The symbol that Anna Orlova had drawn on a piece of paper we found in her room,' he said. 'A Glagolitic symbol. *Slovo* – meaning, as a professor called Lapshin told me, speech. And the papers I found in your office, Comrade Baikalin . . .'

Vishensky's head snapped towards the academic. Baikalin looked uncomfortable.

'. . . Lists of names,' Rossel continued. 'Hundreds of names. At first, I thought they must be of people like yourselves, people whom the state would call traitors. But there are too many. Then I understood. They're the names of victims, aren't they?'

For a moment, no one answered. Then Kovalyova spoke.

'The martyrs of Polye,' she said. 'I have carried their names in my head, more than three hundred of them, for two decades. But you know how life is in the Soviet Union. We all have suitcases in the hall. I could be arrested at any moment. And what good would my prodigious memory be then? It was time to write them down – but in such a way that they remained indecipherable. To have a written testament that Anna could take to the West. Slovo was what we called ourselves because it was time for us to speak.'

Rossel sat forward a little.

'You, I imagine, Comrade Kovalyova, are the one who persuaded your friend Anna to get close to Comrade Abazi. My guess is that your MGB comrade here' – he gestured towards Vishensky – 'discovered the Georgian's origins in Gori, his youthful friendship with Stalin, and directed Orlova to get to know him better. To see what he would divulge in his pillow talk. A longer-term project, maybe, but what an incredible source of intelligence Abazi might have proved. If only he hadn't said something to Stalin that annoyed him or scared him. Prompting Stalin to order his swift removal – no arrest, no confession, no talking. The killers had not anticipated him being involved in a romantic assignation, but no matter – they saw their chance and took it. It turned out to be not so much a crime of passion as a crime utterly bereft of it. A cold and calculated tidying up of the books.'

Kovalyova nodded. 'Yes . . .' she began.

'Enough, Vika,' said Vishensky. His tone was quiet but authoritative. 'Comrades, this man is an officer from the militia, however lowly his rank and however unreliable his past. He is correct to say that the state will regard us as traitors. Counter-revolutionaries. Leave here now. I will deal with him.'

Kovalyova touched Vishensky's arm. 'Maybe that is not the way?'

Vishensky scowled. 'If he does not die, we will,' he said.

'How did you find us?' asked Rossel. 'It's not like I left a note.'

Keep him talking.

The colonel waved a hand. 'I called on Comrade Kovalyova, she was not at home. Tried the others. Same result. So, I came to the place we usually meet.'

Surkova stood. She was trembling. 'Hasn't there been enough killing?' she said. 'Think of Anna.'

Vishensky aimed the barrel of the pistol at Rossel's head. 'This is Russia under the power of the Soviets,' he said. 'There will never be enough killing.'

Rossel looked around the room, at this unlikely collection of people. Proud, scared, motivated by a grief and a horror that had been fermenting inside their souls for two decades. And, he thought, courageous beyond belief. Led by a man at the heart of the Soviet Union's apparatus of fear and control, who, for reasons he did not yet understand, was working against his own masters. He filed that thought away for later.

He moved his head a little closer to Vishensky's weapon. A gesture of defiance.

'You were right,' he said.

'Right about what?' whispered Kovalyova.

'About the things a man like Tamas Abazi might know.'

'Things?' said Baikalin, his voice wavering.

'You wanted to take Abazi alive because of information you believed he might have about Stalin. Secrets I now hold. Information about Stalin. Information that will destroy him. So why kill me now? Don't you want to know it too? Even better, I have documents that prove their authenticity. Their truth.'

Baikalin ran a hand through his hair. Surkova and Kovalyova exchanged agitated looks. Vishensky's jaw rippled under his cheek.

'Five minutes, gun dog,' he said. 'You have five minutes to talk. No more.'

*

Kovalyova, Baikalin and Surkova stared across the table. Vishensky was still standing, his Nagant trained on Rossel.

'I now know that, apart from the colonel, you all met many years ago,' said Rossel. 'You are all connected to Ukraine in some way, and I would guess that you either experienced this famine you speak of or you had relatives who died in it.'

'*Holodomor*,' said Vika, rapping her knuckles on the table. 'It already has a whispered name, this famine. It means death by hunger.'

Rossel bowed his head. Then, staring at Vishensky, he began to speak. Everyone else was still and mute.

'The names of those who perished in the famine sat in Comrade Kovalyova's head for years,' he said. 'But you decide to write them down – if she disappears, those names are lost for ever. Here, Comrade Anna Orlova proves most useful, because not only does she have a cipher that accords with her academic expertise, but practically no one else can read it. And through her attendance at international academic conferences, Comrade Orlova had access to something invaluable. Access to the West.'

The small, sardonic smile that was fixed to Vishensky's face disappeared.

'While the papers I found in Comrade Baikalin's office contain names . . .'

'Only that,' said Baikalin. His tone strained. 'Just names.'

'. . . My bet is other documents in Orlova's possession contained places, dates, details, numbers,' continued Rossel. 'But if she writes them down on curling yellow parchment, decorates them with some gold leaf, then she has what looks like an eleventh-century chronicle or sermon. Which she takes with her to her academic conferences on early Slavic writing and hands to a person who seems to be a typically dull American or British academic but is in fact someone whom Comrade Vishensky, thanks to *his* professional expertise, knows to be working for a very different organisation. Am I right?'

Vishensky eyed the pistol. 'Tamas Abazi,' he said quietly. 'You claim to know his secrets. And more. So far, I haven't heard any of them.'

'You wanted to bring knowledge of the famine in Ukraine to the attention of the West,' said Rossel. 'Then you wanted to go further. You wanted to reveal the true character of the Soviet government, and of the man who leads it, to the world. Therefore, you reasoned, who would have better access to the shadowy, bloodstained depths of that man's soul than his childhood friend?'

He paused to examine his jury. Their faces remained set in stone, but he could sense his deductions were hitting home.

'A few days ago, I travelled to Gori, to the birthplace of Abazi. And, as you also know, the birthplace of Iosif Vissarionovich Dzhugashvili. Our beloved Comrade Stalin.'

Baikalin sat up in his seat. 'You've been to Gori?' he said.

Comrade Baikalin can sense the release of secrets, like genies from their lamps. He looks nervous. Why?

Rossel nodded. 'Abazi still lived there but would make occasional visits to see his old friend in the Kremlin,' he said. 'He made one such visit only a few days before arriving in Leningrad to see his niece.'

'That we already knew,' said Surkova, unimpressed.

Vishensky turned his left wrist so Rossel could see his watch. 'One minute left,' he said. 'And still you've given me nothing.'

Rossel glanced around the table. 'I have documents, comrades,' he said. 'Ones that will cause a scandal not only in the West but here in Leningrad, in Moscow, in the whole of the Soviet Union.'

'Of course you do,' said Vishensky. 'Forty-five seconds.'

Rossel addressed Kovalyova. 'You were right. Abazi *was* privy to Stalin's deepest secrets. Even though, until the end, he was too stupid to realise it. The generalissimo was once a brigand, a bank robber, a strike organiser, a rabble-rouser, a kidnapper, a revolutionary without mercy. Even a poet. But he was also, for a while, something else.'

'Something else?' she asked.

Rossel nodded. 'A spy for the Okhrana, the Tsar's secret police. He informed on his fellow revolutionaries. And I have brought written evidence of that from Gori. Evidence which clearly proves that the man who now leads Lenin's revolution once betrayed it.'

Vishensky gestured at his watch.

'An unlikely tale,' he said. 'Every corpse begins to pray just before the screws go into the coffin lid. Ten seconds left. You say you have proof? Where is it?'

Rossel reached across the table and enclosed Kovalyova's hand in his.

'I am with you all, comrade. In a different way, I have spent twenty years caring about one person. Searching for her without finding her. We are the same. In a world where millions have died, why should anyone care about one person? And yet I do. As you all do about the boy Petro. I want to join you.'

The poet held his gaze. Then looked up at Vishensky.

'I believe him,' she said.

The colonel took a moment to lower his pistol.

'Proof,' he said to Rossel. 'I'm still going to need it.'

*

They cross-examined him a while longer – about the search for his sister, about aspects of his investigation. Rossel did not ask any questions in return, even though he had many. Chief among them was how they were going to smuggle so much as a jar of pickled cucumbers out of the country now that Anna Orlova was dead.

'If what he says is true,' said Kovalyova, 'think what the capitalists will do with it. What a story that will be in the West. The truth will be out. They will broadcast it back to us on their radio stations. In time, every citizen will know.'

The prospect brought a smile to her severe countenance.

They talked more until the euphoria evaporated. Once again, apart from the colonel, they looked frightened and out of their depth.

'Is this really everyone?' Rossel asked them. 'All of your group. All of Slovo?'

No one answered. Vishensky fidgeted with the barrel of his pistol before holstering it. The others looked at the floor.

Finally, the poet opened her mouth to speak, about to confirm Rossel's worst suspicions.

Vishensky held up a hand to stop her.

'They don't know. But I do. There is one more,' he said.

* * *

A hand roughly shaking her awake. A man standing by her bed.

Comrade Beria took off his pince-nez glasses and used a handkerchief to polish them. Then placed them with exquisite care back on the bridge of his nose.

Zlata sat up and covered herself with the blanket, preparing to fight off another assault.

'Good evening, Comrade Sidorenko,' Beria said.

She glanced at the luminous green alarm clock by the bed. Round and squat. Like a mechanical toad.

Three in the morning?

Beria's voice was low. His diction ponderous and sarcastic.

'I have brought something that belongs to you to give to Comrade Stalin,' he said. His voice carried an almost imperceptible note of . . . anticipation. 'A painting of yours,' he added. 'Not as good as the one you did of your lover, Marshal Tukhachevsky. Much more abstract, and sadly lacking in all the virtues of Socialist Realism.'

Beria's eyes lingered on her as if she were a bottle of fine claret he had uncorked to let it breathe.

'I could have saved you, Zlata,' he said. 'But you wouldn't pay my price.'

She glanced at his polished black shoes.

Small feet, yes. Like a devil. But no hooves . . .

53

Rossel and Vishensky drove to the State Public Library in the colonel's car. Once there, Vishensky flashed his ID at a terrified nightwatchman and Rossel retrieved the documents – the payments book, the arrest warrant and the briefing note written by the Okhrana agent on their most valuable informant – and handed them over. Vishensky had issued instructions on where to meet the next day near the Moscow Station and dropped him off near his apartment.

Can I really trust the colonel?

It was just before midnight.

What choice do I have?

Rossel pulled his sleeve over his watch and turned into his own street. He put a gloved hand to his face to wipe at his eyes. More than anything, he needed sleep – even a few hours would do. He stopped at the door to his building and began patting his pockets, fumbling for his keys.

Where are they?

He yanked them out of his coat pocket but dropped them into the snow. They disappeared into a drift.

'Shit!'

Rossel began pushing back the snow with his fingers.

There . . .

He reached out and picked them up. Something caught the corner of his eye.

A pair of polished black boots.

With a feeling of resignation, he looked up at their owner.

A muscular man in a black trench coat stared at him.

Behind him, a Black Raven was pulling up to the kerb. The man nodded at him in genial fashion. Then he booted him twice in the stomach and, as Rossel fell forward into the snow, put a gun to his head.

*

Black Trench Coat still hadn't said a word. Neither had the driver. Another shit-kicker in a well-tailored brown coat.

They had been driving for about half an hour now. Through Ozerki, past Shuvalovo, heading northwards away from the city.

He had asked questions but got no answers.

Only shrugs, smirks, silence.

Rossel squinted through condensation on the passenger window.

A rusted road sign said Toksovo was another ten kilometres.

There were rumours about the forests around Toksovo. But no one knew for certain. And it was not sensible to ask.

'We're going to Toksovo?' Rossel said to the trench coat.

Not even a shrug this time. But he sensed he was right.

Oh, well, at least I know where I'm going. Even if it's to the edge of a freshly dug pit.

*

Another pine branch slapped him in the face as Black Trench Coat shoved him forward. It threw wet snow in his face, some of it sliding down the space between his neck and the collar of his coat. Rossel stopped to wipe his eyes but got another prod with the barrel of a Nagant in the small of his back.

He stumbled.

'Keep moving, keep moving!' It was the first thing Rossel had heard the driver say. The man hauled him to his feet.

'Why don't you just get on with it?' Rossel said. 'Too lazy to dig a pit?'

No answer. Just the Nagant prodding him between the shoulder blades again.

He was pushed into a clearing. A car was parked. The headlights came on, blinding him. His two captors walked past him and beyond the light.

A door opened and shut with a harsh clang that echoed around the forest, scattering wood pigeons, which shook thin trails of snow off the topmost branches.

Silhouetted by the headlights, a figure of a man with a hat pulled down over his eyes trudged towards Rossel. Then, stomping his feet to remove the packed snow on his boots, stopped in front of him.

'You're a difficult man to pin down, Comrade Rossel,' said Major Nikitin. 'Then again, you always have been.'

'So, it is to be you,' said Rossel. 'I suppose there's a little poetry in that.'

Nikitin shook his head. 'No,' he answered, 'this isn't *that*. That's why you keep fucking up, Revol, because you think life has a mysterious rhythm to it that some great bard or composer has got down in a couplet or two. When a man like me was born knowing there's no rhyme, no reason, only what today demands from each of us before it becomes tomorrow.'

*

Rossel and Major Nikitin stood to the left of the clearing, next to the large stump of a tree that had only recently been felled. The car's headlights had been dipped and Rossel could see Nikitin's two men sitting inside to keep warm. By the calls they were shouting every now and then, it sounded like Durak, a game in which the last player with cards in their hand was the *Durak*, or Fool.

Tchaikovsky's lyric from *The Queen of Spades* floated back to him down the years. The one about card playing that Galya loved so much.

Nikitin pointed over his right shoulder. 'This is where prisoners were taken in the thirties,' he said. 'Around here, in these clearings. They'd dig their own pits, then line up and . . .' He made a pistol with his fingers. 'One in the back of the head . . .' He took a small step to the side. '. . . Step to the right, next one . . .' Nikitin almost sang the words. '. . . Another step to the right, and so on.'

'You must have enjoyed it,' said Rossel.

Nikitin took a handkerchief out of his pocket and blew his nose.

'I wasn't here,' he said. 'I was carrying out the interrogations in the Bolshoi Dom. Before they sent some of the jolly folk I'd been chatting with to places like this. Don't look at me like that – back then, we called it "work", comrade. A simple man does not make life complicated. That's what I've always told myself. The Party knows best.' Nikitin looked around, as if seeking something. 'But these days, after thinking things through, I'm not so sure.'

'And why is that, exactly?'

The moon appeared from behind a long, thin cloud, turning the clearing into a scene from Russian folklore, all trees and snow and twinkling beauty.

'I have many . . . not so much old friends, more short-lived acquaintances, buried out here,' Nikitin said, gesturing to a dense thicket of pine behind him. 'Sometimes, I see their faces and think about the people who must miss them. That's all.'

'A field of bones,' said Rossel. A hard edge to his voice, refusing to accept Nikitin's maudlin self-indulgence. 'The whole country's full of them. Ask the people of Krasa and Polye.'

'Kras-what? Pol-where?'

Rossel shook his head. 'It doesn't matter.' He glanced around the clearing. 'Why bring me all the way out here?'

Nikitin raised two fingers again and curled another into a trigger.

'This is where I've been for the past week. No one's been buried here for years, but with all this talk of capitalist plots, metropolitan elements, Jewish doctors . . .' He sniffed. 'Some people think we might need to re-examine that. Leningrad is going to be at the heart of it again, Revol. Stalin wants our great city brought to heel once and for all. So, Comrade Khrushchev has asked me to look at feasibility – driver availability, truck capacity, average journey times from The Crosses and the Bolshoi Dom to Toksovo. That kind of thing. The practicalities.'

The major spat into the snow.

'Personally, I'd like to do things differently. But when did I ever have a say about anything? I told my men to find you and bring you to me wherever I was. And tonight, I am here.'

He reached inside his coat pocket and pulled out a curled manila file with a red elastic band around it.

'You asked me to do some rooting around. I did some,' he said.

Nikitin removed a glove and ran a finger across the scars on his face, as if tracing the path of his own pain. Or the part he had played in somebody else's.

Rossel opened the file. It was a list. Another list of names.

Each had a red cross next to it.

Nikitin's fat finger ran over the top of the paper.

'It's from 1934. Look down.'

There were forty-nine names in all.

Numbers thirty-seven and thirty-eight he recognised.

'Early victims of what was to come,' said Nikitin. 'Betrayed by an informant – not just any old informant, either. A fellow traveller among the cadre of Old Bolsheviks who assembled for the Seventeenth All-Party Congress. Most were executed without delay. A few may even lie beneath our feet. Some were sent to the camps. A few weeks before his release, your father had a heart attack and died. When your mother found out, she tried to kill herself, slit her wrists. A camp doctor saved her. But two weeks later, she walked out between the wire and the guard tower and was shot.'

Rossel's fingers curled around the file, crumpling the paper.

'And the informant's name?' He could hear the tremor in his own voice.

Nikitin turned his head slightly. Rossel could see the scars flowing over one side of his face.

'Like your parents, a delegate at the Seventeenth All-Party Congress in January 1934. Poor bastards. All proclaiming their loyalty and purity, just as Stalin was about to purge them.'

He kicked at the snow.

'Sensing which way the wind is blowing, in June 1934, this piece of shit proposes a deal with the People's Kommissariat for

Internal Affairs and offers to supply them with evidence of treasonous behaviour at the heart of the Party itself. It may be that he was trying to head off an accusation against his own person. The note recording his offer is not clear.'

Moonlight flitted over Nikitin's squat, muscular body before sliding back behind a cloud.

'Since investigators and interrogators love evidence,' he said, 'they agreed. Of course, a couple of years later, once the purges were well under way, we were drowning in confessions, conspiracies, traitors desperate to save their own skins by giving up their friends and neighbours. But by then our man has volunteered – volunteered, mind you! – to serve as a political education officer in a Siberian penal colony. A demonstration of exceptional zeal that also happens to get him out of harm's way when the purges begin in earnest.'

The trees seemed to sway at impossible angles, making Nikitin appear huge and ogre-like one moment, puny and ridiculous the next.

As if from afar, Rossel heard him say: 'A very clever man, this Comrade Baikalin. Two years ago, they even accepted him back into the Party.'

A peal of harsh, mocking laughter from inside the car. One of the men had played a final hand and was pointing at the other, shouting – 'Durak, durak . . .'

Nikitin glanced towards them. His voice dropped to a whisper. 'I have been called back to Moscow. Who knows what awaits me there? In the Kremlin, paranoia reigns. Beria, Khrushchev, and the rest, they're at each other's throats. The only thing that binds them together is their fear of Stalin. Beria, I know, has been looking into Stalin's history. Desperately searching for something, anything, he can use as leverage, as protection. Or as a weapon to attack the malevolent old bastard when the time is right.'

'I know he has,' said Rossel. 'I bumped into some of his men in Gori.'

'Of course you did,' said Nikitin. 'Beria always seems to be one step ahead of everybody else.'

The major took a small step forward.

'I know you have already been asking questions of Comrade Baikalin,' he said. 'Indeed, your name has come up more than a few times recently. There will soon be a reckoning. I'm certain of it. You need to disappear. Get out of Leningrad, go to Magnitogorsk or Irkutsk, somewhere remote. Or one of those new cities they're carving out of the Siberian ice. Go down the mines. Drive trucks. Run away to sea. I don't care. Become one of the missing. I can't help you any more after this, Revol. Do you understand?'

Rossel pushed the file into his pocket. Took out a cigarette and lit it.

'Moscow,' he said. 'I'm going to Moscow, too. But there's something I need to do first.'

He began to walk towards the car.

Nikitin's voice followed him. 'While you are there, you might look in on your sister,' he said.

Rossel swung back around.

'Galya?'

'Have you got another? There's a show trial of an underground Orthodox sect due to take place in a couple of months' time. The Party is clamping down on religious worship again. Five ringleaders in all. Currently detained in Moscow. They are to be made an example of. I understand that Galina Rossel is one of them.'

Rossel's heart was racing. 'A religious sect?' he said.

The major nodded. 'Under interrogation, she told the blue-hats she'd joined to atone for something terrible she did.'

Under interrogation . . .

'Atone for what?'

Nikitin glanced around the ghostly clearing. Then the major stared back at Rossel.

'Apparently, she believes that when your mother and father were first arrested by state security, she was the one who betrayed them.'

54

Black Trench Coat and his driver dropped Rossel off on his street, metres from where they had abducted him.

He had spent the journey with his face pressed against the passenger window, staring out into the drifting snow flurries thinking about Galya.

She's alive.

Not only that, despite her resentment at being his twin, it seemed she was so like him, they even shared the same sin. Each of them had betrayed their parents.

Rossel watched the two men drive off. He let himself into his apartment, pulled out an old toolbox from under the sink and took a claw hammer from it before returning to the street.

It took him an hour to reach Lesnaya District and find the building he was looking for.

The *kommunalka* stairs were filthy and unlit. Without a torch, he could have fallen through the missing handrail, or cracked a knee on the piles of discarded wood planks and masonry. Comrade Baikalin's rehabilitation had not extended to the kind of accommodation given to privileged members of the Party elite. But it was better this way – just another communal building where people came and went.

Once inside, Rossel took the steps two at a time. On the third floor, he paused to listen before pulling the claw hammer from his coat. It took only a couple of brisk shanks to break the rusty lock on the door.

As he stepped into the corridor on Baikalin's floor, he removed his pistol and looked left and right.

It was half three in the morning. The corridor was empty and dark.

The door at the 'end of the hall'. That was what the academic had said when he had talked to him at the Titan cinema's café.

He could use a pillow as a silencer. Or simply break the bastard's neck. But, before that, he would wake Baikalin, make him confess and make him beg for his life.

The door to the academic's room was ajar.

Rossel pushed it. With a creak, it swung open.

He felt for the light switch. But thought better of it as his eyes adjusted to the shadows.

To the left was an empty bed.

To the right, Baikalin sat in a narrow armchair, still in his coat, asleep. A bottle of cheap cognac stood on a table at his elbow. He had not finished the glass.

Rossel stepped towards him and rammed the barrel of the gun against the academic's cheek, then roughly covered his mouth with his left hand.

Baikalin's head slumped backwards. His eyes were open, glassy and still.

'There's absolutely no need for you to bother yourself, comrade,' said a voice behind Rossel. 'I already broke the bastard's neck.'

Rossel turned. Vishensky was standing in the corner. The colonel pointed at the body.

'I had a nice chat with him before he went. He had planned to inform on us all to help secure his university tenure and, ultimately, his final rehabilitation as a Party member.'

The snarl on Baikalin's greying face betrayed the agonies of his last moments. Rossel gestured towards him.

'I wanted to do it,' he said.

Vishensky shrugged the shrug of a man who had got there first.

'I followed you home, just to be on the safe side,' the MGB man said. 'I saw you beaten and bundled into a car. But here you are, still alive. Ready to kill, so you say. But I don't think you would have. Vika's right – you're the moonlight, not the axe. It's a weakness.'

'How did you know for certain he was an informer?' said Rossel.

'I've had my suspicions about Comrade Baikalin for some time. Inconsistencies in the telling and retelling of his own history. But when you told us that he had some of Anna Orlova's lists in his office . . . he was never meant to have those. I believe he was planning to turn them in to the MGB at any moment.'

Vishensky pulled on his gloves.

'I am letting you live because I need your help. Meet as agreed tomorrow. Now let us both go and get some sleep.'

The colonel pushed himself off the wall and patted Baikalin on the head, ruffling his hair, as he exited the room.

'You know the thing I always like about Leningrad?' he said. 'The people here are so nice, so friendly. A much more welcoming city than, say, Moscow.'

6

ВОЛК

Wolf

55

On the wall of the carriage were two pictures. Small, black-and-white, and stuck, side by side, in cheap, gold-lacquered frames. The first was of a statue – Peter the Great's on the banks of the Neva. The second, hung askew, of a tomb – Lenin's, in Moscow's Red Square. Neatly cut from the pages of the travel magazine *Vokrug sveta*. They were meant to be testaments to the glorious history of Mother Russia.

Rossel offered Vishensky a *papirosa*.

The colonel shook his head. He had said little since the mid-morning train to Moscow had set off some three hours ago. And although it had been almost nine hours since they had exchanged pleasantries over Baikalin's corpse, the MGB officer had not said a word on the subject.

At least the carriage was warming up. Vishensky stood, removed his coat and hat and hung them on a hook on the door. He had ordered Rossel to come not in militia uniform but in civilian clothing – dark blue jacket and trousers, and a long black coat. For the first time, Rossel noticed that the two of them were dressed similarly.

Retaking his seat on the hard bunk, the colonel picked up the pillow that sat on top of the sheets provided by Soviet Railways and slid it behind his head.

'I went to the Hermitage a few days ago,' said Rossel.

'How cultured of you. The Deyneka exhibition? People say it's good. But I'm not so keen on his war material. All that blood. Too much like work.'

Rossel exhaled some smoke and shook his head. 'I don't like him. A clumsy propagandist. No, I found it a useful place to think.'

'You think too much,' said Vishensky. 'It unnerves people.'

'You see, I saw Vika and Baikalin meet there once. In a room full of Soviet military heroes. At the time, I couldn't understand why they were so interested in gazing at a bunch of old generals. Of all the rooms in that grand museum to meet for a cosy tête-à-tête, why that one?'

The train rattled as it took a bend. Rossel readjusted himself in his seat. Vishensky closed his eyes.

'They paid particular attention to a brass plaque that was almost illegible, apart from a few letters,' Rossel went on. 'One that clung to the wall, like a memory, or an old love affair, that refused to fade. When I asked the curator about it, I discovered it belonged to a painting that no longer hung there. Another Soviet military hero. And after far too long, I realised that Vika and Comrade Baikalin were interested not in the paintings that were on the wall,' he continued, 'but in one that was *not* on the wall. And that the remaining letters on the plaque, I-K-O-L-A, were not from a first name, nor a last name, but a patronymic. Marshal Tukhachevsky. Mikhail *Nikolayevich* Tukhachevsky.'

Rossel would have liked nothing more than to lean against the wall and sleep. But this was a scab that needed picking.

Vishensky opened an eye. 'I believe Tukhachevsky was shot before the war,' he said, sounding bored.

Rossel nodded. 'Yes, alas. A great Soviet military theorist, a decorated, venerated soldier, adored by his men. Practically invented modern Soviet tactics. When I served, I knew little or nothing of his theory of deep operations. Few ordinary soldiers did. But some of our senior officers whispered of its brilliance. However, just as the patriotism and abilities of thousands of other Red Army officers did not save them from execution in Stalin's purges before the Great Patriotic War, his patriotism did not save him.'

Vishensky pressed the smooth tips of his fingers together. 'Yes, a truly great man,' he said. 'A Slavic hero.'

Rossel reached into his jacket pocket and took out the carved figure he had found dangling from a piece of string outside the disused children's theatre.

He placed it on the table that was fixed to the wall between the bunks.

'Here's another Slavic object of veneration,' he said. 'Perun. The ancient god of war.'

Vishensky was sitting up straight now. He picked up the little carving; he was passing it from one hand to the other.

'He had some strange and mystical beliefs, the marshal,' the colonel said, his tone reflective. Almost as though he was speaking to himself.

Rossel pointed to the figure.

'I have another one of those,' he remarked. 'I found it next to the statue of Lenin outside the Finland Station. Not far from the scene of the murder of Anna Orlova and Tamas Abazi. You left it there.' He settled into his seat and looked out of the window. 'How did you get to the scene of the crime so fast?' he said. 'The answer tormented me for a long time – and then, it came to me. It was obvious. It was because you were already there. You left the carvings as a signal to others that it was safe to meet. On the night of the murders, it was to indicate that you were nearby, and ready to act. Orlova could rest assured that you were in position to kidnap and, later, interrogate Abazi to mine for gold about Stalin's mysterious past.'

Vishensky nodded. 'Yes,' he admitted. 'I left the carving so that Anna would feel safe. Alas, she was anything but. My own quiet inquiries suggest Stalin himself placed a call to the headquarters of the Leningrad MGB and arranged for two officers he could rely upon to be utterly discreet. To remove Abazi – and to get the militia, who should have done what it was bloody well told, to rubber-stamp it as an accident. Orlova was simply collateral damage.'

The colonel tilted his head back.

'Funny how life is,' he said. 'A few days ago, I would have slit your throat for knowing all this. But perhaps you really are one of us now. The fact that you were resolved to kill Baikalin reassures me. Have you understood the rest?'

Rossel shook his head. 'Some. But not all. Why Perun, the god of war?' he asked.

Vishensky stared back. Lights flickered for a moment through the window as the train rushed past a village. Then the darkness was restored.

The MGB agent placed the carving on the table.

'Did you know that the marshal's signed confession is spattered with his own blood?' he said at last. 'The words upon it are meaningless. But the bloodstains are powerful and eloquent. The work of Blokhin, Stalin's hand-picked executioner. The marshal deserved at least a death with honour, death by firing squad. He deserved medals and glory. But he got Blokhin.'

Rossel fumbled for his matches. His fingers felt tense, leaden, cumbersome. What brutalities, he wondered, had this executioner Blokhin visited upon Tukhachevsky?

He lit a *papirosa* and sat back on the uncomfortable bunk.

'For a long time, it didn't make sense,' he said. 'Why would an MGB officer, a ruthless senior agent in the Second Directorate, charged with weeding out and exterminating foreign spies and traitors, support and protect a bunch of dreamers? Poets, painters and music lovers who genuflect before a dead child, memorising the names of hundreds of peasant corpses, bearing witness to an atrocity that will never be avenged. Pointless, futile defiance.' Rossel tapped the side of his head. 'Then I saw it. You don't really care about an infant who was left to starve twenty years ago. Not in the same way as the others. No, you saw something else in this little group that calls itself Slovo, a silly gathering with silly code names. You saw an opportunity. They had something you could use. Access to foreign travel and those academic conferences of Orlova's, for one thing.'

Vishensky picked up the carving again and gripped it in his right hand.

'When the marshal was taken prisoner during the First World War,' he snapped, 'he kneeled and prayed to a carving such as this, one he had made himself. When he escaped, he carried one with him.' The colonel held it up. 'Just as he worshipped it, I worshipped him. A true hero. A "Red Napoleon" who could have led our nation to greatness. As a young officer, I was under his command and saw his genius close to. I will never forgive what that cut-throat in the Kremlin did to the marshal.'

Vishensky placed a hand on the worn brown rucksack next to him. He looked out of the window. 'Do you know, my hunch about Slovo was right,' he said. 'Without them, without the murders outside the Finland Station, I would not have encountered you, Comrade Senior Militiaman Rossel. And had we not met, I would not now be carrying information that is enough to condemn the greatest traitor of them all.'

*

As the train came to a halt, Rossel awoke with a start. Sitting up, he knocked over a metal ashtray piled high with butts. A blizzard of stale ash filled the carriage, making him and Vishensky start coughing.

A cheery ticket inspector with a drinker's nose stuck his head around the door and surveyed the scene.

'What are you hiding behind that cloud, comrades? A stash of *samogon*?'

Rossel wiped his mouth with a handkerchief. Then waved Vishensky's worn rucksack at him.

'The best stuff, made from the gooseberries in my dacha garden. One sip and you'll be ready to go to war with the Nazis all over again.'

The inspector smiled. 'Rise and shine, gentlemen, welcome to Moscow.' He stepped back out into the crowded corridor and shut the door behind him.

Still coughing, Rossel pulled down the window. Vishensky took back the rucksack. Taking out the manila envelope, he handed it to Rossel.

'Here,' he said. 'It will be safer if we both carry something. That way, if we're chased and only one of us gets away, the other will still have something to get to the West. If you think you're about to be captured, get rid of it – try to hide it somewhere.'

Rossel took the envelope and pushed it into his inside pocket.

The platform was busy. Announcements of departing trains blared out almost without a break – 'Platform Four for

Kuibyshev', 'Platform Six for Gorky', 'Platform Nine for Sverd-lovsk . . .' A cramped line of black, brown and grey coats, topped off with fur hats, thick caps and headscarves, shuffled past. A huge poster of Stalin in military uniform rippled above their heads. A slogan written on it in red and white declared: 'Onward with the people towards perpetual revolution.'

Rossel straightened his hat. 'What now?' he said.

'Later, we will meet a friend,' replied Vishensky.

'A friend? Where?'

'Somewhere you'll feel at home, comrade,' said Vishensky. He reached up and straightened Lenin's picture on the wall of the carriage. 'Next to a dead body in the middle of Red Square.' Vishensky picked up his hat and centred it. 'But first, I have a car waiting.'

Rossel blinked. 'The MGB are expecting us?'

'Of course,' said Vishensky. 'As the marshal once told me, the last place they search for traitors is inside the belly of the beast.'

56

En masse, Muscovites looked grey, harried and reluctant to remain outside in the biting cold any longer than necessary.

Like a different species, Rossel thought, one that if they sensed the presence of aliens in their midst would spit out an accusation: *Enemies of the people . . .*

A large black car was waiting in front of the station's clock tower. As the two men walked down the steps through the crowd, a huge driver in an MGB uniform got out and opened the passenger door for them. Nervous civilians pretending not to notice the man mountain in the blue-hat scuttled out of the way.

'Where's Zakharov?' Vishensky asked the driver.

'Sick, Comrade Colonel. A duodenal ulcer.' The giant saluted, looked eager to please. 'It burst. He went to the clinic. I was ordered to pick you up instead.'

Vishensky cast a look across the teeming square.

'Duodenal?' he said. 'You a doctor now, Popov? I thought you had to study for years to learn big words like that.'

Popov opened the door wider.

'I didn't need to go to medical school, Comrade Colonel. That's what they told me to tell you, and you know me, what they tell me to say, I say it. Where do you want to go?'

Vishensky took a moment to ponder this last point. He

turned to Rossel and gestured to the back seat. Rossel got in, shuffling across the polished leather seats. The colonel sat next to him.

Popov shut the passenger door and got behind the wheel.

'The Lubyanka, of course.'

Just hearing the name of the building spoken out loud made Rossel feel queasy.

MGB headquarters, the joke had it, was the tallest building in the Soviet Union, because you could see Siberia from its cellars.

Rossel turned to the colonel. 'The Lubyanka?'

In the driver's mirror, he saw Popov glance upwards and stare at him.

The colonel looked at his watch. 'I have a little work to do before our appointment,' he said.

He took off his gloves and rubbed his right thumb over the smooth tip of his index finger. What was it that Nikitin had said? *Even ghosts leave a chill. Vishensky leaves nothing . . .*

The car picked up speed.

'Work. Yes, of course, Comrade Colonel,' said Popov.

*

Bumping along on cobbles, the car swung right out of Milyutin-skiy Pereulok, a small side street, and passed a bright-blue neoclassical mansion.

Not far now.

As they sped around another corner, Vishensky unbuttoned his coat. He turned towards Rossel.

'At the end of the war,' the colonel said, 'I fought in Manchuria against the Japanese. A wise, introspective people. They had

357

a saying I liked. "Death surprises us all because he brings with him many disguises."'

Rossel slowly raised his hands. A Nagant pistol had materialised in Vishensky's hand.

'I get ulcers too, Popov,' Vishensky said to the driver. 'They give me terrible burning acid in my throat. Sometimes it's my own fault – too much *kolbasa*, too much Armenian cognac . . . but other times, it's when something's not quite right.'

Over Vishensky's right shoulder, the squat orange block of the Lubyanka came into view.

Maybe if . . .

Rossel glanced at the passenger door handle. Then back at the barrel of the colonel's gun.

Too risky.

Vishensky whispered into Popov's ear: 'I've decided not to go into work after all. Too nice a day for paperwork.'

Popov smirked. 'The Shooting House?'

Vishensky kept the weapon trained on Rossel.

'Not the big one on Nikolskaya Street,' he said. 'The small one on Kuznetsky.'

*

They stopped at number 114, a small house with shuttered windows at the end of Kuznetsky Street. Popov turned the car into a scruffy alley. He climbed out to open a rusting gate and parked in the yard on the other side.

'Out,' said Vishensky, gesturing towards Rossel with the Nagant.

Popov opened the door for him. Rossel took his time getting out.

Now . . .

Slamming the door shut with his right hand, he rammed his left fist into Popov's belly. As the big MGB man crumpled, Rossel grabbed him by the hair, pulled his face downwards and smacked his right knee into it.

Popov groaned but wasn't finished. Seizing Rossel by the waist, he hoisted him into the air and threw him into the side of the car.

As he did so, Vishensky ran around the back of the car and pressed his pistol into Rossel's temple.

'That's enough,' he said.

Popov stood, nose bleeding. He towered over Rossel.

'I take after my mother and she's a sensitive soul,' he growled. 'Normally, I don't like to watch the things they do to people here. But in your case, *svoloch*, I'll make an exception.'

Vishensky gestured to the door at the back of the building. 'Open up,' he said.

Popov pulled some keys out of his pocket and turned. Vishensky flipped the gun in his hand, took three quick paces forward and slammed the butt into the back of Popov's head. The driver fell into the wet snow and lay still.

'My apologies for that little charade, comrade,' he said to Rossel. 'But I've seen this bastard take on four men on his own before and win.'

He picked up the keys from the wet snow.

'Maybe Zakharov really does have a bad stomach today. But I'm not taking any chances. Let's get him inside.'

*

In the corner where Rossel sat was a dirty sink with an old sponge, a dried mop, a pile of used cloths and a bucket in which a dead fly floated on a dark, shallow pool of blood.

The Shooting House's rooms were bare. Damp crawled up the plaster. The faded velvet curtains were drawn and iron bars guarded the windows. A single light bulb hanging from the ceiling cast an eerie light. Two short filing cabinets on the other side of the room looked clean and dust-free, but the contents of a tray on top of them – razor blades, a hacksaw, a pair of pliers – spoke with nightmarish eloquence of the room's purpose.

The house, Vishensky explained, was used by the MGB to 'welcome with particularly effusive felicitations' those who visited the Lubyanka but who were not fortunate enough to earn a ticket to the camps. A bigger building at 23 Nikolskaya Street, a little closer to the prison, served the same purpose. Kuznetsky was the back-up. A busy day at Nikolskaya and the blue-hats opened it up.

Popov, gagged and bound, was locked in a smaller room along the corridor. The colonel's chilling reputation had served him well. He'd only had to pick up a scalpel from the tray and stare at it for Popov to start talking, eyes wide and fixed on the blade. But despite persistent enquiries, the driver hadn't been able to tell them much. Only that he had been asked to replace Zakharov at the last minute.

'I saw Blokhin working in here once – the man who executed the marshal,' said Vishensky. 'Always wore an apron, long gloves and sturdy boots. He set new records for the most killed in one day.'

He pointed to the bucket, sponge and cloths.

'Careless,' he said. 'Blokhin would have put those away, got out a scrubbing brush and a bottle of bleach. And when he was finished, it would be as though the victims whose brains were smeared over the walls had never existed. Their bodies gone, their bone, blood and gristle wiped away. Imagine that? You're born, you live, make a life for yourself, a wife, children . . . One day you disappear without a trace. Not even leaving a stain.'

Rossel rubbed at the stub of one of his missing fingers. 'When did you join Tukhachevsky's staff?' he asked.

'In 1933. I barely left his side for three and a half years,' replied Vishensky. 'Straight out of military academy. I was the most junior member of the cadre he took with him wherever he was posted. And almost the only officer in that group to survive the purge after the marshal was arrested and shot. There was no pattern to it. Officers around me were reporting for duty one day and disappearing the next. But I like to think Perun watched over me.'

A drip of rusty water fell from the tap in the sink.

'Camouflage, distract, confuse,' Rossel stated. 'That's the essence of deep military operations, isn't it?'

Vishensky nodded. 'The marshal did not invent the theory, but he developed it, refined it, trained the Soviet armed forces in it,' he said. 'Multiple co-ordinated operations behind enemy lines, never letting your opponent settle or understand what your ultimate objectives are. That last point being key.'

'After his death, you left the Red Army and joined state security,' said Rossel. 'You must have needed help.'

Vishensky looked at Rossel. 'By the time he knew they were coming for him, the marshal was making plans,' he said. 'He ordered me – not just me, but others, though most were murdered not long after – to bury myself deep inside the state. And now . . . well, you can't get that much further behind enemy lines than rising to become a colonel in state security, can you?'

Rossel looked at his watch. 'Time is passing,' he said. 'When do we meet your American friend?'

'I didn't say he was American.'

'You are in the Second Directorate of the MGB. Counter-intelligence. The CIA always on your radar, and you always on theirs. Not easy to contact them and suggest a meeting, even for yourself, but possible. And they would be interested. You would be a prize. A big one.'

Vishensky held his gaze. Then examined his own watch. 'Another hour, that's all,' he said.

'The marshal should be proud. He taught you well,' said Rossel. 'A ruthless yet valiant defender of the motherland is the last place anyone would look for a traitor.'

'Traitor?'

Vishensky glared at Rossel. In that moment, Rossel realised exactly why people confessed to Comrade Vishensky.

'Marshal Tukhachevsky and the officer corps around him were loyal Soviet patriots,' Vishensky said, his grey eyes blazing. 'Warriors. Prepared to sacrifice their lives for the cause of communism, to defend the workers and the peasants from the jackboots of fascism. And our reward? On the eve of the most terrible war in history? To be lined up for the slaughter by a collection of senseless cowards led by a blackarse Georgian who was happy to do a deal with the German Führer.'

The colonel wiped his mouth. He looked on the verge of losing control.

'The only *traitors* are Stalin and Beria and all those other sycophantic cocksuckers in the Kremlin.' He slapped a hand on his rucksack. 'To me, Tukhachevsky was Perun – a god of war. And this is his revenge.'

Rossel stood. 'There's every chance that the blue-hats will be waiting for us by now. You must realise that?' he said.

The colonel shrugged. 'At times like this, the marshal liked to quote von Clausewitz. "The enemy of a good plan is the dream of a perfect one." I will take my chances.'

Rossel walked towards the bucket and dropped the butt of his cigarette into it. It fizzed, flickered out and began to float towards the dead fly.

57

A muted sun was playing hide-and-seek behind the domes of St Basil's as Rossel and Vishensky walked past the squat quadrangle base of the Nikolskaya Tower into Red Square.

To their left was what looked like a huge railway station. Before the 1917 Revolution, it had been a temple to capitalism, a magnificent department store in granite, marble and glass. But Stalin had driven out the mercantilist gods and their worshippers and turned it into a hive of administrators, clerks and bureaucrats whose task was to run the Soviet economy – every factory in every region, no matter how far-flung, every collective farm . . .

On this side of the square, ahead of them, was Lenin's tomb. A site for pilgrims from all over the Soviet Union. Although the afternoon was wearing on and the sun dipping, the square was crowded. A huddled, respectful column of devotees snaked from the red mausoleum.

'We'll stand in that queue,' said Vishensky.

The two men joined the line of boots, scarves, coats and ushankas shuffling forward to meet Lenin. A few fat flakes of snow began to fall, and people began to stamp their feet and slap their hands to keep out the cold.

Rossel scanned the square. Lenin's tomb? The walls of the Kremlin right next to them?

This really is taking deep operations a step too far.

There was no sign of Vishensky's American. Then again, how would Rossel know? What would they look like? Would they roll up chewing gum and sing American songs, like some US troopers he had once watched with fascination in Germany?

There was no sign of anyone else, either. The usual soldiers standing to attention, but no patrolling, prowling troops from the military or from state security. Rossel conceded that Vishensky had picked his spot well. They were among a faceless crowd, unlikely to be seen while able to see most of the square.

Rossel and Vishensky moved forward again. A woman in a blue headscarf in front of them pointed above the wall in the direction of the Kremlin. Bending down, she spoke into the ear of her child, a small, pink-cheeked girl of Dasha's age.

'Grandpa Stalin lives up there,' she said. 'From there, he looks out for all of us. Grandpa Stalin never sleeps.'

Vishensky glanced at his watch and smothered a yawn with his hand.

If the colonel was nervous, Rossel thought, he was good at hiding it. Vishensky completed his appraisal of the square and tugged at Rossel's sleeve. They were on the move once again, heading towards the huge building opposite.

A single bead of cold sweat began to run down Rossel's back. He reached inside his coat, pulling at his shirt collar which felt tight around his throat, giving him the urge to be sick. An urge he fought.

Everybody they passed – a thin man pushing a bicycle, a woman wrestling with a pram, two teenage girls, arm-in-arm and giggling – seemed to be staring at them. As they reached the middle of Red Square, Rossel glanced over his shoulder at the Kremlin, half-expecting to see a familiar moustached face peering down from a window.

She's right, he thought. *Grandpa Stalin never sleeps.*

They arrived at the far corner of the former department store. Vishensky began to slow his pace and Rossel fell in beside him. Three soldiers carrying rifles in their left hands, all in dress coats, peaked caps and braiding, marched into view and began goosestepping across the square. It was what every tourist in the huge crowd had come to see: the hourly changing of the guard at Lenin's tomb.

'Keep going,' muttered Vishensky. 'Down Ilinka Street.'

Reaching into his pocket to find the little stone, Rossel walked on.

*

Ilinka Street ran northeast off Red Square. When the two men turned into it, they saw a tall man wearing a black ushanka and a fur coat, leaning against the wall of a building reading a copy of *Nauka i Zhizn*, a science magazine.

He closed the pages, rolled it up and shoved it into a pocket before setting off up the street. They followed, keeping on the opposite side of the road while the magazine reader wove in and out of the arches and steps that lined the building on his side. He turned left again, into a narrower street – a trap, Rossel thought straight away, until he saw the green Moskvitch parked at the other end.

The man walked halfway down the alley and came to a halt next to the Moskvitch. Few people were about – it was too early for the evening rush hour. As the two Russians came closer, they could see another man, younger and bigger, with a shaved head, sitting in the driver's seat, his hands on the wheel.

The contrast between this outsized American and the tiny Soviet car was almost comical – he must have had to pour himself in through the window. The driver was deeply tanned. In the snowy Moscow alley, it made him seem impossibly exotic. A recent arrival, Rossel thought. Perhaps he lived a life of capitalist decadence, hopping on and off yachts in the Caribbean.

Welcome to the workers' paradise, comrade.

'I don't understand science,' said the tall man, removing his ushanka to scratch his head and revealing a thick mass of grey hair. His Russian was excellent. But he had a strong accent. 'I don't understand it when it's written in English, and I understand it even less when it's written in Russian.'

He pulled the magazine out of his pocket.

'And you've had me reading this shit for thirty minutes, Colonel.'

'Sorry,' said Vishensky. But he didn't sound it.

'Who's this?' said the American, pointing at Rossel.

'A comrade,' replied Vishensky.

'We said no friends.'

Vishensky gave the American a cold stare. 'Then you have a decision to make,' he said.

The man thought for a moment. Then opened the back door of the car.

'All right, both, get in.'

Movement behind him. Rossel peered over the American's shoulder.

At the end of the street, a Red Army soldier stepped into view, and then two more. All were holding semi-automatic rifles.

The first Red Army soldier pointed at them and shouted something to his comrades.

'Let's go,' said the tall American, jumping into the Moskvitch.

Vishensky placed a hand on the rear door. But the soldiers were already opening fire. A bullet whistled past Rossel's ear. They heard yelled orders to put their hands up.

Rossel and Vishensky ran.

Rossel's shoulder blades cramped as he imagined the next volley biting into his back and neck.

About twenty metres ahead, he could see a rear entrance to the old department store. They reached it almost before the Moskvitch did. The car's engine was screaming as the scowling driver with the exotic tan discovered how little acceleration a Soviet vehicle had.

The car swerved left and right. A second bullet shattered the back window. But the Americans got lucky. It reached the end of the alley and disappeared.

'In here!' shouted Vishensky.

He and Rossel jumped up a short flight of steps to the former store and headed inside, the colonel pulling out his ID card and shoving past the militia officer who half-heartedly tried to stop them.

'MGB,' he shouted at both the officer and a terrified receptionist who was putting on her coat. 'Stay out of our way. Soldiers are coming.'

Rossel pushed through another set of revolving doors and was faced with a huge central atrium, punctuated with giant crystal chandeliers and screened off into sections, each one containing a forest of metal desks and chairs. Most were empty. A middle-aged man in a green cardigan stood and pressed himself against the wall.

Rossel and Vishensky raced past him. Behind them, the soldiers burst through the doors.

'What now?' said Rossel, his breath coming in short, sharp bursts.

A woman with bright orange hair pushing a metal trolley full of files appeared around a corner. Unable to stop himself, Vishensky barged into her and she cannoned into the wall. The trolley flipped on its side and Rossel jumped over it, skinning a shin.

Another shot, this time shattering the pane of a nearby door. He felt something on his cheek. His hand came away sticky with blood. A shard of glass must have nicked him.

Rossel glanced down the corridor. More soldiers ahead, forcing their way through the heavy doors. At least ten in total now.

'This way,' shouted Vishensky, turning right.

Another long corridor, more desks, more chairs for the colonel's brown rucksack to smack into. Two more huge glass chandeliers hanging from the ceiling. A web of crystal beads shattered as a bullet hit them, turning them into rain. Two office workers were hiding under their desks, no doubt wishing they had taken the day off.

Rossel was lost in the labyrinth, keeping up with Vishensky, placing his faith in the MGB man. Another door appeared at the end of another new corridor. As Rossel spotted it, it opened and two more soldiers charged in.

Vishensky stopped, looked left, right, and left again.

He turned around. For the first time, uncertain.

Rossel searched for an escape route. There was none.

We're done for.

He saw a samovar on a trolley, gushing boiling water out of a jagged bullet hole. He instantly dropped behind it, out of sight of their pursuers. Hands fumbling, he turned a key in a drawer. Opened it. Slipped the envelope with the documents inside under two ring binders. And closed the drawer.

Rossel jumped to his feet. Began running again. Vishensky was barely a metre ahead of him

Something?

In front of him, the remaining government clerks were scrambling for a way out; heading for a side door with a large glass frame, off to the right.

There.

Rossel pointed to it. Vishensky nodded.

They began to sprint, bursting out into a long, busy street, not knowing or caring which one or where it led.

'To the river,' said Vishensky, clutching his rucksack to him like a mother defending a child.

Grateful for the gathering dusk and the crowds of commuters, Rossel and Vishensky slipped into a small alley and headed for the Moskva.

58

Pale moonlight glittered on the snow that covered the length and breadth of Gorky Park.

Rossel and Vishensky sat on a workman's bench inside a rickety bandstand, not far from the icy expanse of the Moskva River, at the park's southern end. It was sleeting, but the bandstand was covered by a tarpaulin, meaning they could stay dry and not be seen from any direction. Their hiding place backed onto the wall of a small warehouse that stored equipment for a carousel and a children's playground. Before the park had closed for the night, every now and then they had heard footsteps crunch nearby and both men tensed in readiness for fight or flight.

But now, the park was quiet, and they risked conversation.

Peeping through a gap in the tarpaulin, Rossel could see in the distance an ethereal array of red and white lights suspended in mid-air – Moscow State University. One of the huge new skyscrapers being built around the Soviet capital. The tallest in Europe, Vishensky claimed. Rossel drew up the collar of his coat.

'You're certain they'll try again?'

Vishensky rubbed his hands together to keep out the cold. 'What did I already tell you?'

That he had met his American contact in a location approximately three hundred metres south of here on three occasions at 10.10 p.m. precisely. That if they were to have any chance of survival, they had to hope the Americans would know what to do.

'Does your friend have a name?' asked Rossel.

'Fowler,' replied Vishensky. 'That wasn't him earlier, though.'

'I hope not. They were useless.'

That was as much information as the colonel had given in the past four hours.

After another few minutes of silence, Vishensky pointed at Rossel's cigarettes. Rossel passed him one.

'Our chances are not good,' Vishensky said. 'Vanishingly slim, in fact. Anything the Americans try, the blue-hats will be watching.'

'I had worked that out,' said Rossel. 'But, I assume, you have some sort of back-up plan?'

The colonel exhaled. 'That may be a grandiose description of it. But yes, we are only plan B. Even plan C. I can't quite remember.'

'And plan A?'

Vishensky didn't answer.

Rossel drew the tobacco deep into his lungs. The solution came to him.

'Kovalyova,' he said. 'We're the decoy. We are the sacrificial battalion that clears the way, as the marshal would have put it. And Vika Kovalyova, our poet with the miraculous memory, is the one that finally makes it.'

Vishensky tapped the side of his head with his finger. 'Our success, as you say, has always been unlikely. Hers more certain. She has memorised everything. All the key details, at least. In a few hours, Vika will be at the Finnish border, where someone is waiting to take her across. While state security are concentrating on us, no one will be looking for her.'

Rossel dropped his cigarette into the slush and felt for a new one. To his dismay, he had only one left.

'Who gave us away?' he asked.

'God knows,' said Vishensky. 'Baikalin, most likely. Perhaps he made a call before I got to him. Perhaps one of the others talked too much. Perhaps your investigation drew unwelcome attention our way. It doesn't really matter now.' He pulled up his collar against the sharp wind from the river.

'And *Peter and the Wolf*?' said Rossel.

Vishensky shrugged.

'Music to summon the members of Slovo to their gatherings. It was Natalya Surkova's idea – as were the code names, using the characters in Prokofiev's composition. As it happens, the marshal was a good violin player, did you know that? Knew Prokofiev personally; they were friends. It seemed fitting. And, of course, because of the boy, Petro.'

The colonel sighed. His face was in shadow. 'When I first uncovered their amateurish activities, I could have had them all shot. But then, in our poet's miraculous ability to remember names, and in our academic's Glagolitic cipher, I saw an opportunity.'

Rossel thought for a moment. 'Names,' he said. 'The names you have aren't just the names of victims. They're of Soviet agents operating in the West, too. Names you're handing to the Americans. So, you really are a traitor?'

Vishensky shook his head. 'Last month, my niece took me to the Pushkin Museum,' he said. 'They had taken all the art out – the art with real value, I mean. The basement is full of Monets, Raphaels and Picassos. But the galleries are filled with kitsch rubbish – gifts people gave to Stalin. Vases, tapestries, statues, sculptures, paintings, sweets. Even his image drawn on a grain of rice. One thing is from the miners of Tashkent to the Great and Glorious Comrade Stalin. Another is from the steelworkers of Azerbaijan. And so on. There are worms wriggling among the confectionery, but no one dares remove them because it would mean tampering with a gift to Stalin. Can you believe it?'

Rossel chuckled. 'I can.' He mimicked the tones of a Soviet prosecutor. 'As curator of the Pushkin Museum, you took it upon yourself to dispose of a chocolate bar and a grain of rice upon which was engraved the image of our wondrous Comrade Stalin. Ten years in Vorkuta without correspondence privileges.'

Vishensky nodded. 'The system is as riddled with rot and decay as those sweets. And yet you accuse me of being the traitor? I say *he* is. As do those documents you brought back from Gori. If we tell the Americans where they are, let's hope they can get to them before anybody else does.'

Rossel sat back. 'All around us are corpses and ghosts,' he said. 'Millions of lives thrown on the bonfire, most of them at random. We Russians are as familiar with grief as we are with tiredness at the end of a long day. And yet we still hold out for one person. You for the marshal. The others for the boy Petro. Me for my sister.'

'Holding out isn't enough,' Vishensky said. 'Grief isn't enough. Grief doesn't win wars or overthrow tyrants. Hatred will serve you better.'

After a moment of silence, the colonel's shoulders began to heave. He was laughing.

'A good impression,' he said. 'You sounded just like a pompous prosecutor.'

Rossel grinned. He took a last puff at his cigarette and

dropped the still-glowing butt on the floor, grinding it under the heel of his boot.

'One more question,' he said. 'Back at the children's theatre, you said there was one more of you. Who is it?'

Vishensky's mood changed. 'As a senior counter-intelligence officer, lots of files come across my desk. A few months ago, I saw a list of three names. All artists. One to be chosen to paint a portrait of Stalin. On it was a name I knew. The other two I spread some rumours about, so they were no longer considered suitable candidates for such a prestigious commission.'

'Who is it?'

'Someone who loved Tukhachevsky even more than I did. Someone who, given the opportunity, might—'

A noise outside. Distant but distinct.

Rossel put a finger to his lips. He gestured to a hole in the tarpaulin.

*

Another sound – a car slowing to a stop on the tarmac.

Vishensky put his eye to a gap in the tarpaulin. 'A Moskvitch,' he whispered.

Rossel began to stand.

The colonel held up a hand to still him. 'Wait.'

Headlights blinking on and off three times.

'That's as agreed,' murmured Vishensky. 'It's them. I was beginning to have doubts, but it's them.'

Checking left and right, the two men clambered down from the bandstand and headed towards the car, which was parked thirty or so metres away on the road running alongside the park.

As they drew closer, Rossel could see the silhouettes of two people in the front, and a third man in the back seat.

'Fowler,' said Vishensky.

Fowler waved a hand to beckon them forward.

*

In the camps, before violence broke out, you knew it was coming.

The way a cloud moved across the sun. Or the sound of a felt boot plunging into a drift, too hard and sharp. Or the way a Thief scratched his spoon across his bowl. Anything could be a sign. Of rage. Of intent. Of—

Out on the river, a tugboat sounded its foghorn.

'Keep walking,' said Vishensky to Rossel.

The back door of the car swung open.

A voice from inside – fluent street Russian with an accent. 'Fuck, comrades, hurry up.'

A second blast of the foghorn.

They're here . . .

The headlights of a GAZ truck lit up the scene. A twitch of the tarpaulin covering its back. A growling burst of machinegun fire, pin-sharp in the cold night air. Rossel threw himself on the ground.

A puff of snow, centimetres from his head.

Vishensky pirouetted like a Bolshoi principal. Then crumpled, splashing blood onto the snow as he fell.

Rossel could see MGB troops jumping down in twos and threes from the back of the truck. A dog – a huge Alsatian straining at the leash, roaring its fury. A second GAZ screeched to a halt at the other end of the street, more men leaping down. All shouldering rifles. Both groups closing fast.

The car door slammed. The driver swung the wheel hard left, but the back tyres slipped and spun on the ice. It hardly moved.

Leaving us again? You bastards . . .

Rossel jumped to his feet. He grabbed the colonel underneath both arms, dragging him back towards the car. But Vishensky fought him off.

'The rucksack,' the colonel shouted. 'Take it and go.' He glanced at his chest. 'Shit.' He began fumbling for his pistol.

Rossel could smell burning. The Americans' car battling for traction. Inching forward. More bullets whistled past his head. One of the dog handlers tripped and the animal slipped the leash. It charged forward. Vishensky rolled and shot it.

The American driver changed tactic. The car reversed and headed for Rossel – going straight over parkland was now the only route out.

For a moment, Rossel thought the Americans meant to run him down, but the car slid to a halt a metre away and the back door swung open again.

Fowler, his face contorted, was bellowing, 'Drag Vishensky in!'

Rossel heaved at Vishensky's heavy body. But once more the colonel punched at his arms and screamed at him to take the rucksack and go.

Other arms pulled at Rossel and dragged him into the car. Somehow, he hooked his right hand around the rucksack's handle and kept hold of it.

Two MGB riflemen were metres away.

The door slammed shut. Fowler wrenched the rucksack out of Rossel's grasp.

The Moskvitch roared into Gorky Park, bucking over the uneven surface and sliding like an ice hockey player chasing a puck.

Fowler was dressed in a smart blue suit, including waist-coat, and wore tiny spectacles. All three Americans were broad-shouldered and sleek. They smelled of cologne and exuded aggressive confidence, revelling in the adventure.

Fowler twisted around to look out of the back window. Then at Rossel.

'Do you think Vishensky's dead?' he asked in fluent Russian.

Rossel looked at him. 'I'm not certain.'

Fowler sighed. 'I hope for his sake he is,' he said.

*

They changed cars twice.

Big men in identical black coats and polished shoes vacated the new vehicles and disappeared into the night.

Rossel did not understand the babble spoken by his new accomplices but could make out one word they kept saying.

Spaso.

They were not far from the Arbat, one of the few parts of Moscow Rossel could recognise. At last, they rounded a corner and pulled up before a set of iron gates and a large guardhouse. The gates were opened by an unseen hand. The driver pressed on the accelerator once more and the car slipped into the grounds of a large, brightly lit neoclassical building.

As Rossel stepped out of the car, another big man in a blue suit pushed him up against a wall and frisked him.

'Welcome to America,' he said.

59

Rossel was sitting at one end of a long, polished table in the library of Spaso House – not the embassy, Fowler had told him, but the American ambassador's residence in Moscow.

For a library, it didn't have many books. A couple of wood and glass cases filled with aged, leather-backed titles. Most of them looked as though nobody had turned any of their pages since they were first placed on the shelf.

Facing him, at the back of the room, was a long wooden side-board, also polished with military thoroughness, on which shone a phalanx of six identical table lamps, each with white shades shaped like mitres. They looked, he thought, like a con-clave of cardinals ready for an inquisition.

To Rossel's right sat his current inquisitor – a fat, middle-aged man with a wide mouth and a brow beaded with sweat no matter how much he wiped it with an ostentatiously monogrammed silk handkerchief. He had introduced himself as Raymond Mander-ley, a deputy consul at the US embassy. To his left was a blonde woman in a yellow skirt and tight sky-blue top – a stenographer and translator; no one had bothered to introduce her. Fowler sat next to the woman.

On the wall behind the deputy consul was a picture of a man Rossel recognised. Franklin D. Roosevelt, US wartime leader, once a friend and ally of the Soviet Union. Next to him was another man – 'Our current president,' said Manderley. 'Eisenhower. Damn fine man.'

'I know who Eisenhower is,' Rossel said.

The stenographer was interpreting for the deputy consul, which Rossel found strange – didn't Fowler speak good enough Russian? But the American men had briefly argued and while Rossel didn't understand the words, he realised it was about the presence of the woman. For whatever reason, Fowler wanted the monopoly on translation and for her to leave. He lost the argument.

They don't even trust each other.

Rossel glanced at Vishensky's rucksack in the middle of the table.

So why should I trust them?

Manderley began to speak.

At intervals, the deputy consul paused to give the stenographer time to interpret. The woman had lipstick on her teeth, Rossel noticed. And smelled heady, exotic. Of money. Not roubles. Dollars. Unimaginable riches. She was young. Thirty, maybe. Poised and confident. A Statue of Liberty in a crisp cotton top. When she'd walked in, he'd noticed her shoes – green leather with a small golden clasp. A pair of heels like that, he thought, would have every woman in Leningrad queuing down Nevsky just to gaze at them in *Passazh*'s window.

'Mr Rossel,' she translated. 'Or perhaps you prefer comrade, comrade? Deputy Consul Manderley says we have people here who will talk to you in an abrupt fashion.' She emphasised the Russian word for abrupt. But did so somewhat apologetically. 'He means some of them won't be quite as friendly as we will be. So his advice is to tell us everything you know right now, and then we can see if we can help you.'

'I prefer "Mr",' Rossel said. 'It makes me feel like I'm already in America.'

She turned to Manderley, but the consul raised a hand.

'I understood,' he said. Then to Rossel, in a rough, plodding Russian. 'I speak enough of your language, comrade. We mostly just use Grace here, Miss Callaghan, for the Kremlin high-ups.'

Fowler leaned forward. 'When key details are important,' he broke in with a grin. 'Conversations where, if you fuck up and use the perfective instead of the imperfective, or get your verbs of motion wrong, everyone starts sweating like Hirohito on the day they dropped the big one on Hiroshima. If you follow?'

Rossel nodded. 'Hiroshima, yes, I understand. Mistakes can be costly. Cigarettes,' he said. 'Regrettably, I'm out of *papirosy*. Can I have some?'

'Sure,' said Manderley. He made an elaborate show of tapping his breast pockets. 'Shit, I'm out, too. You got any, Grace?'

She nodded, reached under the table and pulled out a white pack with a red circle on it from a cream leather handbag.

'Aw, give him the pack, Grace,' said Fowler. 'And your lighter. I'll get you a new one.'

She gave Fowler a chilly, distant glance. But then did so.

Rossel stared at the lighter. It was golden – surely not real gold? – and the flint wheel was on the side. He wondered what he could swap it for on Leningrad's black market. A sizeable haul of Maksi Bondar's caviar, undoubtedly. He rested it on the table.

'Good girl, Grace – Lucky Strikes,' said Manderley with a laugh. 'Good tobacco can . . .' He faltered, searching for the right Russian words. A wry smile. 'Some of you Reds have been known to defect after just one puff.'

Rossel picked up the pack, took one out and lit it. He pulled the smoke right down into his lungs. It tasted like silk. Like he'd spent his whole life smoking horseshit. He held it down for as long as he could.

Manderley spoke. "'Be happy – Go Lucky!' That's what it says on the Lucky Strike posters, Mr Rossel. And that's you. Am I right?' With this, his Russian seemed to run out and he switched back to English. 'Because you're a nobody from nowhere, but you're the one sitting in that chair. And Colonel Vishensky, he was a real somebody. He was everything we needed. But either he's lying dead in the snow or, worse, strapped to a chair in the Lubyanka.'

Grace looked at Rossel as she interpreted, rendering 'nobody from nowhere' with emphasis.

Rossel returned her gaze. 'That's me all right,' he said. 'Comrade Manderley has me exactly.'

Manderley pulled the rucksack close to him and emptied the contents onto the table. He spread out the curling sheaves of Glagolitic script.

'We're going to get this all deciphered, of course we are. But that might take some time. Meanwhile, I was wondering if you could tell us . . . what this shit is all about?'

Rossel tapped out some ash into a small metal ashtray that had an eagle embossed on it. He picked up the gold lighter and placed it on top of the pack of Luckies. He glanced around at the Americans. All pale, thanks to the Russian winter, but well fed. Grace had the beginnings of a double chin. Fowler's muscles were toned by plenty of red meat. What did they eat in the United States? Steaks, whole chickens, enormous pies. Rossel had not eaten for hours and felt dizzy at the thought. He wanted to ask for food. But decided against it.

'Water,' he said. 'Can I have a glass of water?'

After a moment, Manderley nodded.

*

Rossel finished his water and set the glass down on the table.

'Thank you,' he said to Manderley. He gestured to the Glagolitic script spread out before them. 'I'm presuming you have received documents like this before?'

Manderley scratched his chin. 'And what makes you say that?'

Fowler cursed and then barked something guttural at Manderley that Rossel did not understand.

'Yes, we got something,' Fowler said to Rossel in Russian. 'Of course we did. From the academic Anna Orlova. You know her?'

'She is dead,' said Rossel.

'We heard. She handed them over one time at a conference in Finland and once again in Berlin. Either she took a lucky guess or was pointed in the right direction by Vishensky. The American to whom she gave material like this alerted the CIA. He knew they were forgeries right away. He translated them. Just long lists of names. We didn't get it at first. But one word kept coming up again and again. *Holodomor.* You know about that?'

'I do,' said Rossel. 'Death by hunger. And then what? Vishensky made contact?'

'We have places in this city, and other cities, where, shall we say, friendly locals can leave us messages,' said Fowler. 'One day, not so long ago, we found another scroll like this with strange writing . . .' He turned to Grace. 'What's the Russian for gobble-degook?' he asked.

'*Abracadabra,*' she translated.

Manderley nodded in agreement.

'That then – *abracadabra* all over it,' said Fowler. 'Now, our people are smart. They remember the documents from the lady at the conferences and match the script. Then they translate this new message and find only one new name. But what do you know? It's an American name. A damn CIA name. And, to cut a very long story short, the name turns out to be a double agent working for your lot. The CIA arrest the name, hold a press conference, drop in the word *holodomor*, and there you go, the CIA have passed the test. After that, Vishensky gave us a few more names – and I assume these are yet more. Using the same method of *abracadabra*. Give me one of those Lucky Strikes back.'

Fowler grabbed the pack and lit one. Manderley began to protest – not at Fowler's demand for a cigarette, Rossel assumed, but over the amount of information he was sharing – but Fowler ignored him, as Grace translated at speed.

'And how do we know we passed the test?' Fowler blew a large smoke ring into the air and chased it with another. 'Well, a couple of weeks ago, there I am, enjoying a high-level Soviet-American evening of cocktails, a banquet, a movie, top brass from both sides comparing war wounds, everyone smiling even though we're ready to drop the bomb on each other tomorrow . . . And this one man who never smiles starts lecturing me about Russian history, and Russia's place in the world, and how Russian civilisation is a million times older than American civilisation. And how the Slavs *even invented their own alphabet* to express their souls. And at *that* point, comrade, alarms go off in my head like all the bells of St Basil's Cathedral. It's two in the morning, everyone is shit-faced, and this guy, speaking in a very rounda-bout way, gives me a time and a place where we might meet . . . and the rest you know. Now, over to you, comrade. Let's have your story.'

Rossel shifted in his chair, taking a moment to process the information. He felt chastened. He had spent days running around Leningrad trying to pick up the scent of people close to Anna Orlova, and of anyone who knew Tamas Abazi. Groping in the darkest recesses of the past, missing clues, overlooking connections. Lifting the lid on a conspiracy of people of virtue, principle and courage, endangering their lives. Meanwhile, Colonel Vishensky had found a way to contact the American secret services, make them join the dots on an existing contact and her method of conveying information without Soviet security suspecting anything, and persuade them to meet him and arrange for his defection.

Like his hero, Marshal Tukhachevsky, the man was a master of strategy.

Rossel picked up one of the scripts. 'Yes, these documents are also fake, of course – artificially aged – but once translated you will find the contents invaluable,' he said. 'I can vouch for both Colonel Vishensky's motives and his methods. But more than anything else, I'm a militiaman. So, for me, this is a tale about murder. Murders, in fact. The murder of a great Soviet general, a military genius, a man whom Vishensky worshipped, is one of the victims.' Rossel toyed with the flint of the lighter. 'Not just Marshal Tukhachevsky, though,' he added. 'The annihilation of a village in Ukraine. A few hundred people out of many millions who were sacrificed to the Revolution. One of them a child called Petro Petrenko.'

He looked at the three Americans. Only Grace Callaghan appeared to grasp what he was saying.

'In every case, the murderer was the same man,' Rossel said. 'The exact same person who ordered the death of the renowned academic Anna Orlova. That's why I'm here. To make sure he gets to pay for her and the boy, Petro Petrenko, and maybe a few others.'

'Others?' said Grace.

'Old friends I knew who disappeared in the night. A good friend, a drunk, an honest man, a militia captain. My father. My mother. My missing sister . . .' Rossel rolled the flint and lit the lighter. Let the flame go out again. 'Names that will mean nothing to you. But there is one person you will be interested in. Another victim of the same cruel mind. One of the murderer's childhood friends, in fact. A man called Tamas Abazi . . .'

Manderley held up a hand. 'Slow down, Mr Rossel, you're not making much sense to me.'

A phone rang in the corner of the room. The stenographer got up and answered it.

'McCluskey is on his way,' she said to Manderley.

Rossel turned to him. 'McCluskey?' he said.

Manderley scratched his unshaven chin. 'He of the abrupt methods.'

'Is this the bit where people usually ask if they can go to America?' said Rossel.

Manderley nodded. 'Usually it is, yes. But, for the most part, it's only the *somebodies* who get to go.'

60

McCluskey never seemed to stand still. He paced restlessly while the others sat at the table.

The CIA man looked the way Rossel had imagined all Americans did. Rich, overfed and tall. In his fifties, he was heavy-set and olive-skinned. His white hair had been brushed until it had surrendered. It topped off a tight-fitting suit, the whole giving the impression of a snow-capped mountain. The two men who had arrived with him and were guarding either side of the door wore the same kind of suit and were similarly large. For a couple of minutes, McCluskey barked questions at Fowler and Manderley. Rossel could only pick out some names, Vishensky's among them.

McCluskey stopped pacing. He became a little calmer. He turned to Rossel.

'That room our boys first brought you through when you arrived here at Spaso, Comrade Rossel, the one with the big chandeliers.' His Russian was fluent, almost unaccented. 'There was a famous party held there in the thirties. Old Bill Bullitt, the ambassador back then, got in three performing seals, Misha, Shura and Lyuba, to do tricks. They say one of them even played the fucking *"Internationale"* on an accordion. What do you think of that?'

'I've always liked the *"Internationale"*,' said Rossel.

McCluskey grinned, pulled out a chair and sat down. 'The

trainer got smashed on the free champagne, the seals took their chance and made their escape.' He took out a toothpick and picked at his brilliant white teeth. 'You know that story, Grace?' he said to Callaghan.

She nodded. 'Sure,' she said. 'You've told me it lots of times.' She turned to Rossel. 'I think the moral is supposed to be that even Soviet seals try to defect.'

McCluskey snapped the toothpick in two. 'Maybe you're not who you say you are, Comrade Rossel? That's what I'm thinking. Just a trained MGB seal they taught to whistle "The Stars and Stripes".'

Rossel pointed at the scripts and the rucksack. 'I can't really whistle. Never could. So far, I've told you gentleman nothing but the truth.'

McCluskey took out another toothpick and removed a speck of dirt from one of his nails with the sharp end of it. 'Vishensky was an asset we could use,' he said. 'An MGB colonel. But you? You don't ring true, comrade. A small-time militiaman with a big fairy tale. A story about a conspiracy. A story about a famine in Ukraine. A few million people starved to death and yet no one in the whole wide world knows anything about it . . .'

He nodded at the photograph of President Eisenhower on the wall. Stood up and started pacing again.

'Ike's a former captain in the engineers. A polished-buttons man. Likes to spit on the cloth before he shines his shoes. I don't think he's going to think you and your story pass muster, comrade. You need to give me something else.'

Now's the time to tell them about the document – where they can find the signed confession . . .

Rossel leaned forward. 'I know—'

A knock on the door.

'Yes,' barked McCluskey.

A marine sergeant stepped inside.

'Phone call, sir,' he said to McCluskey.

'Not now, sergeant. I said no interruptions.'

'It's not for you, sir.'

'Who, then?'

The marine pointed at Rossel. 'Him.'

61

Two big men in blue suits were standing on either side of the library door. Only Rossel, McCluskey and Callaghan were sitting around the table.

They brought a phone in, tethered to a lead that trailed out of the room and out of sight. *People will be listening in*, Rossel thought.

He didn't know if he wanted to go to America. But he knew the person on the other end of that phone was Russian, knew they would try to persuade him to stay in the Soviet Union, and knew with equal certainty that nothing in the world would get him to do that.

The phone rang. A shrill, brittle jangling that echoed around the room. The phone was cream-coloured and gleamed as if freshly polished.

'Pick it up,' said McCluskey.

Rossel did so. He felt calm. Almost in a trance. For the first time in his life, he was out of reach of the MGB.

He pressed the handset to his ear. A crackle of static.

'Comrade Rossel?' The voice was familiar.

'*Slushayu vas*,' Rossel said.

How does he know where I am?

'This is Major Nikitin,' replied the voice. 'My instructions are to facilitate your release from the American ambassador's residence as soon as possible. You are a Soviet citizen and have been detained illegally. This matter is being dealt with at the highest levels. I am simply calling to reassure you of this and ascertain whether you are in good health and being treated in line with the standard diplomatic accords.'

Nikitin's voice was stilted, and he stumbled on a couple of words. He was obviously reading from a script.

'But it's pleasant here, Comrade Major,' said Rossel. 'They tell me they have jolly parties with seals who play the accordion. What if I don't want to leave? And, more to the point,' he added, glancing at McCluskey, 'why would the capitalists let me?'

A pause. He could sense Nikitin considering his options.

'We also have some news that may be of interest to you,' Nikitin said.

Rossel had never heard the major sound so nervous. 'News?'

'More news of . . .'

A crackle of static. Nikitin's voice floated into the far distance, became ethereal, seemed about to disappear. Then it returned.

'. . . News of your sister.'

Rossel ran a hand over his head. McCluskey peered across the table at him, his eyes curious, suspicious.

'Galya?' Rossel whispered.

'Yes.'

McCluskey scratched at his chin. A shaman trying to decipher the runes. He mouthed a question: 'Galya?'

'You still there?' said Nikitin.

'Yes. Where is she?'

'Safe.'

'Where?'

'Here with us. I . . .'

A stranger's voice in the background. Quiet. Authoritative.

Issuing an order. Another burst of crackling static. A pause. Then a rough, Georgian accent.

'You know me?'

Instinctively, Rossel's back straightened, as if he were a small child being reprimanded in school.

'Yes, I . . .'

Rossel glanced at McCluskey, who was staring at him so intently, his eyes looked in danger of popping out of their sockets.

'I hope you enjoyed the mountains. Is it with you?' asked the voice. The accent more distinct this time.

Rossel swallowed, tried to gather his wits. 'Is what with me?' he replied.

A low chuckle. 'I'll take that as a no, then.'

Rossel, glancing at McCluskey, said nothing.

'I am told that diplomatic protocols stipulate you will have to demand your release from American custody before they will let you out,' said the voice. 'Can you do that for me?'

Rossel cradled the phone in both hands and cleared his throat.

'As I told Colonel Nikitin, it is very pleasant here,' he replied. 'And they tell me America is the land of opportunity. I am not sure why I would do as you suggest.'

Silence. Only the crackle of static. And the sense of someone making, for the millionth time, a calculation – how to play the cards he had been dealt and win.

'I have a condition,' Rossel said.

'Name it.'

'My sister comes in here. As I come out.'

A brief pause.

'Agreed.'

A dull tone as the phone went dead.

Rossel turned to McCluskey.

'I am a Soviet citizen, held against my wishes,' he said, 'I'd like to officially request my release now.'

'And I'd like to go back to Nebraska and take my wife on a nice boat trip up the Platte River. But it's not going to happen.'

Rossel replaced the receiver and pointed at the phone. 'Comrade Stalin says it is,' he said.

At the sound of the name, one of the suits at the door let out a long, low whistle.

McCluskey held up a hand to silence him. He leaned in a little closer. His voice hushed.

'Is *what* with you?' he said.

62

As the line of inquisitorial lamps watched on, Rossel sat, next to Grace Callaghan, half in and half out of the light they cast, smoking his way through the pack of Luckies. Two new blue-suits stood by the oak-framed library door. A changing of the guard.

He only had two cigarettes left. He lit one. Then pushed the pack towards the stenographer.

Callaghan picked up the last cigarette. '*Spasibo*,' she said.

A whiff of her perfume as she leaned forward. He lit her cigarette.

Outside, in the hall, raised voices – Fowler, Manderley and McCluskey.

Manderley, persuasive, pleading.

McCluskey, loud, threatening.

Fowler, considered, playing the reluctant diplomat.

Grace blew a languid trail of blue smoke. Her note-perfect Russian again. 'I don't know why those boys get so heated. They don't get to decide whether you stay or go, anyway. In theory, they don't have a choice, of course. In theory, you're a Russian citizen who has asked to be released, and therefore international diplomatic protocols say we have to let you go. Can't keep a Soviet citizen in the US ambassador's residence against his will.'

'And in practice?'

'In practice, you're a pal of Colonel Vishensky who just had a personal call with Uncle Joe. In practice, forms can take a few hours to fill out, and in the meantime you can be subjected to those "abrupt methods" until you tell them what they want to know. In practice, anything can happen.'

'Who does, then?'

'Does what?' she asked.

'Get to decide if I can go.'

She waved a hand in the direction of the portrait of Eisenhower on the wall. 'That guy, maybe? Especially now you've had a conversation with Stalin. But that means talking to his chief of staff, Sherman Adams, first. So, things may take a little time.'

'What's he like, this Adams?'

Another puff on the Lucky. Another languorous exhale. 'The real power in the kingdom,' she said. 'We've got a game kids play back home called "Simon says". I don't know if there's a Russian version. Simon says "jump" and you jump, and so on. Well, in the White House, it's all a game of "Sherman says". A mind like a *matryoshka*, packed full of riddles hidden inside mysteries. Plays the long game. Just like your new friend, Comrade Stalin.' She gestured towards the doors behind which Fowler, Manderley and McCluskey could still be heard arguing. 'Everyone else sticks their chests out and goes at it like two cockerels squabbling over the last frisky hen, but, in my experience, *Mr* Rossel, it doesn't mean a thing.'

'I see. "Sherman says". I understand,' said Rossel.

Callaghan gave him a look. 'Why do you want to get out of here? No one does. You're the first sinner whoever knocked on the door of Heaven only to ask for directions back to Hell.'

Rossel stubbed out the last cigarette into one of the small blue ashtrays. He pointed at the smouldering butt. 'Like silk,' he said.

Grace Callaghan put a finger on Rossel's chin and held his gaze. 'Are you a lonely man, *Comrade* Rossel?' she asked.

Rossel breathed in her scent and thought about a girl he had loved when he was a student of violin at the conservatoire.

'Once you've betrayed the people you love,' he said, 'you're alone for ever.'

*

Rossel and Grace Callaghan had been sitting together for an hour. A doorknob rattled. The suits stood to attention. Grace sat up.

McCluskey's head poking around the door. His face red. His brow furrowed.

The translator looked up at him. 'What does Sherman say?' she asked.

McCluskey turned to Rossel and pointed at him. 'Sherman says . . . he goes.'

Rossel reached across the table and covered Grace's right hand with his left. She stared at the stubs of his missing fingers. Then looked up at him.

'One last favour?' he said.

She smiled and, slipping another pack of cigarettes out of her handbag, handed them to him.

63

Snow, whipped up by a frenzied, wailing wind, curled around him.

McCluskey nodded. A hard-faced marine saluted and opened Spaso's metal side gate.

The station chief turned to Rossel. 'Go.'

Obeying the command, Rossel stepped into the street. He blinked in the blazing headlights of a truck and a Packard stationed off to his left. To his right were more cars and two more military trucks with their lights trained on him, illuminating the alley like it was a Lenfilm studio.

It took a moment for his eyes to adjust to the glare.

A voice from the compound bellowed out an order: 'Keep moving!' It was McCluskey, sounding bitter, enraged. Rossel did as he was told.

Running the full length of the right-hand side of the building, the alley was about a hundred metres long. Putting a hand up to shield his eyes from the buffeting wind, Rossel took a few steps forward to the right. As the swirling snow changed direction yet again, he caught a glimpse of something in front of him. Two men standing next to the truck. Two more next to the Packard. One of these was Nikitin. Then they dissolved into nothingness.

He stopped walking and shouted into the gloom. 'Where is she?'

But he couldn't make his voice carry against the wind.

He shouted again. This time louder. 'Galya?'

For a second, the wind dropped. The silhouettes of the vehicles became visible again. And men, too. A line of statues.

Nikitin raised a hand and beckoned him.

From behind the Packard, somebody stepped out and began to walk forward. *Galya?*

His feet felt leaden. He came to a halt. He couldn't move. The next step might bring her closer to him. And he was afraid to take it.

'Keep moving!'

McCluskey again. Impatient and menacing. Bellowing to make himself heard above the wind.

Rossel took a deep breath. He could feel his hands trembling. *Walk. Just walk . . .*

He took one step forward. Then another.

His pace quickened. He looked up.

Among the whirling flurries, there was a shadow to his right. *Can it be?*

'Keep moving!'

This time, the order was barked out from the Russian side. *There . . .*

Next to him. Within touching distance. A woman.

'Galya?' he said. His own voice sounding strained, distant, unfamiliar. As if speaking in a dream.

She looked up.

There were lines around her eyes. A speck of grey in her hair. But, otherwise, she was the same. As if she had been waiting for him here all along, hidden inside the snowstorm.

Galya smiled the saddest of smiles. Then whispered something.

'What is our life? A game!'

He reached out to her.

Again, he heard McCluskey and Nikitin yelling at him.

The command was instantly repeated by Nikitin on the Russian side.

Rossel wiped his eyes, furious because his tears stopped him from seeing her clearly.

'I've been looking for...' he began. But couldn't continue. The words caught in his throat.

'God will reunite us, Revol,' said Galya. 'Have faith. He will bring us to our parents, too. They will forgive us.'

He reached out to her again, and she to him, and their fingers brushed against each other for the briefest second before more shouts and oaths pushed them apart.

'Go,' he said to her.

Galya nodded and walked towards the gate.

Nikitin was booming out another order. 'Keep moving, Rossel. Fuck your mother...'

Rossel walked backwards towards him, committing to memory every step his sister took before the snow and the dazzling light closed around her.

64

As Rossel stared out of the window, he could hear the snow chains around the car's tyres bite into the ice and scratch on the road. Packed rows of birch trees on either side cast long shadows in the moonlight. Damp, fat, half-formed flakes flew through the beams of the Packard's headlights, splattering against the windscreen like insects.

Nikitin, talkative at first but silent since they had passed the first road sign for Kuntsevo, sat next to Rossel. Two brooding Georgians, one driving, sat up front. Both members of Stalin's personal bodyguard.

Before they had set off for Stalin's dacha, Rossel had taken them on a detour – back to Red Square to retrieve the envelope and its incriminating contents. Nikitin had even chuckled when he saw Rossel's improvised hiding place. 'Some poor bastard would have had the shock of his life if they'd found that in their bottom drawer instead of last month's invoices,' he'd said.

In the past, when Rossel had waited in a hallway to break down a locked door to apprehend a felon, there was always nervousness. Mind running overtime, wondering what might lurk behind it. So much so that, as the lock gave way and the militia burst in, he'd half-expect to recoil from the onslaught of a lurking demon – only for some bewildered clerk to step out of the kitchen with his hands up.

And twice, Rossel had found himself pursuing criminals who had murdered not once but multiple times. The unhinged violence of both killers had shocked him.

But the man who lived out here among the pines was different.

His fingerprints were everywhere. His crimes legion. His signature scrawled on the bottom of endless death sentences. Most likely, the sentences of Rossel's own mother and father.

Iosif Vissarionovich Dzhugashvili had dipped his arms deep into the blood of the entire Soviet people.

Anna Orlova and Tamas Abazi were just two more of his victims. The little boy, Petro Petrenko, another. In the labour camps, as Rossel knew only too well, many more. In Leningrad before the war, during the Terror – well, people had stopped counting. It led only to calculations as to how long before the horror came to their own door. Even now, Stalin was accusing Jewish 'poisoner-doctors' of conspiring to murder leading members of the Party. A prelude to yet another masterpiece of murder.

*

After another forty minutes, a break in the trees. High walls topped with barbed wire; a green, corrugated-iron gate. The Packard slowed and stopped in front of two more soldiers, rifles slung over their shoulders.

One of them checked papers and shone a torch on each face. As the light flickered across Rossel's cheek, the man nodded to him. A small, unnecessary courtesy. As if to say, 'So, it's you tonight, comrade? God help you.'

The guard handed back the papers to Nikitin. The gates slid open, and they rolled in.

401

The tree-lined road continued. No sign of a residence. Snow had been packed into neat piles, two metres high, to the right; on the left was a snowplough parked next to a new ZiS truck. A hundred metres or so behind it, a small patch cleared of snow with some skittles piled in one corner, ready for a game of *gorodki*.

What had he been expecting? An ogre's lair – skulls hanging from the birch-tops? A fiery, nine-headed *zmei*, smoke blowing from its nostrils, to guard the approaches?

The car rounded a bend and a squat, green, two-storey building came into sight, lit by flickering lamps. A first-floor balcony was wrapped around it, while a single car was parked before its large wooden front door.

'Visiting is good, but being home is better,' said the driver. His tone gleefully sarcastic.

Nikitin leaned forward and tapped the man on the shoulder. 'I'll take him inside,' he said.

Rossel and Nikitin got out of the car. Rossel took in a lungful of air so cold and sharp that it made him cough.

At the sound, a man swaddled in furs and blankets, sitting on a chair on the right-hand side of the balcony, stood.

Inside Rossel's head, the three growling French horns that evoked Prokofiev's Wolf briefly played their motif.

The face was in darkness. The body small and stout, shoulders slumped. He took another step forward and the lamplight fell on that unmistakable face, scarred by smallpox, twisted further by its many sins.

Puffing on his pipe, Stalin leaned over the balcony.

'Welcome, comrades,' he called down with the cordiality of a generous host.

Rossel stared at the man he had only ever seen in newspapers or on film. The dark eyes, wreathed in a mass of wrinkles, sunk into puffy cheeks. Frost glittered on the moustache. And the smile was one of triumph.

'I sent Minister Molotov to America during the war,' said Stalin. His voice was ageing, too – if still a light, pleasant tenor. He had never shaken off the Georgian accent. Perhaps he'd never wanted to. 'The fool fell in love with the refrigerators there. Big metal boxes filled with milk and cheese called *Frigidaires*. They even make their own ice. Can you believe that, comrade?'

He sucked on the pipe again and pointed the stem at Rossel. 'But you, I'm told, have an artist's soul. A musician. I suspect you have made the correct decision in deciding not to set out for distant shores. In fact, I'm certain of it.'

Avuncular. Concerned. And a shot or two of vodka inside him.

How could he respond? Did it matter? He was dead anyway. But years of collective fearful deference to this man were not easily shrugged off.

Rossel looked up at the icicles hanging from the dacha's guttering. He took a step forward.

'As you say, I could never leave our glorious Soviet Union, Comrade Stalin,' he said. 'Besides, why would I wish to? If there is one thing we will always be able to beat the capitalists at, I'm reasonably confident it is in the production of ice.'

Stalin tapped his teeth with the end of his pipe. Then, enjoying the joke, grinned. He waved the pipe at Rossel. A stage wink, his voice thicker, slurring again. 'Food, then, Comrade Senior Militiaman, if you're hungry? I'll get someone to talk to the chef.'

65

Stalin's chef turned out to be a grey-haired Russian full of respectful concern for the generalissimo's comfort, who withdrew after an insouciant flick of his master's wrist.

They ate in silence, punctuated by the sound of the utensils scraping on the bottom of plates, each man busy with two steaming bowls of *kharcho*, thick with the finest cuts of beef and flavoured with spices and walnuts.

The large table could have sat ten people. The two diners sat at opposite ends. Around them were pictures of Gorky and Lenin. Shelves filled with books covered two walls – books that looked as if they had been read many times.

'Well, what did you expect, Comrade Militiaman?' said Stalin, breaking the silence and jabbing a finger at his plate. 'Milk soup and dumplings? You see, I know everything you have been up to.'

He resumed eating and Rossel did the same. Despite everything, he was still hungry. The Gulag had taught him to take food as and when it came. 'Even if the bastards are going to shoot me in the afternoon, I still eat breakfast. Just in case they miss,' a fellow prisoner had once told him.

Stalin took a last mouthful and dropped his spoon into the bowl with a clatter. He pulled out a handkerchief and dabbed at his moustache. He fixed Rossel with an intense stare. A drifting

blue-green in his irises, the whites tinted with yellow. A scattering of broken blood vessels near the lids and in the corners.
Mocking. Mercurial. Unforgiving.

'You have it?' he said.

Rossel slipped the envelope from his coat pocket and placed
it on the table. Stalin picked it up, opened it and began to read.
His mood changed subtly. He became the perfect host again.
Concerned. Felicitous. Resting back in his chair, he gestured
towards the guards.

'No Russian. They only speak Georgian. Safer for me.' He
smiled. 'For them, too. I'm told you went to Gori. Did you like it?'

Rossel shook his head. 'To be honest, I didn't think much of it.'

Stalin tapped his front tooth with the nail of his little finger,
exposing a line of tobacco-stained teeth. As if calibrating how
much longer he could be bothered to play this game.

'Have you ever heard the Lord's Prayer sung in Georgian,
Comrade Rossel?'

'No, but I suspect I would rather enjoy it.'

'In the seminary in Tiflis, we used to sing it.' The old man
chanted a line, pianissimo. '*Da nu shemiqvaneb chven gansats-
delsa, aramed mikhsnen chven borotisagan . . .*'

His tenor voice was soft, suited to the melancholy of the tune.
For a moment, Stalin seemed lost, beguiled by memories of his
younger self. He stopped and reached out to pour himself a large
glass of brandy from a crystal decanter on the table, set next to
another of red wine.

'If Marx himself had heard it, he would have become a con-
vert, even if for a moment,' said Stalin. 'All religious nonsense, of
course, but such poetry. Such purity. Singing that prayer as a boy
and as a trainee priest made me understand one very simple
thing: people will do anything in the service of a beautiful story.

And, when they have dedicated their hearts to it, their hands become capable of hitherto unimaginable things.'

He drained the brandy in one.

'A tale like that makes the masses weak. Pliable.' Stalin tapped a finger on the envelope. 'So much so, that, in time, they might even mistake a Judas for Christ risen again.'

Rossel glanced at the Georgian guards. Then turned to Stalin. 'You and Abazi really were friends?'

'I was fond of Tamas, yes. We knew each other from the old days.'

Rossel pointed at the documents. 'He visited you from time to time. Perhaps to ask for favours, perhaps for reminiscences. But, most recently, he put a foot wrong. What was it? That he knew about these? Or that he knew your old comrade Tariel was still alive, and where to find him?'

Stalin reached for his pipe but did not answer.

'Perhaps he had one too many and was boasting,' Rossel went on. He dropped his voice to a whisper. 'Or perhaps he lost a round at a game of *gorodki* and his judgement with it – and made a foolish accusation?'

The dictator blew out a cloud of smoke so thick that for a second his head and shoulders disappeared. After a moment, he nodded.

A confession of sorts, then ...

'You ask interesting questions, comrade.' Stalin poured himself a second glass of brandy and drained it. 'Brave questions. Please, help yourself.' He pushed the decanter towards Rossel.

Rossel shook his head and pointed at the envelope. 'And what he suggested supports what's in those documents?'

Stalin held Rossel's gaze. 'What documents?' he said.

A crunching sound on the drive outside – cars drawing up. Stalin glanced towards a window.

'The Politburo arriving,' he said. 'We will drink and watch a film. I'm particularly fond of Westerns. *Stagecoach* is a favourite. John Wayne rides into town and metes out brutal justice at the point of a gun. Who can resist a tale like that?'

Stalin barked a command in Georgian to the guards. They marched towards Rossel and stood either side of him.

'No need for you to fret just yet, comrade,' he told Rossel. 'You still have a little time. Our parties usually go on until four or five. Besides, I have personally requested that a man whose discretion I can rely on totally will interrogate you further. Albeit briefly.'

Stalin nodded and the guards hauled Rossel to his feet.

'I'm told Comrade Blokhin has been visiting elderly relatives. But he is on his way back and assures me he will be here first thing in the morning. I'm sure I'll soon have news of the whereabouts of my old comrade Tariel.'

*

If it was to be his last night, at least he was surrounded by food.

Not that Rossel could eat much of it. The cramped storeroom lit by a flickering wall lamp near the dacha's first-floor kitchen was filled with tins, bags of rice, pickled vegetables of every type, and sacks of potatoes and onions. All uncooked and, in the case of the tins which promised to be packed with fat cucumbers and tomatoes, impossible to open. It was also too cold to sleep. But Rossel sat on a sack of potatoes, surveying these riches, dreaming of the finest Tajik *plov*, the richest Georgian stews, the saltiest cabbage.

It could not be long before it was time.

He drifted off for a moment out of sheer exhaustion. But his own shivering awoke him. He jumped up and down, slapping his shoulders and legs, and tried resting once he was a little warmer. For hours, he played this game, snatches of sleep, periods of near-delirium as he struggled for more, desperate anger as the waiting to discover his fate tore at his nerves. And Blokhin's arrival grew closer.

* * *

Zlata stepped into the room.

Stalin was sitting in the corner, in an armchair, drinking brandy, surrounded by a dense fog of pipe tobacco. He had moved the easel of his portrait so it was in front of him; he was studying it without any sign of emotion. Next to him, resting on the floor and turned around so that anyone approaching could see it, was another, much larger painting.

She recognised it immediately. She had known it was this work since Beria had ordered her out of bed. But seeing it next to Stalin was . . .

A death sentence.

The haunting face of the little boy, Petro, stared out from one corner of the canvas. It was surrounded by a thick, choking, almost impenetrable darkness. A black gouache she had worked into the canvas obsessively. Her palette of shadows.

The child's eyes were an impossible blue, the colour of the summer skies above the endless wheat of the steppe. His skin, white and rice-paper thin, was stretched like a transparent shroud across his skull. At the base was an inscription in Glagolitic, the letters picked out in gold. 'Remember the boy who should not exist.'

Ignoring it, Stalin pointed at his own painting.

'I have had Death followed, Mkhat'vari,' he said. 'Had him listened to. Informed upon. Sent the bastard to the camps, had his bones beaten in the cells of the Bolshoi Dom, stood him beside a ditch, put a bullet into his brain, watched him drop. And yet, he still watches me, peeping out from behind each pair of eyes that meet my own. Even from the eyes of my own *doctors. I know I won't survive another stroke.' He pointed at the Walther on the table. 'What is that?'*

'A pistol,' she replied, her voice cracking. 'A Walther PP.'

He shook his head. 'No. What is it really? I know you know. I can tell by the way you paint eyes – like Repin would.'

No need to pretend not to understand him any more. My secret's out. He has the painting of the boy.

'A suggestion,' said Zlata.

Stalin nodded. 'For whom?'

'For your wife, for Nadezhda, of course.'

A puff on the pipe. A small smile.

Shape-shifting . . .

'For Nadezhda, yes,' he said.

'Did you tell her you were worried about her living alone in the Kremlin when you were away – assassins, traitors every-where?' she said. 'I imagine that's how you put it. So you got her the weapon as if you wanted to keep her safe. After that, a look every now and then – your eyes flicking across to it, planting a seed. She wasn't happy anyway – that's what Mikhail Nikolayevich . . . that's what the marshal told me.'

The apparition smiled again.

'The Case of the Trotskyist Anti-Soviet Military Organi-sation,' Stalin said. His accent much stronger now. As if he had never left Gori. 'Your marshal, Tukhachevsky, thought he was dreaming. He didn't see it coming. "A spy for Ger-many? Who, me?" How could anyone think such a thing? But . . .'

Two fingers at his temple. Lips mouthing the sound – 'Pop, pop, pop . . .'

Oh, but you're wrong, he did see it coming.

A twisting of the pipe. Tapping out the ash. Hooded lids half-closing. A new expression. Almost saintly.

'As for Nadezhda,' *Stalin went on,* 'I was tired of her. She was more of a mother than a wife. Always nagging. And she never could be Kato. To have her arrested for treachery would have been to implicate myself as suspect. Too close to home. My enemies would have started whispering . . .'

Stalin's voice trailed off. He looked lost in thought. Then he stared at Zlata.

'Why did I want you to paint me?' *he asked.*

'To show you as you really are,' *she answered.* 'That's what you—'

'I know what I said. But why? Why would I want that?'

Zlata did not reply.

'You don't know yet? I'm disappointed. You see, when I'm gone, they won't be frightened any more – Khrushchev, Malenkov, Molotov, Beria, the rest of them. In time, they'll start to tear my pictures and statues down. Chew Stalin up and spit him out. Blame him for everything. But I'm not Stalin. Stalin is Soviet power. And in this painting of yours I'm Iosif, Koba, Soselo . . . I look old, I look frail, I look'* – he spat the word out again –* 'weak. So, this one they will keep. And, in time, people will look at it and say, was Stalin really so very bad. He just looks like an old man. He just looks like me.'*

She pointed at the portrait. 'Not the eyes, though. Not if you let me paint your eyes.'

Stalin pointed at Petro. At the picture of the boy.

'No. I came so close to trusting you,' *he said.* 'But Comrade Beria has saved me from that error. "Remember the boy who does not exist." What nonsense! Beria's rounding them up, your friends. *As well as a few more yids and a few more doctors. They'll all share Marshal Tukhachevsky's fate.'*

Another line from the poet Yesenin came to her: 'If demons nested in my soul, that means angels lived there too.'

'When Yesenin died,' she said, 'I took a silk rope, attached it to a lamp in the ceiling and put the other end around my neck. I stood on a stool and asked myself a question – tell me who you are without speaking. Devil or angel? *I stood there for twenty minutes, but I still could not decide.'*

She reached for the pistol in the middle of the table.

'Until today, that is.'

A grin – a row of broken, yellowing teeth nesting beneath the moustache. Fangs bared. Again, Stalin jabbed his fingers at Petro's image. " Tell me who you are without speaking." Is this who you really are?'

Fingers halfway to the weapon, she looked over at the painting. But she did not answer.

Stalin reached out and pushed the Walther closer to her.

As soon as she picked it up, she knew. She always had known.

Too light . . . the magazine's empty.

Stalin took another drink of brandy. His broad shoulders began to rock back and forth. His face creased with laughter.

She dropped the gun. It spun across the table. And grabbed something else from the easel – a glass bottle.

'No, Mkhat'vari . . .'

Stalin began to get to his feet.

Zlata threw the turpentine at Stalin's portrait. Then grabbed a rag and pulled it across the canvas, smearing the oily black of his coat over the face, above the brow. A shadowy crown appeared on Stalin's head. An apparition wearing it – the demon nesting in his soul.

Breathing heavily, Stalin took a step towards her. Then his body stiffened, his cheeks crumpled.

Zlata sniffed the air. A pungent new aroma in among the tobacco, brandy and cologne. The smell of piss.

The old man's hands began to beat like hammers on his chest as he dropped to the floor.

66

Rossel sat up and stretched. He checked his watch. It was past eleven o'clock in the morning.

Have they forgotten me?

Stiff and aching, he grimaced as he stood and put his ear to the door. Not a sound from the nearby kitchen. Or the hall. There had been some commotion at some point. But little noise after that, at least in this part of the dacha.

Odd, he thought. Breakfast, at least, must have come and gone since his incarceration. And, as far as he was aware, no food had been prepared in the kitchen.

In the corner of the storeroom was a small, cracked sink. He tried the tap and found it dribbled out some icy water, which he splashed on his face. It made him feel better. He sat on the edge of a little shelf, took out one of the cigarettes Grace Callaghan had given him and lit it. Then wished he hadn't. It tasted too smooth. Of America. Of freedom.

At least Galya is safe.

Unlike the tobacco, the thought consoled him. He tapped a finger on the red roundel on the front of the pack of Luckies. In his current circumstances, he found the name bitterly ironic. But he had been lucky, at times – or, at least, had been given good luck as well as bad. His hand moved to the little stone in his pocket. But then it changed direction, and he patted the seabird inked on his chest by a fellow prisoner in a Siberian labour camp. Why not try one last prayer to the god of happenstance? Stalin had been right about the irresistible call of a beautiful story.

Footsteps.

Someone stopping outside the door.

Oh, well . . .

Last night, he had thought he would be braver. But now Death was here, his hands had begun to shake.

As a key turned, Rossel forced himself to stand in readiness.

The door swung open, and an anxious face appeared. It was Stalin's chef. The man's eyes were red and blotchy, and he did not seem surprised to find a man incarcerated in his store cupboard.

'The bastards left him lying on the floor,' he said, his voice cracking. 'We put him on his couch. Make him some *chikhirtma,* I told myself, Comrade Stalin loves my chicken soup. That way, when he's . . . when he gets better, he'll have something to fortify himself, keep him healthy . . .'

Rossel took the chef by both shoulders and shook him. 'What? What is it?'

'A stroke. They say he's had another stroke. That he's . . . But he can't be . . . can he?'

Rossel stepped past the chef into the corridor. He pushed through two doors, the second of which brought him into the dacha's main hall. A housemaid sat sobbing on a chair. MGB guards were marching more of the staff towards the exit.

Ahead of him, he could see the bald, bullet-shaped head of Nikita Khrushchev, deep in discussion with two other men, as he strode down the corridor.

Everywhere, there was chaos.

*

Rossel muscled his way through a group of four soldiers arguing among themselves. As he passed Stalin's office, the huge door with its red star was a quarter open. Through it, he could see Malenkov and a group of other Party dignitaries standing around a man lying on a red velvet couch. Stalin's chest was rising and falling.

Too fast. Too many pauses . . .

The Great Leader's trousers were stained. Molotov was spraying some kind of aftershave out of a bottle, perhaps to mask the smell. Next to the prone figure was an upturned glass. As Malenkov stepped towards the door to close it, he saw another man bend down to pick the glass up.

Rossel walked out of the dacha and gulped in the cold air. For the first time in his life, something tasted better than a *papirosa*.

On the wide drive, three ZiS trucks had parked next to the black limousines of the Kremlin's leaders. More soldiers were jumping out of the backs of them. As the new arrivals clambered down, other soldiers shepherded the dacha's staff into the back of the trucks. There were shouts of protest. A handyman began to weep.

Rossel walked down the side of the building to get out of sight – no one had demanded to know what he was doing there yet, but before long someone would get round to it. And there was also the prospect of running into the fearsome Blokhin. The dacha was surrounded by a layer of tall, thick trees. Another defence against prying eyes. At the edge of the large garden at the rear, he stopped.

A middle-aged woman sat on a low wall, gazing at fragments of broken ice floating in a small ornamental pool. She seemed calm, almost meditative. A point of serenity amid the general pandemonium.

Rossel walked across and sat next to her. He offered her a cigarette. Her nails, he noticed as she took it, had fragments of black paint beneath them. The woman gave him a sideways glance. Above a sharp jawline, she had penetrating, intelligent eyes. The kind that knew how to keep secrets.

'Is he really gone?' she asked.

'I'm not sure,' said Rossel. 'Not yet.'

'I didn't . . . It's just . . .'

She stopped and stared over Rossel's shoulder. He turned and followed her gaze.

Small, swaddled in a thick fur coat and wearing a pince-nez, Lavrentiy Beria was standing among a group of six soldiers and two big men in plain clothes. By the looks of them, MGB. Lazily, the minister raised a hand in the air. All six soldiers stood to attention. He took something from inside his coat and handed it to one of the MGB men. Leaning close, he whispered in his ear. The man nodded. He wrapped it inside his own coat and hurried away.

'Do you know what a Leshi is?' the woman said to Rossel, gesturing towards Beria.

He shook his head.

She drew on her cigarette and stared at the ice in the pond before continuing. 'They're fearsome forest spirits. Shape-shifters.'

As they watched, Beria took a handkerchief from his pocket, slowly polished his glasses and slipped them back onto the bridge of his nose. He barked an order to the soldiers, who collectively saluted him again, before, marching at the double, the men raced into the dacha.

'They don't die,' she whispered. 'They *never* die. They just change form and become somebody else.'

7
Petro

Pravda

6 March 1953

CENTRAL COMMITTEE: TO ALL MEMBERS OF THE PARTY, TO ALL WORKING PEOPLE OF THE SOVIET UNION

The Central Committee of the Communist Party of the Soviet Union, the USSR Council of Ministers and the Presidium of the USSR Supreme Soviet announce with profound sorrow to the Party and all working people of the Soviet Union that at 9.50 p.m. 5 March, Iosif Vissarionovich STALIN, Chairman of the USSR Council of Ministers and Secretary of the Central Committee of the Communist Party of the Soviet Union, died after a grave illness.

The heart of Lenin's comrade-in-arms and the inspired continuer of Lenin's cause, the wise leader and teacher of the Communist Party and the Soviet people, has stopped beating.

The name of STALIN is boundlessly dear to our party, to the Soviet people, to the working people of the world. Together with Lenin, Comrade STALIN created the mighty party of Communists, reared and forged that party; together with Lenin, Comrade STALIN was the inspirer and leader of the great October socialist revolution, founder of the world's first socialist state. Continuing Lenin's immortal cause, Comrade STALIN led the Soviet people to the world-historic triumph of socialism in our land. Comrade STALIN led our country to victory over fascism in the Second World War, which wrought a radical change in the entire international situation. Comrade STALIN armed the Party and the entire people with a great and clear programme of building communism in the USSR.

The death of Comrade STALIN, who devoted all his life to the great cause of communism, constitutes a great loss to the Party and to the working people of the Soviet land and of the whole world.

The news of Comrade STALIN'S death will bring profound pain to the hearts of the workers, collective farmers, intelligentsia and all the working people of our motherland, to the hearts of the warriors of our glorious army and navy, to the hearts of millions of working people in all countries of the world.

In these sorrowful days, all the peoples of our country are rallying closer in a great fraternal family under the tested leadership of the Communist Party, created and reared by Lenin and STALIN.

The Soviet people have boundless faith in, and are imbued with deep love for, their Communist Party, for they know that the supreme law governing all the activity of the Party is to serve the interests of the people.

The immortal name of STALIN will live for ever in the hearts of the Soviet people and all progressive mankind.

Long live the great and all-conquering teachings of Marx, Engels, Lenin and Stalin!

Long live our mighty socialist motherland!

Long live our heroic Soviet people!

Long live the great Communist Party of the Soviet Union!

67

There were no flowers and few mourners.

Only about forty people had attended. The great man, Rossel thought, would have hoped for more.

But Sergei Prokofiev was unlucky enough to be buried on the same day as Comrade Stalin. The two men had died at almost the same time. The composer first, fifty minutes before he might have learned of the demise of the tyrant.

Every rose and lily in Moscow had been sequestered by the Kremlin to pay homage to its deceased leader. All that remained to honour the musician were hastily sketched blooms drawn on his coffin lid and a couple of wilting potted plants donated by his grieving neighbours. Adding to Prokofiev's indignities, his communal apartment was near Red Square and, given the huge crowds milling everywhere, the hearse could not get near the apartment's front door. His mourners, among them his fellow composer, Shostakovich, had to shoulder the coffin and move against the tide, squirming down streets filled with weeping and wailing men, women and children, clutching red flags and pictures of Stalin, jostling to get as close to the square as they could. So packed together, Rossel thought, that in places they resembled vast fields of corn.

By the time they reached the end of the road, Rossel had already fallen fifty metres behind in the crush. In front of him, the composer's coffin was threatening to drift away, like a cork bobbing along in the swell of lost, befuddled, frightened faces. Few paid it much attention. And those who did cast contemptuous glances. To whom belongs this impertinent corpse, their expressions seemed to say, that seeks to share the stage of the very greatest among us? Prokofiev, Rossel thought, might have liked that. Perhaps scoring the humiliating dips and falls of his own final journey in a companion piece to his youthful, astringent piece *Sarcasms*.

Rossel stepped into the doorway of a small shoe shop, so he might lift his hands above the jostling crowd to light a cigarette. He blew out the smoke and looked about. At the conservatoire, one of his old professors, a sardonic Marxist-Leninist, had once posed the question: 'If God and the Devil died on the same day, whose funeral would draw the most mourners?'

Now, he thought, he knew.

Not that, in life, Prokofiev was any saint. Far from it. But within him, he carried something sacred – the ability to set down in music every emotion his fellow man and woman could feel. Even tiny children could sense and understand it. Which is why they enjoyed *Peter and the Wolf* so much, enjoyed it and yet were terrified by it, already able to recognise their own half-formed hopes and fears hidden within its score.

Rossel returned to the pavement and, once again, began pushing against the crowd. A broad-shouldered man, shepherding his wife and two small daughters in front of him, pushed past. His face was weathered and scarred, and he bore himself like a veteran on parade, but his eyes were red-rimmed and tears were rolling down his cheeks. As he passed, he squeezed his wife's hand and muttered to her: 'I can't believe it, Lyuda. It's like the sky has fallen in.'

Up ahead of him, Rossel could see Shostakovich, left shoulder beneath the coffin, right arm holding on to it, glancing myopically around at the distraught masses as the composer's tiny funeral procession began with difficulty to turn a sharp corner that led to the waiting hearse. His expression was one of bafflement. As if he was only now realising who Stalin had really been and what he had meant to the Soviet people.

And something else, too, equally painful.

That the death of Prokofiev was passing unnoticed. Indeed, already seemed forgotten.

As the coffin disappeared, Rossel took a breath and pushed against the crowd. At that moment, a great cry went up in the middle of Red Square and rippled outwards, growing louder and louder: 'Stalin, do not leave us!'

Until all around him were chanting it.

But he did not join in.

68

Sunshine, thin and weak but warming, picked out shining jewels of wet snow and dripping icicles among the rooftops and cupolas of Leningrad. In a few months, it would be the beginning of the White Nights – the early summer days when Leningraders, feeling themselves born anew after their winter hibernation, revelled in the never-setting sun and stayed up all night to stroll in the Summer Garden and the city's other famed parks, or took long boat rides on the canals or out onto the Neva.

Rossel had bought some coffee at a shop on Nevsky and was looking forward to drinking it. As he walked towards his apartment, he passed two teams of workmen taking down from the lamp posts what remained of the banners announcing the city's 250th anniversary. The nation was still mourning, and the celebrations had been postponed.

Vishensky would have hated that, he thought. The MGB colonel's own death had been announced a few days ago. A small obituary in *Pravda*. Name and date only. No listing of his accomplishments or reason given. Hopefully, he had simply died of his wounds.

Rossel turned into his street and began to search for his keys. A magazine – an old copy of *Sovetskaya Muzyka* that Gerashvili had saved for him – slipped from his hand and he leaned down to pick it up.

As soon as he stood up, he saw it. A black GAZ parked at the end of the alley.

Bastards.

Ever since Stalin's death, he had been expecting them. But sooner.

In the last few weeks, he had made a foolish, childlike error – he had begun to hope.

The driver's door swung open. A boot crunched on the ground. A man carrying a large black box in one hand and a round silver tin container in the other began walking towards him.

'Is that coffee?' said Major Nikitin, peering into Rossel's bag. 'Cat's piss, in my opinion. I hope you have something a little stronger?'

*

Nikitin was no cinematographer. It had taken him half an hour, punctuated by many vicious curses, to set the projector up.

He and Rossel sat at a table with a bottle of vodka and two half-filled *ryumki* between them. Next to them was the copy of *Sovetskaya Muzyka,* opened to Prokofiev's obituary on page 116. Given the timing of the composer's death, the first 115 pages had been devoted to adulatory, hand-wringing pieces about Stalin's passing. It might have been a publication dedicated to music, but its editors were not taking any chances.

Nikitin pointed at the cover of the magazine. 'Just like the joke,' he said.

'The joke?'

'Man goes into a newsagent, asks the shopkeeper, "What page are the obituaries on today?" Shopkeeper says, "Same page as they always are." Next day, he's back – "What page are the obituaries on today?" And so on . . . Finally, the shopkeeper says, "The obituaries are always on the same page, page forty-seven. Why do you keep asking me that question?" And the man says—'

'"The one I'm looking for will be on the front page,"' said Rossel.

'You heard it?'

'Everybody has.'

Rossel lit another *papirosa* before standing and switching out the lights. As he sat down again, the projector began to roll.

'I got it from a contact in First Directorate, foreign intelligence, a specialist in capitalist propaganda,' said Nikitin.

Black-and-white images began to flicker across the wall.

'A newsreel?' said Rossel.

Nikitin nodded. 'A British one. Some organisation called Pathé. It's only a few weeks old.'

Stalin's face on a poster came into view, followed by pictures of his huge funeral procession in Red Square. Beria, Molotov, Malenkov and Khrushchev were watching from a balcony. While the other men wore outsized fur hats, Beria was sporting a homburg, much like the one Baikalin used to wear. A considered choice, no doubt, with the aim of marking him out as the coming man. Like the new sheriff in town, Rossel thought, in one of Stalin's favourite westerns.

Nikitin pointed at Beria. 'Nice hat.'

'Very nice.'

'There have been rumours in the Kremlin,' Nikitin said.

'Rumours?'

'About Stalin's untimely end. And about the disappearance of a large number of our agents in the West.'

'And?'

The major shrugged. 'I expect that's all they are. Rumours.'

The film cut to Stalin being laid to rest next to Lenin inside Red Square's mausoleum.

'Those two lovebirds deserve each other,' Nikitin said.

A caption in English appeared.

'First Directorate has had it all translated,' said Nikitin. 'The British announcer, too. Standard stuff. Stalin's dead, who will replace him? Will it be Beria? Will it be Malenkov? And so on. They seem to think Beria is the most likely man.'

Rossel stared at Nikitin. 'And your friend, Khrushchev. I heard his name?'

The major ignored him.

Smoking and drinking, they watched for a few more minutes.

Nikitin drained his glass and slammed it down on the table. He raised a hand. 'This is it,' he said.

As another news item began, a woman with an imposing presence and an angular jaw appeared on screen standing in front of a microphone. It was Vika Kovalyova.

She made it.

Another caption. Rossel recognised the name of a city. Zurich.

Nikitin turned towards him. 'Apparently the announcer says something like, "Defecting Russian poet breaks hearts in Zurich by reading her haunting poem, 'Krasa and Polye', about a great famine in Ukraine." As always, the bourgeoisie lie and exaggerate. They continue with the claim that "Kovalyova uses no written notes and speaks entirely from memory".'

Back straight, staring ahead, her tone undulating and melodic, Kovalyova was addressing a theatre audience of around one hundred people, seemingly mostly journalists, photographers and Western dignitaries. The audience stared up at her as if hypnotised as she chanted the words.

'... Vasylyna Yarovenko ... Teklia Frantsivna ... Ladymyr Kashchuk ... Isai Rudenko ... Arkady Shvets ... Bohdan Mazur ... Daniela Popova ... Daryna Popova ...'

Another caption appeared. This time full screen.

Nikitin translated. 'A poem dedicated to Joseph Stalin. Its only words the names of dead children.'

'How many?' said Rossel.

'In Zurich, she read a thousand. But she's going to other places, too. The Western papers are full of it. Paris, London, Berlin, New York ...'

'Artem Rudenko ... Halya Koval ... Sofiy Tkach ... Alina Savchenko ...' declaimed Kovalyova.

The major refilled his glass. 'And in each city, she offers up a different roll call of corpses. Save for one. Petro Petrenko. That one she always starts with. Kovalyova describes it as a poem without an end.' Nikitin pointed at the screen. 'You'll want to see this last bit.'

The camera began to move through the haunted faces of the crowd. It picked out a woman sitting in the back row. Rossel sat, his *papirosa* not reaching his lips. As the poet continued to list the names of the dead, Galya's intense, curious eyes never left her face.

Authors' Notes and Acknowledgements

Firstly, we'd like to express our profound thanks to Jon Elek for his initial championing of, and constant support throughout, the Revol Rossel series, and his many insightful editorial suggestions. Thanks also to our agent Giles Milburn, especially for his patience. (Sorry we were late, Giles!)

We are very grateful to Jennifer Edgecombe at Mountain Leopard Press for diligently shepherding *Man of Bones* through the editing and proofing stages of the publishing process, and Martin Fletcher for his sharp, considered and astute editing of the manuscript. We'd also like to thank Dr Peter Hammans, our German editor on the first two books, for his constant championing of the series and forensic eye for detail.

Given the 1950s Soviet setting of the novel, research is key to creating a sense of authenticity and the cloying paranoia amongst the general population that living in the Stalin's shadow produced. Both Dr Robert Dale, Senior Lecturer in Russian History at Newcastle University, and Dr Jana Howlett, Emeritus Lecturer and Fellow, Jesus College, Cambridge University, made invaluable contributions to this. Dr Dale's expertise in the late Stalinist period (1945-1953), his fascinating book *Demobilized Veterans in Late Stalinist Leningrad* (Bloomsbury, 2015), and knowledge of Soviet jokes were all particularly useful. Throughout the series, we have regularly drawn on Dr Howlett's vast knowledge of Russian history, ranging from Soviet-era automobiles to the Glagolitic and Permic alphabets.

Once again, Andrew Smith has designed a haunting cover that perfectly evokes the mood of the book. Our thanks to Jake Clewis for his skill in reproducing the Glagolitic text (taken from a passage in the Gospel according to Matthew – about betrayal, of course). Finally, we'd like to mention our copyeditor, Charlotte Chapman, and our proofreader, Jade Craddock, for spotting our many "deliberate errors," as well as the wider team at Mountain Leopard Press, all of whom have made vital contributions to this book seeing the light of day.

Writers looking for inspiration from the realities of life under the murderous reign of Joseph Stalin are not short of material. Yet, while we read and researched widely for *Man of Bones*, this is not a history book. We have always felt at liberty to alter a few dates and places, and to reimagine political rivalries and human relationships, while trying to remain true to the essence of the era. Several people have given us excellent guidance on details ranging from high politics to cigarette brands; any deviations and errors are entirely our responsibility.

We have used the spellings and pronunciations of towns and cities in the Soviet Union that a Russian living in 1950s Leningrad would have used, providing the Ukrainian versions in the map for clarity.